CW00942232

The Modern Nurseryman

The Modern Nurseryman

JOHN STANLEY, NDH
and
ALAN TOOGOOD

FABER AND FABER
London · Boston

First published in 1981
by Faber and Faber Limited
3 Queen Square London WC1N 3AU
Filmset in Monophoto by
Latimer Trend & Company Ltd, Plymouth
Printed in Great Britain by
Lowe and Brydone Printers Limited
Thetford, Norfolk

British Library Cataloguing in Publication Data
Stanley, John
The modern nurseryman.
1. Nurseries (Horticulture)
I. Title II. Toogood, Alan
635 SB88.5
ISBN 0-571-11544-6
ISBN 0-571-11547-0 Pbk

Contents

Tables

METRICATION

Metric conversions throughout this book have been kept at a practical level, and are intended, where possible, to present the reader with working sets of figures.

Illustrations

Photographs *between pages 214 and 215*

Figures

Foreword

John Stanley and Alan Toogood have combined to write a technical work which is certain to meet an identified need in the nursery trade.

The chapters have been carefully selected to cover all aspects of nursery-stock production (apart from that of vegetable production on which sufficient literature is already available) from watering to weed control and from compost to costings. In recent years new techniques have been introduced which are either labour saving or result in marked crop improvement. Propagation is a subject which receives detailed treatment.

The book examines complete production systems in depth. Methods of management, materials handling and marketing, both for field-grown and container crops, are outlined. The text is well illustrated with photographs and line drawings. Literary style suits both students of nursery practice and commercial producers. It will undoubtedly provide an essential reference textbook to both categories of reader.

The authors, John Stanley and Alan Toogood, are well-respected members of the lecturing profession. Both have been on the staff of Merrist Wood Agricultural College, Surrey, since 1972 and closely involved with the local nursery trade which is renowned both nationally and internationally. Since the completion of their book, Alan Toogood has been appointed Editor of *Greenhouse* magazine.

John Stanley began his horticultural career in the Parks Department, Birmingham, before entering Pershore College of Horticulture. Then, after taking the Advanced Diploma Course at Writtle College, he obtained the National Diploma in Horticulture (NDH). Since qualifying, John has specialized in hardy nursery-stock production. John has visited most European countries and is an authority on the latest methods adopted. In 1976, John was awarded the Studley Trust Travelling Scholarship and spent 12 weeks in the United States of America. As a Technical Consultant, he has established a reputation overseas and has returned to the

U.S.A. on several occasions. He and a colleague now have their own nursery consultancy business.

Alan Toogood studied horticulture as a student gardener at the Royal Botanic Gardens, Kew, then Wisley Garden. He entered journalism and spent eight years with *Amateur Gardening* and *The Gardeners' Chronicle and Horticultural Trades Journal*. Alan is an effective communicator and is very knowledgeable on field-grown nursery stock. He has made a particular study of modern propagation techniques for trees and shrubs. In addition, Alan's own specialist interests are alpines and herbaceous plants.

Both authors have addressed the International Plant Propagators Society and other horticultural conferences and conventions in the United Kingdom and throughout the world.

W. J. SIMPSON
Vice Principal
Merrist Wood Agricultural College
Worplesdon
Guildford

Acknowledgements

We are grateful to our colleagues at Merrist Wood Agricultural College, and in the nursery industry, and to Mr B. Hutton, for their help and advice. Our thanks are also due to Haymarket Publishing Ltd for plates 8, 9, 14 and 15; Bloom's Nurseries Ltd for plate 7; Mr J. Whitehead for plates 2 and 3; Mr G. Forster for all the other photographs and to Mr R. Sweetingburgh who drew the line drawings.

Part 1

NURSERY PLANNING

1

Siting a nursery

Choosing a suitable area

To be a successful business a nursery, besides being well managed, efficient and also producing top-quality plants, needs to be situated in a suitable area or locality. The retail nurseryman, especially, will almost certainly find that the location of the business has a direct effect on sales.

When selling to the general public it is a great asset if the nursery is situated in, or near, a densely populated area. A site in one of the new development areas should prove particularly lucrative as many new gardens will need plants. Inner urban areas which are being re-developed, in which houses often have larger gardens, should also create a demand for plants. A retailer, then, generally caters for local customers and should endeavour to build up a good number of regulars to ensure the business has a steady source of income.

There is no doubt that a retail nursery is best sited on a main road, for instance on a busy road between two towns. This will help to attract many casual customers who, it is hoped, will eventully become regular buyers. Unfortunately, these days many people will not bother to search for a nursery; they want one that is easily accessible, on the door-step as it were—so beware of choosing a site in a country area, especially off the beaten track or in a very small village. In such a situation it generally takes years to build up sufficient regular customers to make the business viable: often there are too few local customers.

In such an area one has to rely heavily, at least in the early days, on advertising frequently in the local press, in magazines and in Yellow Pages. But the cost is often high and the success rate may be variable. Mail order is another possibility, but remember a good, descriptive, well-illustrated catalogue will need to be produced and this generally means very heavy expenditure. Also the high cost of postage and packing is causing many businesses to change to other methods of selling. So think very carefully before choosing a country area for setting up a retail nursery.

With a wholesale nursery it is not so important to be in a densely populated area but it pays to be near road and rail links. Delivery and customer collection can be speeded up if the nursery is near to a good main road or motorway. However, be conscious of traffic holdups on approaches to large towns and cities such as London, as a good many hours can be wasted on journeys, when trying to get into major towns and cities. It is a good policy to be near a railway station or one of the road services as plants can often be delivered by these systems, and such services will collect either on a regular basis or when notified of packages awaiting dispatch.

Whether retail or wholesale ensure, as far as possible, there is skilled labour available in the area or workers who can be trained in nursery operations. Other important considerations include essential services, for the site should be near to a supply of water and electricity. There should also be manure readily available in the area if you intend to go in for field production. Check there are local suppliers of oil or solid fuels if you are to have heated glass. Quick and regular deliveries are vital. Many areas have suppliers of nursery sundries and equipment – it is useful to have such a service nearby.

Nurseries tend to be concentrated in certain areas depending on the crops produced. For instance, the main concentration of holdings producing hardy nursery stock is to be found on the Bagshot sands (greensand) of Surrey and Hampshire. These nurseries benefit from the mild climate, acid soils and a dense population. On the other hand, many glasshouse nurseries are found on the south coast, particularly around Littlehampton and Worthing, and on the Isle of Wight, where they benefit from the high light-intensity.

If setting up in such areas, one will be faced with plenty of competition, but this is not necessarily a bad thing as it should help to ensure one grows plants to the highest possible standard. It is quality that is of the utmost importance in the nursery industry today.

History of site

Before buying land find out as much as possible about its history. You need to know what crops have been grown, if any, as they could have resulted in a build-up of serious pests and diseases such as eelworms and *Phytophthora*; or in severe nutrient deficiencies, although the latter is probably more easily cured than serious pests and diseases.

The soil must be thoroughly checked to ensure the structure has not been ruined by the excessive use of heavy machinery. Indications of damaged soil structure are a poor tilth, caking of the surface and poor drainage. You must be suspicious of soil-colour changes and mixtures in the top layer, as these may indicate a great deal of artificial soil movement and excavation. Topsoil and subsoil may be mixed. It will therefore be essential to take soil profiles over the entire site, using an auger.

Soils

Taking the subject of soils a step further, you should ensure the site has good drainage—or is capable of being drained, although this can be cost-prohibitive if a drainage system needs to be laid. An iron pan on sandy acid soils will impede drainage but this hard impermeable layer can be broken up by subsoiling. The same applies to a cultivation pan—this occurs where cultivation to the same depth over a number of years has been practised. Grey soil below the surface indicates waterlogging for prolonged periods—this and any other problems will be indicated when soil profiles are taken. Low-lying areas often have the worse drainage problems and can prove difficult and costly to drain satisfactorily. Also, the surface drainage from higher land can infect crops below with such troubles as eelworm and *Phytophthora*.

The best types of soils for field crops are the brown medium loams. In any case the soil must be workable, particularly in winter and early spring. The soil should not be too stony or the use of machines and equipment could be hampered. Avoid really heavy land which may hold too much water in the winter, making it impossible to get on for lifting and planting. Heavy soil is also slow to warm up in the spring, and newly planted stock may be slow to establish.

Although many nurseries are on light sandy soils these may also have their problems, particularly because of their inability to hold reserves of moisture and nutrients. Large amounts of organic matter often need to be applied on a regular basis, together with fertilizers.

A good depth of topsoil is necessary—in the region of 250–300 mm (9–12 in). A very shallow soil (e.g. overlying chalk) will result in surface rooting of trees and shrubs which makes the crops unstable in the soil. If you intend growing ericaceous crops and other lime haters you will need to choose a site with a soil pH of 5 to 5·5. Soil type is not important for container crops grown on beds but good drainage is. The same applies to glasshouse crops.

especially with the development of bed systems for specialized plants and the hydroponic system known as the nutrient film technique.

Aspect

Ideally, land with a very slight slope towards the south should be sought. In such an aspect glasshouses warm up quickly, as does the soil in early spring. Avoid land with inclinations towards the north, north-east or north-west as these result in colder conditions and late warming-up of the soil.

An exposed windswept site will result in damaged and retarded growth of field-grown crops and increased heating costs for glasshouses. It can also affect outdoor spraying operations and result in the erosion of light sandy soils.

An area with high light-intensity and freedom from atmospheric pollution is important when glasshouses are contemplated. A heavily polluted atmosphere necessitates frequent cleaning of glass as well as affecting plant growth. A shaded site should be avoided, particularly for glasshouses. Also beware of frost pockets, again especially if you intend erecting glass when heating costs need to be kept to the minimum. Generally speaking, a mild area can result in reduced heating costs and better plant growth in the open.

Elevation should not be more than 300 m (900 ft) above sea level and preferably below 150 m (450 ft). In Scotland the site should preferably be less than 100 m (300 ft) above sea level. The higher the site the higher the cost of glasshouse heating and the slower the plant growth in the open.

Shelter

We have already stated the problems of an exposed site but if this is unavoidable then it is essential to provide shelter as soon as possible. Initially shelter can be provided by erecting artificial windbreaks on the windward sides. Living windbreaks (e.g. conifers) should be planted adjacent to these so that eventually they replace the artificial windbreaks. The benefits of windbreaks are: better plant growth; less heat loss from glass; no soil erosion; easier and more efficient spraying; reduced transpiration (water loss) in plants; reduced evaporation of soil moisture; and no loosening of plants in the soil. The object is to reduce the wind speed by filtering, so a semi-permeable windbreak is needed with approximately 40–50 per cent permeability.

The effectiveness of a windbreak is also governed by its height. The sheltered zone to the leeward may extend to 30 times the height of the windbreak but the effect beyond 20 times the height is invariably slight. Maximum reduction of windspeed is generally at a distance of three to six times the height of the break.

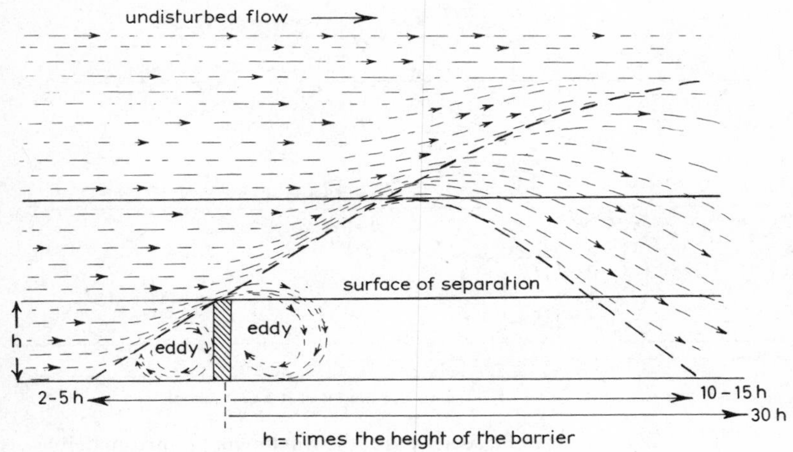

Fig. 1 Characteristic airflow pattern due to a solid barrier

Artificial windbreaks can be made from plastic-mesh windbreak netting (48 per cent permeability), plastic-covered fibre netting (48–50 per cent permeability), coir netting or hop lewing (50 per cent permeability), or vertical or horizontal wooden laths, 25 mm (1 in) wide and spaced 25 mm apart (48 per cent permeability). There is a new material on the market consisting of strips of plastic, which could be used in the same way as laths.

The height of artificial breaks is generally 3 m (10 ft). Laths need a timber framework to support them while other materials mentioned can be supported on a system of strained galvanized wires and hop poles. Additional breaks 18–30 m (60–100 ft) apart may be necessary to protect a wide area.

Living windbreaks are the best long-term solution to the problem, as they are capable of attaining a much greater height than is possible with artificial breaks. Bear in mind, though, that they can create shade problems if too high, and roots may compete with other plants for nutrients and moisture: plant deep-rooters rather than surface-rooters if possible. Hedges do have the disadvantage that they can act as hosts for pests and so spraying may be necessary.

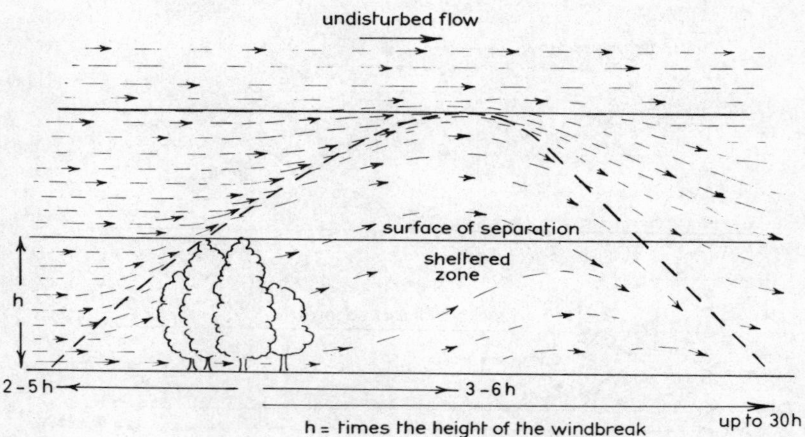

Fig. 2 Effectiveness of a semi-permeable windbreak (approximately 50 per cent permeability)

A number of conifers are suitable for forming windbreaks, including *Pinus nigra* and *P. nigra* 'Maritima', *P. radiata*, *Picea sitchensis* and × *Cupressocyparis leylandii*—the fastest grower.

Conifers can be grown alone or mixed with hardwoods; or hardwoods could be used alone although deciduous types will provide less protection in winter. Hardwoods which are often used for windbreaks include *Acer pseudoplatanus*, *A. platanoides*, *Populus alba* (which produces a lot of surface root that has an extensive spread), *Salix alba*, *Quercus ilex* (evergreen), and *Alnus incana* and *A. cordata*.

Plant preferably in double staggered rows, spacing the plants 2–2·5 m (6 ft 6 in–8 ft) apart each way. For very quick shelter, plant 1 m (3 ft 3 in) apart each way and thin out before the plants become overcrowded.

The future

Ideally a nursery should have sufficient land to allow for future expansion. Land that is not being used at present can be put down to grass leys. These can be rented out for grazing, providing an additional source of income.

2

Layout of a nursery

In Chapter 1 we aimed to show the importance of choosing a suitable site for a nursery. Once an acceptable piece of land has been acquired, a great deal of consideration must be given to the layout of the site. The efficient running of a nursery depends very much on the way in which the various buildings, roads, fields and container beds are laid out, particularly in relation to one another, and these considerations will be discussed in this chapter. The advice offered is also applicable to those contemplating improvements to an existing nursery.

Access to nursery

The main entrance to the nursery should allow for easy access by large lorries. The entrance gates must therefore be set back well off the road to provide space for lorries to wait if necessary before entering the nursery—or perhaps more important, to allow lorries to wait for the road to clear when leaving. A suitable layout for a main entrance is as follows: a 9 m (30 ft) long standing area between the road and the gates, which is 9 m wide at its junction with the main road, and has a width of 4·2 m (14 ft) for the entrance gates. The standing area between the road and the gates should not have straight sides: the sides should preferably 'bulge' outwards or curve to allow lorries to 'swing' easily off and on to the road.

It is essential to have a clear name-board at the entrance to the nursery to direct deliveries, customers and other visitors. Planning permission is required for this. Ideally, another name-board should be placed a suitable distance from the main entrance to give vehicles time to indicate and slow down.

The present trend is to do away with hedges, solid fences and the like near the entrance so that the holding is clearly visible from the road. Several entrances and exits may be desirable on a large nursery but planning permission for them—this is essential—is often difficult to obtain, especially on A-class or major roads.

Nursery roads

A suitable width for the main road or drive, from the entrance and through the nursery to important buildings, delivery areas, glasshouses and collection areas, is the same as for the entrance gate at 4·2 m (14 ft). Make it at least 1 m (3 ft 3 in) wider on bends to allow easy turning for large lorries. Try to avoid sharp bends in this road as many vehicles have a long wheelbase.

Passing places or lay-bys may be desirable on this main drive and they should be 18 m (60 ft) in length to allow articulated vehicles to draw in, and may be centralized (the road widens out on both sides) or off-centre (the lay-by being on one side of the road only). Whatever method is used, the combined width of road and lay-by should be 7 m (24 ft).

We do not want to go into too much detail on construction, but we must add that the main road or drive must be adequately constructed to take the weight of heavy lorries delivering such things as loam, manure, oil and peat. It should be 150 mm (6 in) of concrete overlying a 300 mm (1 ft) deep foundation of consolidated hardcore, such as railway-track ballast.

Internal roads to be used only by nursery vehicles (tractors, vans and the like) are often constructed simply of well-consolidated track ballast about 300 mm (1 ft) deep. This gives a reasonably hard and well-drained surface. A minimum width of 3·5 m (12 ft) is adequate for tractors with a width of 6 m (20 ft) to allow for turning.

A question one should ask before laying the main road is: 'Do we need roads all round our buildings and glass?' We feel that the answer is yes. A continuous band of road (preferably used as a one-way system) is more useful than, say, a large concreted yard in the centre. The delivery and collection areas should of course be sited alongside the road. However, a yard is useful, and one can often be found on nurseries, but there is a temptation to store loose materials on it, such as sand and peat bales; these materials tend to expand, with the result that there is less and less space in the yard for vehicles to manoeuvre. If a yard is to be laid it should be adjacent to materials and packing sheds, etc. Remember that lorries will need to turn round in a yard, unless there is room for them to back in, and some of the largest lorries need a turning circle of 21–22 m (70–75 ft) – so to be efficient a yard must consist of a big area of concrete. This is why we would prefer a continuous band of road right round the key buildings.

Gates

It is desirable to be able to lock entrances to the nursery and therefore suitable gates need to be chosen. Tubular-steel barred gates are often used to stop traffic and pedestrians entering (they do not provide security owing to their height) and they come in various widths. Single and double gates are obtainable. If there is a risk of livestock getting into the nursery fit the gates with cattle-proof latches: a herd of cows can cause havoc on a nursery! Gates 2 m (6 ft 6 in) high, constructed of chain-link fencing material on an angle-iron framework, will be needed for better security.

Fences

These may be needed for various purposes: security, protection against livestock, or protection from rabbits and hares. The most efficient type for security is a 2 m (6 ft 6 in) high chain-link fence with barbed wire strained at a height of 1·5 m (5 ft) above ground and at the top. Such a fence should also keep out deer – a real pest in many areas these days, as they strip the bark off young trees. If you just wish to keep out livestock (cows, sheep, etc.) then a woven-wire farm fence, available in various widths, is suitable. A height of about 1·5 m (5 ft) is generally adequate. Use barbed wire at the top and about half way up as an additional deterrent. To keep out rabbits and hares one needs to use 1·5 m wide galvanized-wire netting with a 30 mm (1·5 in) mesh size. The bottom should lap at least 150 mm (6 in) outwards, about 300 mm (1 ft) below ground to prevent these animals burrowing underneath.

One should really consider the problem of fencing when choosing a piece of land for a nursery as it could result in a large financial outlay. Try, if possible, to avoid a piece of land of a very irregular shape as a great deal more fencing material will be needed around the boundary than, say, for a reasonably square or rectangular site of the same area.

Buildings

The main buildings should preferably be located centrally on the nursery, as a group – so forming the 'hub of activity'. The advantages of grouping all the main buildings together are:

1 To reduce to the minimum the distances that both supervisors

and nursery workers have to walk to and from jobs—walking-time costs money.

2 To reduce the use of transport, which uses fuel—another high expense.

3 To make deliveries easier: drivers soon get to know where to aim for.

4 To reduce the cost of supplying services like electricity, gas and water. (Permission must be obtained to ensure that all supplies are available.)

The types of buildings which form the central complex include: offices; machinery workshops, tool and equipment stores; dry stores for fertilizers, chemicals and sundries; packing and dispatch sheds; cold store; staff mess rooms and cloak-rooms; potting shed; compost-mixing area; loam-sterilizing area; storage area for compost materials; propagating houses; growing houses and tunnels; and frames.

Some of these could be combined in one building if convenient—this is certainly cheaper than putting up many separate buildings. Often, nowadays, a large pre-fabricated concrete building is erected, using the portal-frame construction with a reinforced concrete framework, the walls being concrete blocks or panels and the roof corrugated asbestos. Such a building gives a clear floor area that can then be divided into a number of different sections with partitions, perhaps of timber, bricks or concrete building-blocks. Or you may find an open-plan layout more desirable. Be careful what you combine in this case: for example, one cannot incorporate a potting shed and a packing shed together as different temperatures are needed. The potting area needs to be kept warm for staff comfort, while a packing shed for lifted stock, cut flowers, etc., needs to be kept as cool as possible under moist conditions. However, it is efficient to have a potting shed next to a compost-mixing area, with materials-storage bins and bays in this area.

Propagating and growing houses (including tunnels and frames) should be as close as possible to the potting shed to cut down the distances that plants have to be moved. Again, if container growing, try to locate the standing grounds as near as possible to the potting area, growing houses, etc. As mentioned earlier, if a continuous band of road encircles this group of buildings then deliveries and collections will be very much easier.

Remember that planning permission is required from your local authority before any building work is started. It is desirable to contact the planning department before buying land to ensure permission will be granted for horticultural buildings. Also gain permission at the same time for future buildings. Planning permission is required for glasshouses as well as other types of buildings.

It is important to remember that concrete and tarmac roads and the roofs of buildings (such as glasshouses) shed many thousands of gallons of water during periods of rain, which can either be run off into a storage reservoir or into a drainage system capable of handling large quantities of water at certain times – often when normal field drainage systems are already overloaded. There could be a problem, though, when storing water collected from roads – this is the possible presence of disease spores in the water, particularly those of the soil-borne disease *Phytophthora*. However, there should be no such problems with water collected from the roofs of buildings. Needs for such items as water storage or drainage systems should always be over-estimated rather than under-estimated. (The same applies, of course, to electricity requirements and to oil storage for heating.)

Internal layout of the main work areas will have an effect on the efficient running of a nursery. For example, potting sheds and compost-mixing areas need to be especially well organized to ensure a continuous flow of work through or round the areas (but not across in more than two directions, as this can result in congestion).

The component parts of a work area like a potting shed can be divided into three sections as follows:

1 Space for movement of labour, barrows and materials.
2 Benching to work at.
3 Storage: so that materials for potting, propagation, etc. are readily accessible.

Efficiency at work is dependent on integrating these parts. Movable potting benches, for example, give greater flexibility to the work area. Try to ensure there is adequate space for placing potted plants; and space for trucks, trailers, etc., which are used for transporting pallets of potted plants.

The bulky materials (peat, sand, loam) needed for compost mixing should be in bays adjacent to the mixing area to avoid transporting them any distance. Fertilizer bins should be in the mixing area and compost bays or bins as near as possible to the potting area. Fig. 3

shows a suggested layout for a compost-mixing area. This layout allows for a through 'flow' of materials from storage bays (peat, sand, loam) to potting area, which means minimum handling of materials.

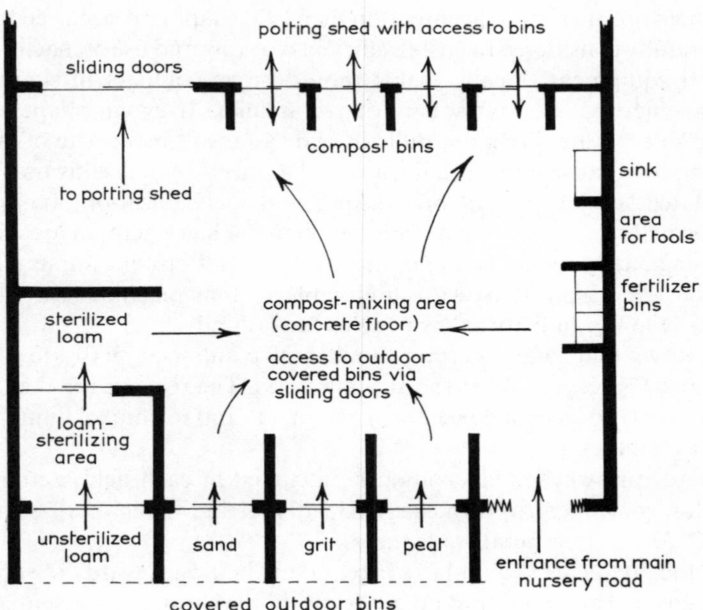

Fig. 3 A compost-mixing area

Car parks

Car parks are necessary for staff as well as customers and other visitors. Try to have a separate car park for staff, as they justifiably become annoyed if they cannot park owing to the car park being full of visitors' cars. Staff and visitors' car parks should be near the main building complex. Try to provide a hard dry surface – tarmac laid on a track-ballast base is suitable but expensive. Track ballast covered with fine shingle gives a well-drained, cheaper surface.

Nursery fields

Despite the boom in container production many nurserymen still favour field production for some crops, such as trees, roses, hedging shrubs, herbaceous plants and some conifers (see Part 5). Plant growth is often superior in the field as opposed to in containers, no matter how well the latter are managed, although there have been, and will continue to be, heated debates on this topic! Nevertheless, if field production is the intention then field shape and size need to be carefully considered to ensure efficient working and use of machinery and equipment. Ideally, fields should be as compact in shape as possible, that is, near square or rectangular. Irregular shapes can make accurate lining out difficult and can result in a waste of land, simply because crops are lined out. The size of your fields must be related to the method of working and mechanization. It is not normally feasible to have fields less than 0·4 ha (1 acre) in area. For lining out by tractor and planting machine, sections of a minimum of 1 ha (2·5 acres) in area are preferable so that machines can get a really long run before they need to turn round.

Rows that take a certain number of plants (say 500) are often aimed for, especially in forestry nurseries. The reasons are that it is then easy to calculate piecework payments and to control lining-out programmes.

Adequate headlands should be included in each field section to allow machinery to turn easily. Headlands in the region of 8–10 m (27–33 ft) are generally adequate.

Ideally, fields should have a gentle inclination towards the south to ensure early warming-up of the soil in the spring. It is essential to provide windbreaks if the fields are exposed: the sections could in fact be divided up by living windbreaks (see Chapter 1 for further details of windbreaks). Choose the best soil on the site for your field crops and leave the less suitable land for the building complex, container beds and glass and tunnel areas. There should be adequate roads between the field sections for tractor access. The roads may be either beaten soil or, for a better-drained surface, rammed track ballast.

Container-production beds

A great many nurseries are now producing plants in containers, either in preference to field production or in conjunction with it. The subject is covered in detail in Part 4, but a few preliminary comments on siting will not come amiss in this chapter. Soil type is not important but it should be well drained or capable of being drained.

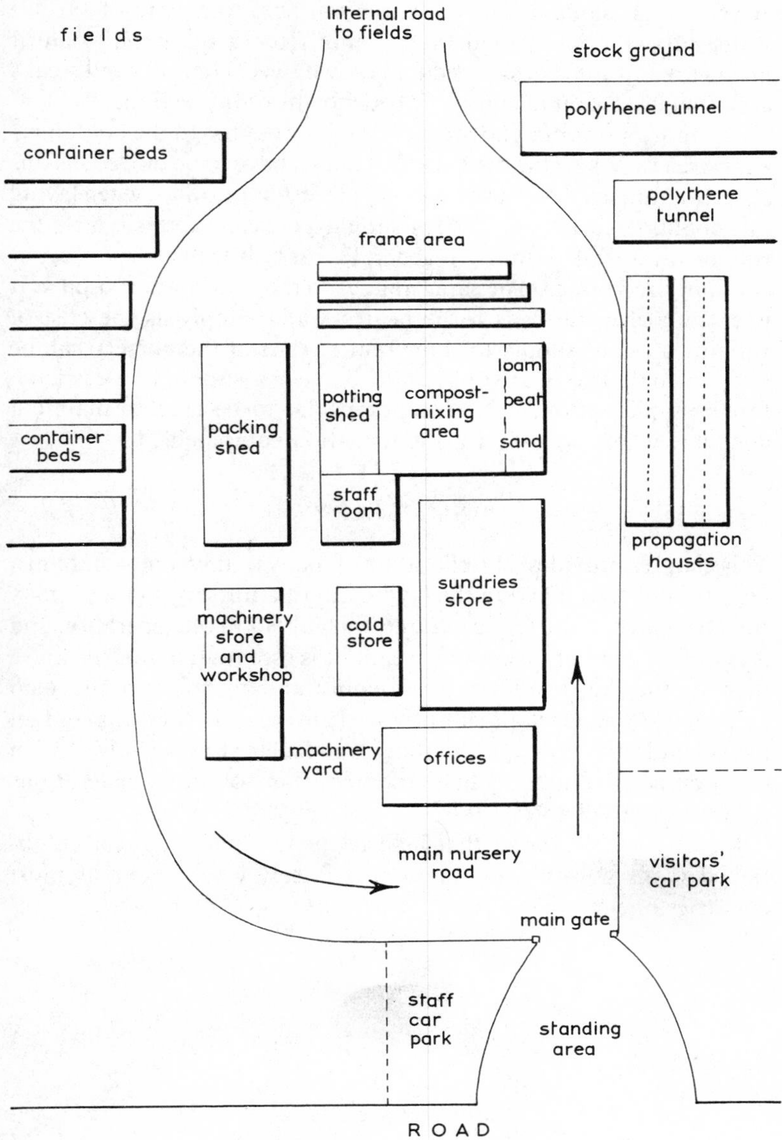

Fig. 4 A nursery layout – designed for efficient working

A very slight slope in one direction will help to get rid of surface water. As with field production, shelter from wind is important if plants are not to be desiccated and blown over. Netting windbreaks are often used around container beds to afford protection.

Try to locate container beds as close as possible to the containerizing area to reduce the distance that plants have to be moved, as this costs time and money. Space is of the utmost importance when laying out container beds, as all beds should be easily accessible by the tractors and trailers that are generally used to transport pallets of containerized plants. The same applies to the collection of orders. It is essential for the beds to be near a water supply as the cost of running a mains supply to some remote part of the nursery can be phenomenal. The beds should also be near a supply of electricity, for the same reason, if electric pumps are to be used to maintain adequate water pressure for the irrigation equipment.

SUMMARY

This chapter provides a brief outline of many of the points that must be carefully considered in the laying out of a nursery so that it may run efficiently. A nursery can rarely be laid out in one operation and is generally built up over many years. It is essential, in this instance, to plan the entire nursery thoroughly and to stick to the plan throughout the development period. It is the only way to avoid an inefficient hotch-potch of buildings, roads, etc. Fig. 4 shows a plan of a well-laid-out nursery that embraces many of the considerations covered in this chapter.

Finally, do not forget that help in nursery planning can be obtained from government advisory services, which exist in most countries, including the UK.

Part 2

STOCK-PLANT MANAGEMENT

3

Seed orchards

Seed origin or provenance

Seed provenance is the geographical source or place of origin from which a seed lot has been collected. Historically, foreign seed was often painted with red lead for identification purposes.

Any plant that occurs naturally over a large area develops different ecotypes; for example, *Pinus sylvestris* grows in Europe, West and North Asia and can therefore be found in Siberia and the Mediterranean regions; this means it can adapt to different latitudes, elevations, climates and soil. After the Ice Age, small colonies were isolated and these formed the differing ecotypes:

Pinus sylvestris var. *scotica*—Scottish form
Pinus sylvestris var. *lapponica*—Narrow head, Lapland
Pinus sylvestris var. *rigensis*—Slender trunk from Baltic regions

The result of these variants is that seed collected in warm areas may react differently in colder areas and vice versa.

Normally, the best source of seed is that collected locally although seed of *Ulex europaea* is often imported to the British Isles, as insects frequently eat the seed of native plants.

The relevance of seed provenance to the nurseryman is twofold, depending on whether he is raising for forestry or ornamental outlets.

RELEVANCE TO FORESTRY NURSERYMEN

It is now common practice in most countries for seed that will eventually be used for forestry purposes to be registered. The records must show the seed source, year of collection and species. Obviously it is best to obtain seed from a source which is as near to your climatic conditions as possible as this will produce the best-timber trees.

Provenance can be divided into two for forestry purposes. Natural provenance is where seed is collected in the wild; this can be unselected and collected from a wide area, or registered with the source identified, or obtained from selected natural areas. Alternatively, seed can be of a derived provenance such as an arboretum or nursery selection.

Once a selected area has been found for seed then an ideal seed tree must be selected. Fig. 5 shows the points to look for.

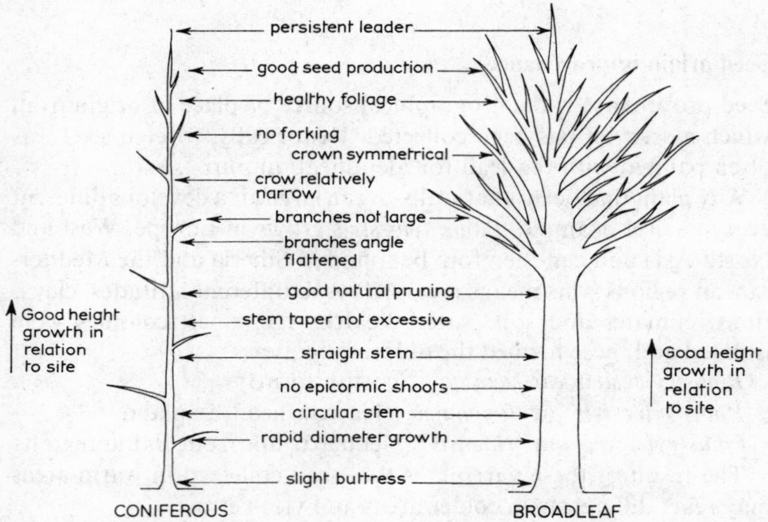

Fig. 5 Ideal seed trees

RELEVANCE TO ORNAMENTAL PRODUCERS

Normally, the ornamental producer is not concerned about maximum timber values, and registered seed is just an added expense.

Provenance can affect plants in various ways and the following points are worth considering by ornamental producers:

1 Autumn colour: plants are often selected for their colour intensity in the autumn months. Provenance can have a bearing on this, some sources producing better autumn colour than others.

2 Hardiness: as mentioned earlier some plants have large natural growing areas. This means a plant collected in a warm location may not be hardy in a colder climate, although plants of the same species may grow naturally there. An example is *Elaeagnus umbellata* Cardinal strain which will withstand zero temperatures, while *Elaeagnus umbellata* direct from Japan will not withstand such temperatures.

3 Pest and disease resistance: an example is *Larix decidua* which shows wide variations in its resistance to larch canker. Seed from Scotland seems to be highly resistant, while seed from Central Europe is susceptible to the disease.

SEED ORCHARDS

Collecting seed is one of the oldest nursery occupations, but as labour, time and techniques become more expensive and precise we need more control over where we obtain seed and how we manage the trees to obtain maximum yields.

The idea of seed orchards is not new: during the 1880s the Dutch in Java attempted to increase the content of quinine of *Cinchona ledgeriana* through growing them in an orchard situation. Seed orchards have been used since 1919 in Malaya for breeding *Hevea brasiliensis* for rubber.

In nursery production the aim of a seed orchard is to produce superior seed in a controlled environment similar to a stock ground for cutting production. An example of the process as used in forestry production can be seen from the following diagram.

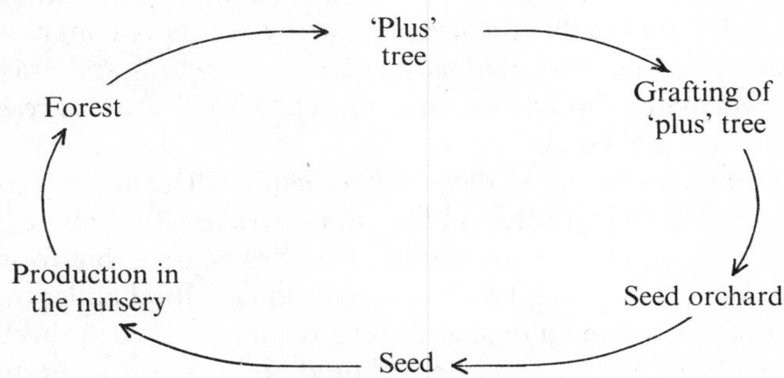

A 'plus' tree is the term used for superior seed-bearing trees in the forest.

In ornamental-tree raising, a seed orchard could be set up along the same principles as in forestry production, and a few nurserymen are now beginning to start their own orchards. It must be stressed at the outset that seed orchards use up valuable production land and are long-term crops in the sense of length of time before any worthwhile crops are produced.

Siting and planting

The siting of an orchard is important, the first consideration being isolation in order to avoid cross-fertilization with inferior trees. The site should be well sheltered, drained and have a fertile soil, preferably on the heavy side as a more abundant crop will be produced.

Various planting designs have been devised for seed orchards, but for the ornamental nurseryman a square pattern or triangular arrangement is easily managed. It is important that trees are labelled correctly at planting, with species, source, planting date and rootstock, as most 'plus' trees will be grafted to speed up the production cycle.

Management of seed orchards

The initial aim is to establish the young mother plants as early as possible, to ensure they develop as healthy plants and to promote them into early, regular fruiting with the minimum amount of capital involved.

In the establishment period it is desirable to leave a 500 mm (18 in) radius circle of clean land around the plant to ensure there is not competition from other plants until the plant is fully established. This can be achieved by the use of a harrow, or more commonly by using a herbicide. Once the plant is cropping, weeds and grass can be grown under the tree as this will encourage water stress and promote the seed crop.

Nutrient deficiency of the mother plant will result in reduced foliage and carbohydrates and in some species this can result in biennial bearing. Fertilizers should therefore be used, but for maximum benefit there should be no competition for food under the tree from other plants and if regular feeding is adopted then the herbicide treatment around the trunk base should be maintained. Fertilizers used should include nitrogen, phosphorus and potassium as an application in the spring at a rate of 1,000 kg/ha (80 lb/acre) of a compound fertilizer 10:10:10. Fertilizers will increase the weight of seed and germination energy although more research is required to assess the effect on pollen production.

Irrigation is important on dry sites and if available could be used for frost protection on early flowering species.

The pruning programme should be tailored to make seed collection as easy as possible. The grower should aim to produce a tree with a short, wide, bushy habit, except where seed is collected from the ground as with oak and beech. The technique of pruning is similar to that adopted for fruit-tree pruning, that is, light should be allowed to enter the centre of the crown and short seed-producing spurs should be encouraged. This technique works with most species, but has a detrimental effect on Scots pine and Norway spruce and we suggest that this technique is not used with them.

The initial spacing of the mother trees should allow for full crown development, but in time thinning out in the orchard may be needed to maintain isolation of each tree, in order to ensure that sunshine reaches each plant, that harvest equipment can get around all the trees and that inferior trees can be removed. The other important consideration in tree management is an adequate pest and disease control programme to ensure trees remain healthy. Slow seed-producing trees and heavier crops within a year can be produced by giving the mother plant 'shock' treatment. Various methods are available, but normally root pruning, stem girdling and strangulation are used. In recent years the chemical gibberellin has been sprayed on members of *Cupressaceae* and *Taxodiaceae* to induce flowering and there is no reason why this chemical should not be tried on other species.

Seed harvesting

Seed can now be obtained from one of three sources:

1 Seed orchards.
2 Collected from local sources.
3 Purchased from a seed house.

Obviously, from a labour viewpoint, the third source is desirable, as many problems are associated with seed collection and collection methods have not changed much since early nursery-production days.

Seed ripening varies with species and Table 1 gives some idea of the seed collector's calendar.

Methods of collecting vary according to the species of plant and the natural method of seed dispersal. Species such as *Quercus* and *Aesculus* can be picked up from the ground, while *Ulmus glabra* seed must be swept up. Another alternative is to place sacking or polythene around the plant and then shake the tree or shrub until all the seed has dropped on to the sack.

Table 1 The seed collector's calendar

Time of collection	*Species*	*Age of plant when first good crop produced*
January	*Pinus sylvestris*	15–20 years
May	*Betula* *Populus* *Salix*	15 years for each species
June	*Acer saccharinum* *Daphne mezereum* *Prunus* species *Ulmus glabra*	25 years 25 years 20 years *Note:* Cherry germination potential decreases the longer it is left on the tree 30–40 years
July	*Mahonia aquifolium* *Morus* species *Rosa hugonis* *Sorbus aucuparia*	4 years 10 years 3–4 years 10 years *Note:* Very appetizing to seed-eating birds
August	*Acer ginnale** *Carpinus betulus** *Euonymus* species* *Fraxinus* species* *Hamamelis* species *Magnolia* species*	25 years 30 years 4–5 years 25–30 years 6 years 10 years
September–October	Bulk of seed collected	
November	*Viburnum* species	4 years
December	*Ilex* species *Larix decidua*	20 years 15–20 years

* Collected before ripening and sown immediately.

Other seeds, especially berries, have to be collected from the plant. These should be collected in a bucket, bag or basket. Polythene bags are undesirable as they have no ventilation, resulting in sweaty seed which can reduce viability. Other methods include using hooks on long poles to hook material off and even shooting the seed off branches where seeds are produced at shoot tips high in the tree.

More mechanized systems are now being developed for collecting large batches of seed of a single species and this will make collecting more efficient, but care must be taken not to injure the seed, as this can reduce viability in some species.

4

Vegetative stock plants

Cutting material

The first stage in any production cycle is obtaining propagation material of the right quality in the quantity required. As production techniques become more exacting it is becoming increasingly important to have full control over propagation material from the earliest possible stage. This thinking has brought about an increasing awareness of the use of ornamental stock beds for vegetative propagation material.

SOURCES OF VEGETATIVE MATERIAL

Cuttings can come from one of three sources:

1 Saleable plants in the nursery. It is only feasible to take cuttings if this fits in with normal trimming, otherwise you may be cutting away saleable material.

2 Plants outside your control. Many nurserymen still collect cuttings from local gardens, the wild, and parkland areas. This material inevitably has an unknown history and often involves excessive labour and transport costs to obtain.

3 Stock beds/hedges. The advantage of a stock area is that the history of the plant is known and can be controlled. In a stock area the plant is grown purely for the purpose of producing the right type of cuttings at the right time. Large batches of cuttings are within easy reach, which reduces time and money when collecting. The plants can be easily managed and even manipulated to produce the cutting material required. The disadvantages of a stock area are that it takes up valuable land, and extra costs are involved in the daily management of such an area. Many growers often imagine a small arboretum mushrooming in their nursery, but by planting hedgerows in lines 3 m (9 ft 9 in) apart and 450 mm (18 in) in the row, it is possible to plant 6,500 stock plants per ha (2·5 acres) and still manage the crop using a tractor.

Selection of plant material

There are many plants in the trade that are grown under different names or have clonal variations. It is essential that before planting a stock plant you know the source and continually check and compare the identity of plant material.

Where possible, the best clonal form of a particular species should be used. Various research stations are now gathering plants together to find the best forms for release to the trade. Clonal selection in fruit production has been carried out for many years (see Chapter 16) but now similar work is being carried out on ornamental plants.

Obviously, once material has been selected it must be labelled correctly. A system we have used successfully is to give each plant an 'entry number' before it is planted. The first two digits of the number signify the donor and the last two the year in which they were received. For example in '*Hamamelis mollis* 1577', '15' indicates nursery, and '77' indicates the year of purchase.

Siting of stock grounds

Cutting-hedges or beds are long-term crops and therefore initial pre-planting preparation must be thorough. A site must be selected that is fairly sheltered from wind and frost pockets, yet has plenty of light, as plants in shade often produce undesirable material for cuttings. The soil should be of the correct structure and of a suitable pH for the plants being selected. The site should be suitably drained and free of perennial weeds, pests and soil-borne diseases.

STOCK-BED MANAGEMENT

At the end of this chapter we give a routine management programme for a stock ground. It must be stressed that this is a rather extensive programme and can be altered depending on plants grown, and on land and labour availability. A number of important points are worth covering in more detail when managing a stock ground.

Juvenility

Plant growth can be divided into a number of phases as follows: an embryo phase; juvenility, when shoot buds cannot become flower buds; a transition stage, when shoot buds begin to respond to induction; an adult phase, when flowers and seed are produced; and finally senescence and death which often occurs as a constant production of flower buds and no vegetative bud production.

A number of reasons have been put forward on why juvenility occurs: the main reasons are, firstly, that in a natural crowded environment, such as a forest, it is advantageous for a plant to grow strongly without flowering until it is in a position where it can obtain the right amount of light; secondly, it is an advantage to be able to regenerate quickly from near the ground once the top of the plant has been destroyed by browsing animals or fire. Many plants in their juvenile stage produce spines, thorns or prickly leaves and this is considered to be a deterrent to browsing animals.

The change from a juvenile to adult phase is thought to be stimulated by light and temperature, but it is important to realize that the plant does not change genetically. The duration of juvenility in a plant varies according to the species; e.g., *Pinus sylvestris* stays juvenile for 5–10 years while *Quercus robur* stays juvenile for up to 30 years.

Juvenility shows itself in different ways. One is by heteroblastic development or different leaf shapes; examples of this include *Hedera helix* and *Eucalyptus* species.

Alternatively, plants may show marcescent growth; or juvenile parts may retain withered leaves throughout the winter months. Examples of this are *Fagus sylvatica* and *Carpinus betulus* and this factor is used when considering these plants for hedging purposes.

Some plants produce thorns on juvenile portions, e.g. *Malus* species, while others produce a differing growth habit, e.g. *Euonymous japonicus*.

RELEVANCE OF JUVENILITY TO THE PLANT PROPAGATOR

Juvenile plant material roots more easily than the adult phase as juvenile stems have a good carbohydrate food reserve and are relatively free of lignified cells in primary tissues.

It must be remembered that it is the base of a plant which retains its juvenility. With this knowledge we can manipulate the plant to maintain or regenerate its juvenility, or in some cases shorten the juvenile phase to induce flowering to speed up breeding programmes.

Age of stock plant

The older the mother plant, the more senile it becomes and the lower the capacity for vegetative production, as most of the plant's energy

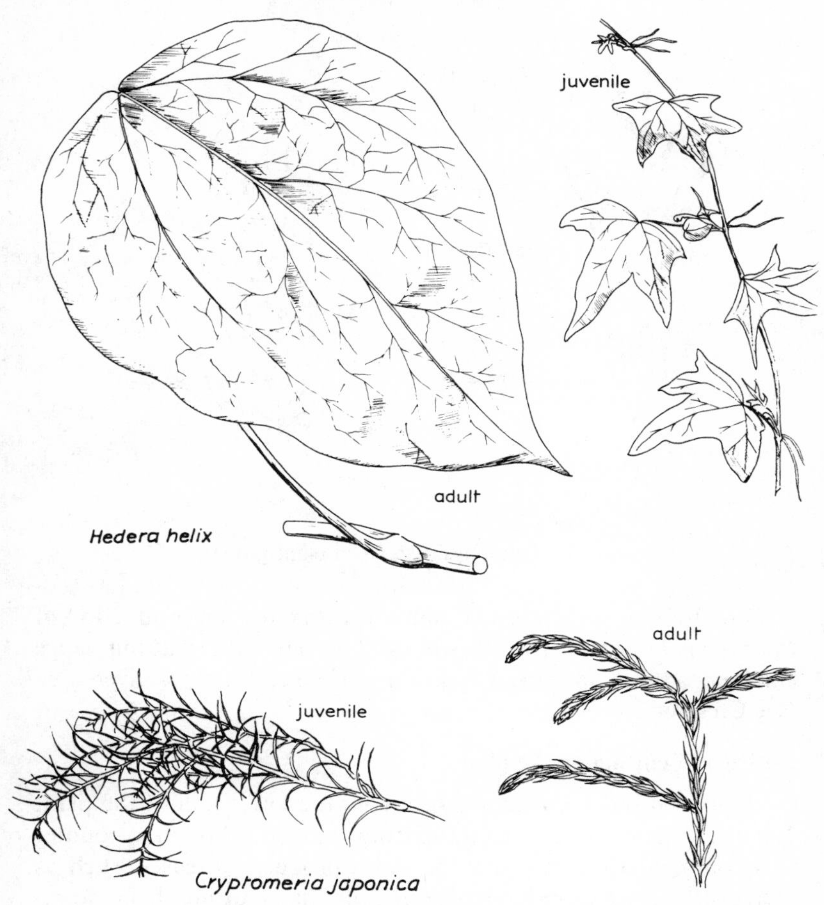

Fig. 6 Visual growth differences due to juvenility

goes into flower and seed production—therefore, stock plants should be replaced at regular intervals with new mother plants. The replacement programme will vary according to the natural life of the plant, e.g., *Erica* stock plants should be replaced every few years while *Platanus* stock plants will produce juvenile material for 20 years.

The alternative approach is to upset the root/shoot ratio of the plant and induce rapid juvenile growth to occur from the base of the plant.

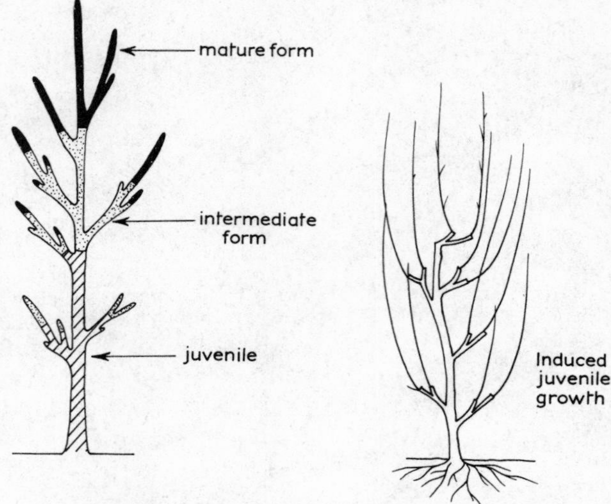

Fig. 7 Topophysis effects in plant growth

This stooling system is a common practice for the production of *Salix*, *Populus* and fruit rootstocks. Alternatively a cutting-hedge can be produced and this will produce more cuttings per given area (see Chapter 16).

Position of cutting on the plant

On a normal plant, cuttings taken from the lower half of the plant will usually root better than those from the top, although to counter this comment they may also be more prone to diseases, such as *Phytophthora* which reduces rooting potential. Cuttings from dominant growing points will normally produce better plants than those from side laterals; it has been noted on a number of plants that constant taking of laterals for propagation can result in a crop which is broader than the original stock plant.

Type of plant produced

The type of plant required by the customer will also influence the type of cutting material taken. Obviously if an adult plant is required then it is far easier and quicker to root adult-phase cuttings and vice versa. The following example illustrates this point:

Euonymus fortunei radicans is juvenile, bearing no fruit; its sport

Euonymus fortunei radicans 'Variegatus' is a popular ground-cover plant and therefore to produce this plant cuttings must be collected from juvenile stock plants. *Euonymus fortunei* 'Carrierei' is the adult form of the same plant, producing a variegated sport, *Euonymus fortunei* 'Silver Queen'; to obtain plants of this cuttings must be taken from adult stock plants.

Nutritional status of stock plants

It is important to maintain a vigorous mother plant, while also remembering that the rooting of cuttings depends on the nitrogen: carbohydrate ratios in the plant. An excessive nitrogen feed can result in the wrong type of cutting and a reduction in rooting potential.

Very little work has been carried out on stockbed feeding but foliar feeding is preferred by many nurserymen, as nitrogen and potassium can move freely within the plant.

Weed control

Perennial weeds should have been controlled prior to planting and any remaining perennials should be controlled by spot treatment with a suitable herbicide. The main weed problem will be annual weeds and normally a residual herbicide will keep these under control. Residual herbicides can be root pruners if used constantly on the same piece of ground around the same plants. We therefore recommend that a selection of herbicides is used, both residual and contact.

Irrigation

The rooting of cuttings is in relation to their water content, although the water content of such material varies with species and age. It is therefore important that the cutting is removed from the stock plant in a turgid state and remains so until it is in the rooting environment. It is therefore important that the stock plant must be healthy and turgid when cuttings are removed which, in dry spells, may mean irrigating the plants the day before cuttings are taken. The cuttings must not be allowed to wilt in transit to the cutting-preparation area.

Table 2 Routine maintenance of stock ground

Month	*Stoolbeds*	*Layering*	*Pruning*	*Spraying*	*Collecting*	*Lifting*	*Miscellaneous*	*Planting*
JANUARY	Unearthing, lifting, grading		Fruit and ornamentals for budwood production	Propyzamide for couch control	Hardwood cuttings (ornamentals and fruit) and hard prune stock plants *Buddleia* cuttings (softwood) Conifer cuttings	Perennials for division and plants for root cuttings	Drainage Ditch maintenance	
FEBRUARY		Simple layering: lift tip layers of blackberries and loganberries Lift ornamental layers			Hardwood cuttings (ornamentals and fruit) for cutting bin (hard prune stock plants) Conifer cuttings	Perennials for division	Check labels, tree ties and stakes	
MARCH		Trench layering: peg down *Prunus* F.12/1 French layering: pegging down	Stock for soft and semi-mature cuttings Stock for hardwood cuttings	Simazine to weed-free beds	Scion wood for grafting and hard prune stock plants Conifer cuttings and pruning			Final planting and moving of deciduous stock

APRIL	First earthing up of *Malus* root-stocks, Quince A and *Aronia prunifolia*	Simple layering: ornamentals pegging down	Broadleaved evergreens for cutting production	Lenacil – perennials, heathers, etc. Fruit and ornamentals for aphids Junipers for webber moth	Softwood cuttings, e.g., *Hypericum*, *Spiraea*		Set up irrigation for stool-beds and layerbeds	Perennials, conifers, evergreens
MAY	Second earthing up of stoolbeds	Trench/French layering: first earthing up Simple layering: ornamentals pegging down		Kelthane against conifer spinning mites (especially junipers)	Softwood cuttings		Mulching: rhododendrons, heathers	Perennials (then spray lenacil) (irrigation)
				Benomyl soil drench to cherry layer beds to prevent *Thieloaviopsis basicola*. Rate: 150 g to 90 m row				
JUNE	Third earthing up of stoolbeds	Trench/French layering: second earthing up	Summer pruning of conifers	Paraquat if necessary Spray aphicide	Scion wood for budding Cuttings of heathers and other ornamentals			

Month	*Stoolbeds*	*Layering*	*Pruning*	*Spraying*	*Collecting*	*Lifting*	*Miscellaneous*	*Planting*
JULY	Final earthing up of stoolbeds	Layering: strawberry runners Trench/French layering: final earthing up		Weed control: hand weeding of layer beds Repeat residual herbicide applications if necessary	Cutting of ornamentals Scion wood			
AUGUST		Layering: tip layering blackberries and loganberries		Early August spray against juniper webber moth (malathion) Spray weeds as necessary	Cutting of ornamentals Scion wood			
SEPTEMBER				Apply soil sterilant for new heather and conifer beds	Cutting material of conifers and broadleaved evergreens		Check labels, tree ties and stakes	Conifers and broad-leaved evergreens
OCTOBER			Raspberries, blackberries and loganberries		Cutting material of conifers, evergreen shrubs, *Berberis*, etc. Seed of trees/shrubs		Deep ploughing of fallow land, incorporate farmyard manure prior to planting	Conifers and broad-leaved evergreens

NOVEMBER	Unearthing, lifting, grading	Simple layering: lift layers of ornamentals then prune mother plants			Hardwood cuttings (ornamentals and fruit) and hard prune stock plants Cuttings of conifer and broadleaved evergreens	Raspberry spawn for lining out		Deciduous stock, through to March
DECEMBER	Unearthing, lifting, grading	Trench/French layering: lifting and grading		Fruit with tar-oil or DNOC/petroleum oil to control overwintering pests	Hardwood cuttings (ornamentals and fruit) and hard prune stock plants Conifer cuttings	Plants for root cuttings		Replant for future root-cutting material

THE FUTURE OF STOCK-PLANT PRODUCTION

A few major developments may occur in stock-plant production. Firstly, if the trend continues in nursery production, as it has in other areas of horticulture, we may see our stock plants grown hydroponically under cover (see Chapter 19).

The second advance may be by scientists inducing cuttings that start rooting while on the mother plant. We can already see this with the dwarf cherry rootstock 'Colt' and other plants may be induced to react similarly. In some countries nurserymen are using giberellic acid to manipulate plant growth and it seems a logical progression to use this type of chemical in the stock ground.

Part 3

PROPAGATION SYSTEMS

5

Propagation programme

Part 3 of this book deals with the major subject of propagation on the nursery. The two basic methods will be dealt with: raising plants from seed and producing plants by vegetative or asexual methods. This chapter, by way of an introduction to this subject, is intended as a guide to planning a propagation programme.

An annual programme

A nursery producing hardy stock will need to formulate an annual propagation programme, taking into account the following considerations:

1 First consideration must be given to the range of plants that are to be produced. This is a case of trying to determine future demands, for a line that is in demand now may not have a ready market at the time the plants are saleable. One never really knows what the demand for plants will be in maybe a couple of years time—one can only make a shrewd assumption based on the current situation. Do not let this situation tempt you to produce a very wide range of subjects, or to build up vast stocks of plants, in the hope of selling some, especially if you have only a small nursery. This can only result in a great deal of wastage of plants, space, time, labour and propagation and growing facilities. It is generally far better to concentrate on fewer lines (those that are usually in steady demand) and to produce top-quality plants. Avoid lines that are being produced in quantity by specialist nurserymen, e.g., roses, heathers and possibly conifers.

2 Propagate subjects only in the most efficient propagation period—this is often a case of experience, and of knowing the optimum period. It results in, for example, quicker rooting of cuttings plus a higher percentage 'take', quicker germination of seeds and so on.

3 Know the average time that subjects (e.g., cuttings, grafts and seeds) should be in a propagating area in order to calculate space needed for rooting, germinating, etc., at the optimum time.

4 Consider the growing-on procedures and timing following propagation. There must be suitable facilities and space available for young plants to grow on, and there must be labour available to handle batches of young plants once they leave the propagation area.
5 Keep all propagation facilities (e.g., glasshouses, mist benches and frames) at full capacity all the year round – empty propagation space is a sheer waste of facilities.
6 Estimate the quantity of plants that you need to produce for sale. This is discussed in more detail later in this chapter, in the section on forward planning.
7 Know the subjects that give the quickest returns, the lowest risk of failure and the highest risk of failure. You must also know the subjects that involve the highest production costs and those that involve the lowest production costs. Labour must also be taken into consideration: some aspects of propagation such as bench grafting require highly skilled labour, while other methods like hardwood cuttings can be tackled by relatively unskilled staff. Propagate only those subjects that can be successfully tackled by the available staff. These considerations are outlined in more detail below.

Quickest returns ↑

Open-ground hardwood cuttings
Cold-frame hardwood cuttings
Layering trees and shrubs
Cuttings under low polythene tunnels
Root cuttings in cold frames
Seed out of doors
Softwood summer cuttings under polythene
Cuttings under mist
Conifer cuttings under cold glass
Seed under glass
Budding trees/roses summer outdoors
Grafting trees spring outdoors
Bench grafting (closed-case grafting)

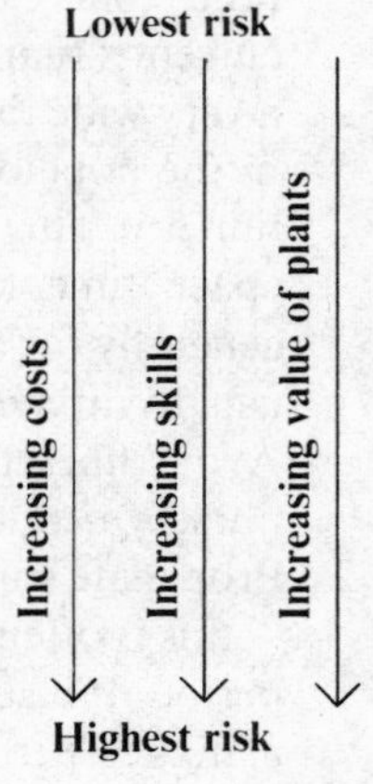

Table 3 Annual propagation programme

Method	*Jan*	*Feb*	*Mar*	*Apr*	*May*	*Jun*	*Jul*	*Aug*	*Sep*	*Oct*	*Nov*	*Dec*
Bench grafting												
Hardwood cuttings												
Softwood cuttings												
Field grafting												
Layering												
Seed under glass												
Seed outdoors												
Semi-ripe cuttings												
Budding—field												
Conifer cuttings												
Root cuttings												
Division of herbaceous plants												

An annual programme for the propagation of hardy nursery stock can be summarized as in Table 3. It is not envisaged that a nursery will be carrying out all of these methods. It depends on the types of plants that are to be produced, the facilities available and the amount of skilled labour employed.

A system of recording for the propagation programme is recommended and a record sheet is shown below in Table 4. Record sheets are also useful to refer to when planning in the future. The propagation record sheet is reproduced by courtesy of J. Gilford, Toddington Nurseries, Littlehampton, Sussex.

Table 4 An example of a propagation record sheet

Propagation Record Sheet

LINE SYSTEM PROPAGATION DATE

PLANNING DATE SALES PERIOD

	Planned	*Actual*
1. Estimated sales 2. Replacement % 3. 1st revision 4. Final pot losses/grade out/carry over 5. 2nd revision – final potting numbers 6. % losses in liners 7. 3rd revision – number of liners 8. Propagation loss % 9. 4th revision – cuttings required		

Propagation spacing
Propagation space required
Liner spacing
Liner space required
Final spacing
Final space required

	Planned	*Actual*
Propagation date Propagation time (week numbers) Propagation time Propagating labour input		

Forward planning to estimate plant requirements

The number of plants to propagate depends on:

1 Final plant numbers required.
2 Rooting percentage.
3 Plant establishment losses.
4 Number of inferior and unsaleable plants.
5 Contingency allowance for mishaps such as pests and diseases, weather, etc.

Let us illustrate this with an example.

Example

We require 1,000 *Chamaecyparis lawsoniana* in three years' time. Experience tells us that:

90 per cent root
90 per cent establish
15 per cent are unsaleable
20 per cent are lost via *Phytophthora*

We can calculate numbers required as follows: if we take 1,000 cuttings

1,000 less 10 per cent (100) = 900
900 less 10 per cent (90) = 810
810 less 15 per cent (121) = 689
689 less 20 per cent (138) = 551 (55 per cent of original)

So, take 20 cuttings to obtain 11 saleable plants.

We require to take 1,818 cuttings of *Chamaecyparis lawsoniana* to get 1,000 saleable (calculated in the following way)

1,818 less 10 per cent (182) = 1,636
1,636 less 10 per cent (164) = 1,472
1,472 less 15 per cent (221) = 1,251
1,251 less 20 per cent (251) = 1,000

MAKING MAXIMUM USE OF EXISTING FACILITIES

Often it is unnecessary to invest large sums of money in propagation facilities. Try to make use of what is already available on the holding; for example, cold frames can be used for many aspects of propagation, as conifers, heathers, semi-ripe cuttings, root cuttings and hardwoods can be rooted in these conditions. Low polythene tunnels provide a cheap means of rooting a wide range of semi-mature evergreen shrub cuttings (see Chapter 10). If you do not have a mist-propagation system then heating cables could be laid on existing benching in a glasshouse where a wide range of soft and semi-mature cuttings could be rooted (see Chapter 9). With tree and shrub layering no special facilities are required (see Chapter 15). Existing polythene tunnels and unheated glasshouses can be put to good use for rooting hardwood cuttings, heathers, and a wide range of semi-ripe shrub cuttings.

Hygiene

To prevent losses due to diseases like *Phytophthora* and *Botrytis* you must maintain a strict hygiene programme for propagation. For example, sterilize all used containers by soaking them in a solution of formaldehyde. Always use sterilized or sterile composts and rooting media such as peat and sand, Vermiculite, Perlite, peat blocks, compressed peat pellets, rockwool blocks, etc. Sterilize knives frequently during use and always collect propagation material such as cuttings in clean polythene bags. Prepare material where appropriate on benches covered with clean polythene sheeting. Build into a propagation programme a suitable period for washing down propagating areas and houses with a solution of formaldehyde. There must be no plant material in the area being treated and several days must elapse before introducing plant material again to allow fumes to clear completely.

Introduce into the clean house some lettuce plants which have been germinated in a seed tray, for a day or two before moving in cuttings or other plant material. Any reaction to fumes will be quickly apparent. All ventilators should be opened for some time in order to clear fumes.

Never place containers in direct contact with the soil as this could result in soil-borne diseases infecting plant material – it is better to stand containers on a layer of polythene and sand. As an insurance policy against risk of disease infection, cuttings and other types of plant material in propagation sections can be sprayed regularly with benomyl systemic fungicide (especially under polythene). Cuttings can be dipped in a mixture of hormone rooting powder and captan during preparation as a further safeguard. Foam-rubber disinfectant mats can be placed at all entrances to the propagation area and propagation houses. Make them wide enough so that staff have to walk over them – if they are too narrow there is a great temptation to step over them!

6

Seed raising outdoors

Seed raising can be split into two distinct methods nowadays—growing seedlings in outdoor seed beds, which is discussed in this chapter, and intensive seed production in containers under glass which is covered in Chapter 7. The former method is often used for the production of low-value mass-produced plants like hedging material, plants for conservation areas, windbreak material, and also rootstocks for bench grafting. Outdoor seed beds provide the cheapest means of producing such material, but for high-quality ornamental plants, forestry seedlings, and for large numbers of mass-produced plants for direct planting (say by local authorities), intensive production in containers is gaining great favour with nurserymen.

One of the advantages of outdoor seed beds is that they can be prepared and sown by semi-skilled staff and they represent a low to medium risk in the propagation programme, whereas intensive seed production is a more skilled operation with probably greater risks of failure if conditions are not of the highest order.

SEED PREPARATION AND STORAGE

In Chapter 3 we discussed seed orchards and seed harvesting, but before going on to sowing methods we should first of all discuss the preparation and storage of seed which is collected by the nurseryman. This is indeed a big subject, which is still being researched by many experimental stations, and complete books have been devoted to it. We will therefore discuss the methods we use and there is no doubt that these will suit many nurserymen producing hardy plants.

Treatment after harvesting

Dry fruits (pods and capsules), for example leguminous species such as *Caragana*, *Cytisus* and *Robinia*, are air dried for a period of one to three weeks, probably in trays on a glasshouse bench. This encourages the seed containers to split open for easy extraction of the seeds by hand. Alternatively the pods and capsules can be crushed if not open. The use of seed sieves will separate the seeds from the chaff.

Conifer cones need drying at a high temperature to encourage them to open – ideally a temperature of 46–60 °C (115–140 °F). In forestry the cones are dried in special kilns, but without this facility they could be placed in trays over glasshouse heating pipes. Again in forestry practice the wings are removed mechanically but the average nurserymen could consider their removal unnecessary.

We mascerate fleshy fruits and berries before storing, to expose the seeds, using wooden pressers on a bench. The subjects so treated include *Cotoneaster*, *Sorbus*, *Ilex*, *Berberis*, *Malus*, *Prunus* and *Rosa*. If desired the seeds can be separated from the pulp by flotation in water for several days – the sound (viable) heavy seeds will sink to the bottom of the container while the light non-viable seeds and pulp will float. On no account leave the seeds unattended for more than a day or two otherwise fermentation will start.

Pre-sowing treatments

With many subjects, pre-sowing treatments are necessary to break dormancy and induce uniform germination when sown in the spring. Dormancy can be due to a hard impenetrable seed coat, as in the legumes for example, like *Robinia pseudoacacia*, *Gleditsia* and *Wisteria*. In this case scarification is necessary – rubbing the seed with sandpaper to reduce the thickness of the seed coat. This can be done mechanically on a large scale in rotating drums, or by hand for small quantities.

Then there is internal dormancy – here chemical changes must take place before germination can occur, or the embryo must develop to a certain stage before germination commences. Some subjects are what are known as double dormant and good examples here are *Fraxinus*, *Ilex* and *Cotoneaster*. The North American thorns or *Crataegus* generally take 18 months to germinate although *C. coccinea* is an exception, as it has no dormancy problem. *Rosa* species often take at least 12 months to germinate but this is due to their tough seed coat. There is a new technique now being used called acid treatment, where sulphuric acid is used to reduce the thickness of the seed coat, but it is a highly skilled operation and at the moment is mainly undertaken under laboratory conditions by experienced operators. It is likely that in the future we shall see this method used by some nurserymen. There is no reason why it should not be used for other members of the *Rosaceae*, like *Cotoneaster* and *Crataegus*, which have tough seed coats.

We generally stratify the fleshy fruits and berries after mascerating them. Cold stratification helps to soften hard seed coats and also breaks internal dormancy. Our method is to mix the seeds with one to three times their own volume of moist sand and place this mixture in tins with drainage holes in the base. Each tin is then labelled with the name, source and date of collection and placed in a brick-built stratification bin in a cold aspect. The bins are covered with fine-mesh wire netting to prevent rodents and birds from eating the seeds. In this situation the seeds are exposed over the winter to alternate freezing and thawing and are then sown in the spring. Some species will germinate well after this treatment, but others will not germinate until the second spring and these are sown on a bed which can be left down for two years (see the section on methods of sowing later in this chapter). The alternative is to leave the tins in the stratification bin for the second winter.

Some seeds we mix with slightly moist peat and place in polythene bags in a refrigerator to prevent them becoming desiccated. This is preferable to dry storage. These subjects include *Fraxinus*, *Acer* and *Fagus*. They are then sown in the spring. However, *Fraxinus* will not germinate until the second spring when given this treatment—it is best sown when green. Seeds in a refrigerator must not freeze—provide a temperature of 1–4 °C (34–40 °F).

The dry seeds like the legumes and conifers we store dry in paper seed packets or linen bags and find that they benefit from cold storage in a refrigerator—again we do not allow them to freeze.

OUTDOOR SEED BEDS

Selecting a suitable site

To ensure good germination and subsequent growth of seedlings it is important to choose a suitable site for outdoor seed beds. Ideally the site should have a slight slope to ensure good air drainage and thus lessen the occurrence of frosts. A warm, south-facing aspect will encourage earlier germination of seeds. Shelter from wind is also important as wind can result in water loss from the beds, temperature reduction in the soil, and both reduced growth in the seedlings and physical damage to them. Subjects like *Acer*, particularly *A. palmatum* and *A. japonicum*, the Japanese maples, are particularly prone to wind damage in the seedling stage – the foliage can become 'scorched'. It really goes without saying that a well-drained site is essential, both for the well-being of the seedlings and to allow early preparation and sowing.

Initial preparation of beds

The land must be free of weeds, especially perennial kinds which are difficult to control among seedlings. Annual weeds can be controlled prior to sowing by applying paraquat to 'burn' them off. We make raised beds for our seed crops as these provide better drainage than sowing on the flat – our soil is inclined to be on the wet side. In the autumn, about September, we ridge up the beds with a ridging plough, forming them into 1·5 m (5 ft) wide strips. After this operation we apply dazomet to reduce the annual weed problem on the beds the following year. This is also an insurance policy against *Phytophthora*.

The soil must be moist and warm when dazomet is applied and the structure should be loose. It is applied as prill granules and may be distributed over the beds either by hand or by a fertilizer spreader adjusted to apply the product at the correct application rate. The rate of application varies according to the soil type and the maker's instructions should be followed as to the correct rate for your soil. On our light sandy soil we apply dazomet at the rate of 380 kg/ha (340 lb/acre). If autumn-sowing, dazomet should be applied in the summer. After application the beds are covered with polythene sheeting but ensure the dazomet has been incorporated into the soil by use of a rotary cultivator. Seal the edges of the polythene by burying them in the soil. This retains the gases given off by the sterilant.

The polythene is removed in February (or in autumn when sowing at this season) and the soil loosened to ensure any remaining gases escape. Test the soil by using the cress test before attempting to sow.

Final bed preparation

If drainage is not too good then coarse sand or grit could be incorporated into the bed, but this is an additional expense for what is considered to be low-cost plant production. Sometimes leafmould is incorporated into the bed as this conserves soil moisture on a very dry site and it also results in a much more fibrous root system in some species. However, you must be careful of introducing weed seeds and *Armillaria mellea* (honey fungus) with the leafmould.

The final preparation of the bed includes trimming the sides with a spade so that they slope inwards, to form a bed 1·5 m (5 ft) wide at the base reducing to approximately 1·2 m (4 ft) across the top. The height of the bed is in the region of 150 mm (6 in). The bed should then be levelled and firmed by treading or rolling. This will also break up any large lumps of soil. The bed must be vigorously raked to remove any very large stones and sticks, to create a fine tilth and to make any final adjustments to level. During this raking a fertilizer should be incorporated into the surface. We apply a slow-release tree and shrub fertilizer at the rate of 13 kg/100 m^2 (28 lb/120 sq yd)—analysis: 5% N, 24% P_2O_5, 10% K_2O, and 16% Mg. Then tread again to obtain a very firm seed bed which is best judged by the 'clenched fist test'. Now give a final raking, very lightly, to give a level sowing surface.

Methods of sowing

The main sowing period out of doors is in April although this can be extended into May if soil conditions are wet. It is far better to wait for soil to become drier before preparing the bed and sowing. There are some subjects, however, which are best sown in the early autumn, especially those with short-term longevity—drying out of such seeds can considerably reduce germination. Subjects which are best sown in autumn include *Quercus*, *Aesculus*, *Castanea*, *Salix* and *Populus*. The last two are best sown as soon as ripe and this also applies to *Fraxinus*—in fact, this can be collected green and sown immediately for a one-year crop. If sown in the spring, *Fraxinus* has the characteristic of double dormancy and the majority of the seed will germinate in the second spring. In fact we have a 'double-dormant bed' for the subjects which need a long stratification period. This is an alternative to keeping the seeds in stratification bins for about a year or more. The bed is left down for two seasons, the bulk of the seed germinating in the second spring. In this bed we include subjects like *Ilex*, *Viburnum* species, *Cotoneaster* species, *Crataegus* species, *Cornus kousa*, *Rosa* species, *Tilia* species, *Berberis* species, *Taxus*, and *Fraxinus* if we delay sowing till spring.

Whether to sow the seed broadcast over the beds or in drills is the next consideration. We sow in drills as we feel that we get a better plant stand established than with the broadcast method. We take out drills 100 mm (4 in) apart using wooden drill markers – rather like wide-tined rakes. For small quantities of seed the drills are taken out across the beds and this we feel results in optimum drainage. For large quantities of seed, then, it is more practical to take out the drills down the length of the beds (see Fig. 8).

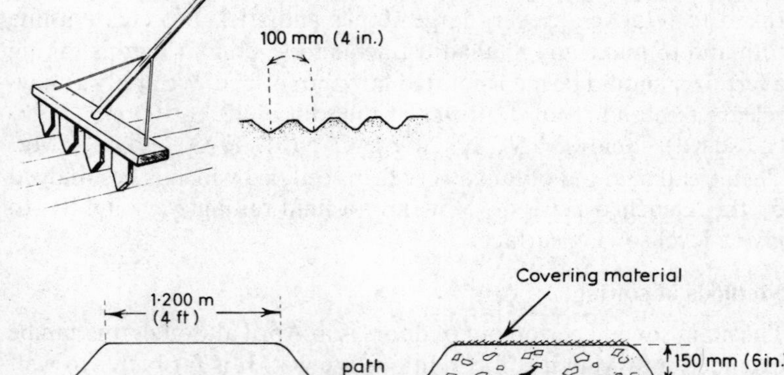

Fig. 8 Cross-section of raised seed beds and drill marker

The seed is then sown by hand. There are seed colourants for use when hand sowing to aid even distribution of small seeds. In forestry waxoline dyes are recommended, especially red as this is a good contrast against the soil.

We have discussed hand sowing here but of course, on a large scale, sowing can be mechanized. However this generally applies only to large enterprises like forestry nurseries, and the average producers of hardy nursery stock still use hand methods.

Seed density

The seed density or sowing rate depends on a number of factors: the required population of seedlings, the viability of the seed sample, the survival rate of the seeds once sown on the beds, and the seed count (the number of seeds per unit weight). The sowing rate can be calculated by using this formula:

$$\text{Sowing rate} = \frac{\text{Population of resultant seedlings}}{\text{Sample viability} \times \text{Survival rate} \times \text{Seed count}}$$

The survival rate of seeds sown on the beds is difficult to estimate as seed losses can occur due to wet or waterlogged conditions and the ravages of seed-eating birds. This is why we recommend really thorough preparation of seed beds to ensure as few losses as possible. When calculating sowing rates it is better to allow for heavier seed losses rather than lighter ones, as a stand of seedlings can always be thinned out if the population is too dense for satisfactory growth and development.

The basis of the above calculation is the population density of the resultant seedlings. It is not possible to give precise population densities for each species but, as a guide, here are a few examples of acceptable seedling densities:

Species with large seeds and vigorous growth: e.g., *Castanea*, *Juglans* and *Aesculus*, 190 per square metre (70·7 per sq ft).

The nuts such as *Corylus*, *Quercus* and *Ginkgo*, 250 per square metre.

Smaller seeds like species of *Acer*, *Carpinus* and *Fraxinus*, 380–500 per square metre.

Seed-bed covering materials

The size of the covering material is important as it can (a) affect the conservation of moisture around the seeds; (b) affect the seedling-shoot emergence above ground; and (c) affect the stability of the cover. Very large material may prevent shoot emergence by the 'large stone' effect while very fine material will form a consolidated layer over the seeds through which shoots may have difficulty in emerging. Very fine material may blow away. The recommended size of grit or shingle, if this material is to be used, is 1·5–4·5 mm (0·06–0·18 in).

Colour of the covering material can affect the temperature of the surface. Dark colours absorb heat and lift the seed-bed surface temperature and this can kill emerging seedlings. Also the surface of the seed bed dries out more rapidly. So light-coloured materials which reflect heat are recommended.

Shape of covering materials is important—a flat shape encourages packing and the formation of an impenetrable layer over the seeds.

The covering material should never have a high pH—in fact it should be acid.

The depth of cover depends on the size of the seeds—it can vary from 3 mm (0·125 in) for small seeds to 12 mm (0·5 in) for large seeds. If too deep for the size of the seeds it will affect shoot emergence, if too shallow, it can result in rapid moisture loss from the surface of the bed.

So what materials can be used? We have already mentioned grit or shingle as often used by forestry nurseries. This is extremely good as it eliminates capping and splashing, gives good aeration around the seedlings, allows for easy removal of weeds and results in even percolation of rain or irrigation water.

Seeds such as *Quercus*, *Castanea* and *Aesculus* are generally covered with soil. Pulverized bark and sawdust are also sometimes used although very fine sawdust should be avoided as it can cap on the surface.

There is a new plastic film on the market which has thousands of tiny slits per square metre. When it is laid over the seed beds the slits are closed, but as the seeds germinate and the shoots emerge above the soil, the film is lifted and the slits open, for ventilation and penetration of water. Irrigation can be carried out without removing the film. The idea of the film is to encourage and protect plant growth. Seeds should, however, first be covered with the usual covering materials.

Labelling

Each batch of seeds should be labelled with a strong wooden label written with a waterproof marker pen. You should include the source of the seed, the sowing date and, of course, the full name of the subject. This should relate to a book entry or some other form of recording.

Irrigation of beds

Irrigation should be carried out throughout the spring and summer during dry periods. It is essential to water if conditions are dry during the germination period. We favour oscillating spray lines as these water several beds at a time and produce the desired fine droplets. Heavy droplets can cause capping, especially if a soil covering has been used.

Weed control

Very often this is carried out by hand on a small scale and if dazomet was used to sterilize the land then there should be few problems with annual weed growth, although with beds left down for two years seeds of annual weeds will almost certainly appear in the second year, and even towards the end of the first year if conditions favour their appearance and growth. If seed was sown in drills then hand weeding is comparatively easy. Two soil-acting herbicides have recently been recommended for forestry seed beds although they would be well worth trying on other trees and shrubs, but carry out small trials to start with. The herbicides are diphenamid and nitrofen. They control germinating weeds, particularly annual grasses. Apply either pre-emergence, immediately after sowing; or post emergence, two weeks after full emergence of seedlings. Another herbicide that could be tried is chloroxuron, applied post emergence.

Shading

We have found it beneficial to shade seedlings, especially large-leaved subjects, from strong sun and the simplest way of doing this is to support shading netting over the beds at a height of about 1 m (3 ft 3 in). A light timber framework can be used to support this material.

Lifting seedlings

In the autumn the seedlings can be lifted either by undercutting or with forks. Their subsequent treatment depends on their purpose. For example, if they are rootstocks to be used for bench grafting the seedlings can be rolled (see Chapter 20) or potted off. Ornamental subjects for eventual containerization can also be potted off. Hedging and windbreak material and subjects for reclamation sites are sometimes large enough for direct lining out in the field. If not, then again rolling is a good method of growing on liners, including forest conifers, trees and shrubs.

7

Accelerated seedling production

Interest in the production of woody-plant seedlings in containers started in the late 1960s and early 1970s in forestry production in North America, Sweden and Finland. The concept of raising trees in containers is not new; it was first used by the early Americans and Aztecs who used fish carcasses to grow and plant young trees.

The advantages of raising trees in containers are:

1 Uniform growing system: plants can be grown in a controlled environment, such as a glasshouse or polythene tunnel. The result of this is uniformity which results in increased mechanization in the growing and planting of the crop. This is an important consideration, especially when skilled labour is getting more scarce and expensive.

2 Increased flexibility: this is especially valuable in forestry regeneration programmes where difficult sites are a common occurrence.

3 Shorter production cycle: it is possible with a controlled environment to accelerate the production; crops being grown in months rather than years.

4 Fewer losses: both in the nursery and on the planting site.

The disadvantages are, firstly, that it is a comparatively new technique in growing and therefore personnel have to be retrained to grow plants under these conditions, especially as containers are likely to dry out more quickly than conventional seed beds. Secondly, to install an intensive seed-production unit initially involves a high capital investment.

The major technical problems are caused by the necessity of aiming at one seed per container, which will produce a healthy seedling. This leads to more accurate work on seed viability or, alternatively, inserting naked germinated embryos (see Chapter 19). Also, seedlings have to be hardened off from the ideal optimum growing environment to normal outdoor conditions.

Accelerated Optimal Growth

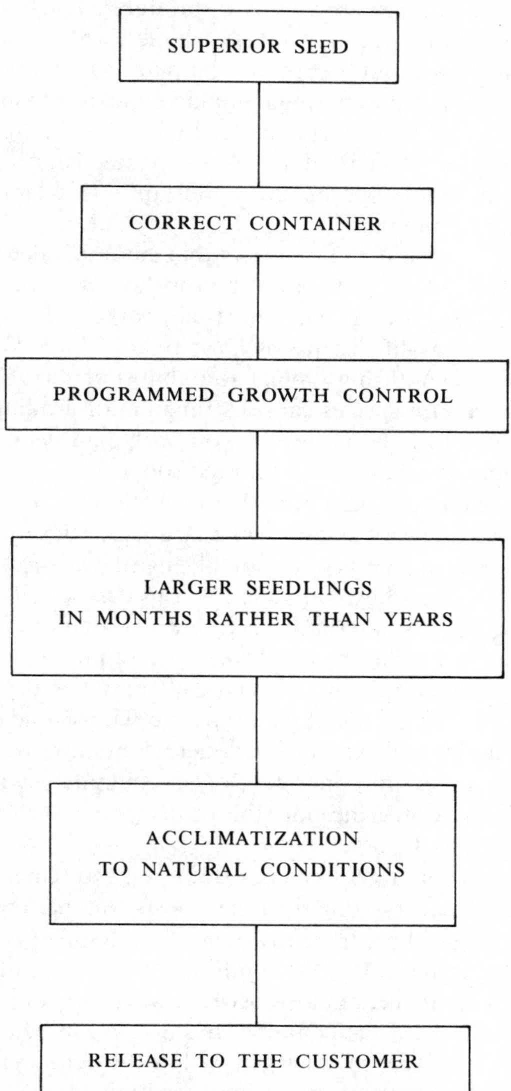

Choice of container

A wide range of containers is now available from various parts of the world in which to produce tree seedlings.

The aim of container growing is to produce a 'plug' of growing medium around the seedling roots to enable it to survive and start growing quickly without a check in the planting situation. It must be remembered that purchasing containers means buying a system and this must suit your particular methods of growing. The container is going to affect the type of root system that the seedling produces and this must be an important consideration when purchasing the container.

It has been known for many years that smooth-sided containers used in nursery production cause the root to curl around the pot. This is no serious problem with short-life crops, but could give rise to damage in long-life crops such as trees. Work by Professor Donald in the USA during 1966 proved that root curl slows growth down and in certain species causes strangulation leading to death. This is evident in forestry production with pine where retarded growth is often associated with knotted roots.

With conventional containers this problem can be easily overcome by slicing the root system. On a large scale this operation becomes laborious and a waste of valuable manpower. The alternative is to improve the seedling container and this can be achieved in one of two ways. The first alternative is to use a container with no walls such as a peat stick, or a very thin wall, for example paper, which can be easily penetrated by roots. This type of container also eliminates the job of removing the pot at planting time. The second choice is to modify the traditional type of container. A number of companies have already done this and developed containers with vertical grooves running down the pot; the root moves down the groove instead of circling the pot.

Whatever the container, the important point to remember is that if the plants are left too long then their roots will mat themselves in the standing area. This can be overcome by the use of chemicals or by air pruning at the base of the container. An opening at the base is important for drainage, but also because when the root tip reaches this point it will die if the container has an air gap below its base; thus, further rooting is encouraged within the container. One disadvantage of the air gap is that it impedes drainage.

Containers at present on the market can be divided into two groups: (a) degradable organic; and (b) inorganic. Both produce a 'plug' seedling, but by different growing systems. It is impossible to recommend an ideal container as this will depend on the system adopted by each individual grower. The following gives some idea of the types of container which are available.

DEGRADABLE ORGANIC CONTAINERS

Most containers are made up of compressed peat either in the form of a conventional container or as a peat stick. Peat pots come in a wide range of shapes and sizes and often are available with ready-made handling systems. An advantage of purchasing a pot/tray system is that handling is easier, small containers have stability and the operations of filling and sowing are made more efficient. Alternatively, the peat stick which was developed in the USA has the advantage that compost is not required; a seed is simply placed in the ready-made hole in the centre of the stick.

In Australia waste pine veneer is being used to roll containers. The veneers arrive in 150 mm (6 in) strips, which are soaked in water to make them flexible. They are then rolled using a 30 mm (1·18 in) pipe tube to obtain the right size. One disadvantage is that pine contains a toxin which has been shown to retard seedlings slightly.

The best-known degradable container is the paper pot. Fifty per cent of Swedish propagation for forestry use is now in this type of container. The paper is bonded together with soluble adhesive. This system has many virtues: it is hygienic, easy to handle and capable of being adapted to a flow-line system. The life of the paper varies from between 4 to 6 weeks, 6 to 10 weeks and 9 to 12 weeks depending on the grade of paper used.

INORGANIC CONTAINERS

Containers can again be sub-divided into those produced by moulded polystyrene and moulded polythene. The polystyrene containers are tapered and come with their own handling system. By using the standard container it is possible to produce 1,200 trees per square metre (1,200 trees in 10·7 sq ft). Polythene containers either come ready-made or hinged and are then assembled on the nursery.

Growing media

Using a container enables production to be carried out in more advanced seed-growing media. At present three composts are favoured by producers: the normal seed-growing compost as used in bedding-plant production; 1:1 peat/Vermiculite mixture; or a normal sandy loam soil.

Obviously people have their own ideas on the best growing media, especially with a relatively new growing method. Potting mixtures developed for normal container-plant production can easily be modified to grow seedlings (see Chapter 21). The main considerations are that the medium is light to make transportation easy; is capable of holding moisture, both for the plants' requirements and to hold the plug together; is suitable for a number of different tree species; and does not contain either insufficient or toxic amounts of fertilizer.

Little is known about the nutrition of broadleaf tree seedlings and often practices adopted are similar to those developed for conifer seed beds.

End of season height and root-collar diameter are improved by top dressings of nitrogen. The major gain for most species is the addition of 5 g nitrogen/m^2 (0·15 oz/sq yd). Subjects such as birch and sycamore benefit considerably from a top dressing while improvements in beech and oak are not quite so pronounced (Forestry Commission Research 1974/5).

Fertilization is important in container-seedling growing as, unlike seed-bed production, the grower is trying to raise plants in a confined space and with a limited root zone. The fertilizer programme must be altered throughout the growing cycle, the seedling requiring far less nutrient in the early stages of its development.

Seed sowing

Earlier we mentioned the problem of getting one seed in a container. Many species produce very small seed and to sow these by hand would be time-consuming and laborious. Sowing is the first important operation, overcrowded seedlings resulting in reduced quality, while containers without seeds in them mean wasted space and money. Two major problems exist: seed viability and seed distribution in the containers.

Accurate information on seed viability is essential for sowing decisions. If viability is as low as 25 per cent then up to four seeds may have to be sown per container, while if it is at 95 per cent then one seed per container is acceptable. In recent years viability testing of seed has improved, resulting in management decisions on how many seeds are sown per container.

Seed-distribution machines have now been developed and are used by large container-seedling producers. Seeds are fed into a rotating drum and are fixed to holes spaced at the correct positions for the containers by vacuum pressure created within the drum. Seed is released by cutting off the vacuum pressure and applying a light air pressure inside the drum.

Environmental control

The aim is to modify the natural conditions to produce sizeable seedlings in one growing season. To achieve this controlled environment some sort of structure to protect the seedlings is required and this is normally a glasshouse or polythene tunnel. Apart from protection one can also consider lighting, carbon-dioxide enrichment and heating to induce maximum growth.

Compared with seed-bed-raised trees, those which are container grown will experience higher air and soil temperatures as well as more plants per given area. The result of this is higher transpiration and if left they will be under greater water stress than seed-bed-raised plants.

Watering can be either manual or automatic, but timing will vary between crops, conditions and containers and therefore will rely on observation and experience.

Carbon dioxide can be introduced by installing CO_2 burners using the same principles which are adopted for glasshouse carbon-dioxide enrichment.

One problem with high-density containerized seedling production is that pathogens can soon damage a large number of plants. The most serious problem is *Botrytis cinerea* which appears as a grey mould on a wide range of plants, occuring on dead and dying vegetation. The disease is most prevalent when plants are grown in high relative humidity and spreads rapidly if plants have been overhead watered and droplets remain on the foliage. Control can either be by using a protective fungicide (benomyl) or increasing air movement over the plants to reduce the time that moisture remains on the foliage.

Diseases such as *Pythium*, *Phytophthora* and *Rhizoctonia* are common, as on seed-beds. They cause damping-off and thrive in warm, humid conditions. The first visual symptoms are normally the seedlings toppling over; on closer inspection the fungus will be visible on the hypocotyl. To control damping-off, drench the seedlings with captan at a rate of 1 kg product in 1,000 litres of water and applied at 5 l/m^2 (1 lb with 100 gal applied at 1 gal/sq yd). Other materials are now available to the grower for incorporation in the growing media and these should also now be considered (see Chapter 21).

Hardening off seedlings too quickly can also result in losses. It is important the seedlings are not placed out of doors until the last spring frost has passed. During the hardening-off process supplementary lighting, if used, is shut off, fertilizer programmes are reduced and the temperature is slowly reduced in the structure.

Planting

The major advantage of 'plug' seedlings is that in forest-tree raising it leads to more efficient planting techniques. Containers can be

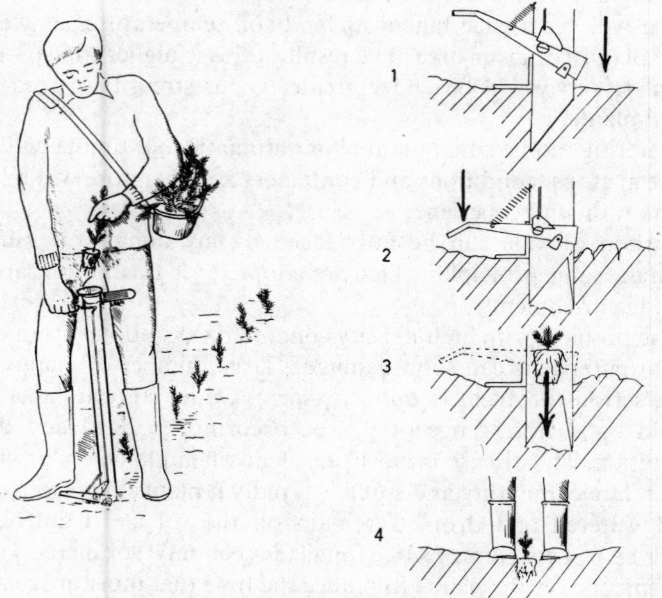

Fig. 9 The Pottiputki planting gun

packed into carrier cases which fit on to a ruck-sack frame for transport to the planting site. At the site the containers hang on a hip holder leaving the planter with two free hands. A plant can be drawn out of the pot at the same time as a hole is being made in the soil.

Various planting implements are now available, but the most commonly available is the 'Pottiputki' from Finland. This planting gun allows planting without uncomfortable stooping, and its mode of operation is shown in Fig. 9.

The point of the 'Pottiputki' is inserted into the ground (1), the jaws are opened by means of a pedal (2) and the plant then drops through the tube (3). The gun is then lifted and the planter firms the soil around the plant (4). One disadvantage of the 'Pottiputki' is that it is difficult to use in brush-covered ground although it is very quick and efficient in open land.

GROWING SYSTEMS

Nurserymen now have the choice between growing seedlings in outdoor seed beds or in containers in a controlled growing environment. The choice can easily be summarized in the diagram on page 80.

Container trees are now an accepted production technique in afforestation and reforestation programmes. The system has now overcome its teething problems and ornamental growers can look on this method as an alternative for certain crops.

Seed-raised tree and shrub crops can be divided into the following groupings:

1 Hedging material.
2 Rootstocks.
3 Forestry seedlings.
4 Plants for conservation areas.
5 High-quality ornamental plants.

Quality requirements will vary according to the market at which the crop is aimed and, therefore, the method of production should reflect this. Low-value mass-produced plants, such as those required for hedging, can be easily and cheaply produced in conventional seed beds, while high-quality specimen plants could be produced in containers, where large losses become unacceptable and a guarantee of quality is required. In addition, one of the major cost

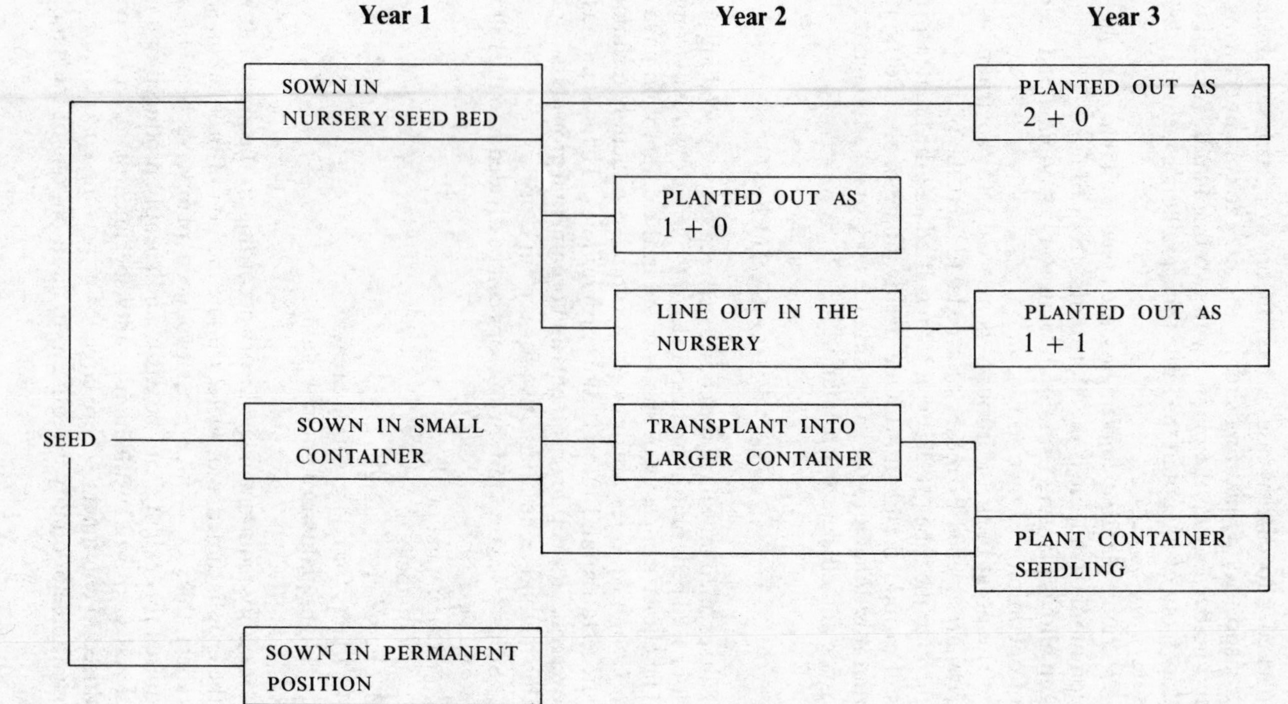
Year 1
Year 2
Year 3
SEED
SOWN IN NURSERY SEED BED
PLANTED OUT AS 2 + 0
PLANTED OUT AS 1 + 0
LINE OUT IN THE NURSERY
PLANTED OUT AS 1 + 1
SOWN IN SMALL CONTAINER
TRANSPLANT INTO LARGER CONTAINER
PLANT CONTAINER SEEDLING
SOWN IN PERMANENT POSITION

and labour areas in outdoor seed beds is weed control. This operation can be eliminated in containers, again resulting in a higher-quality plant and fewer losses due to erratic weeding.

Intensive production can also be of value where mass-produced plants are needed for customers who require large numbers for direct planting, e.g., local authorities and conservation organizations. The advantage here is twofold. Firstly, the nurseryman can handle large numbers of plants easily, without root disturbance, and secondly, the customer can plant the material more efficiently, without a check to the seedling, by using a planting gun.

Management considerations

In planning seedling crops and market requirements the nurseryman needs to select the right species to grow and the right numbers. Often this decision is governed by present fashions, which may be outdated when the crop is ready for sale, leaving him with surplus stock.

With outdoor-grown stock this planning often has to be done two years in advance of the sale date, but with intensive production the plans can be made 12 months ahead to achieve the same product, due to the shorter growing cycle.

Bare-root seedlings do have their advantages. They are normally larger than container-grown plants, which means they have more chance of survival in weedy areas or where there is no maintenance after planting.

In conclusion it must be stressed that the end product governs the system adopted, but as labour costs continue to rise growers must lean more towards intensive methods.

SEED PRODUCTION IN BOXES

For high-quality ornamental plants, seeds may be sown in trays under protection. This technique can be used where small quantities are required or where outdoor seed beds are unsuitable for the crop and facilities are not available for intensive container production. Seedlings in trays have the same advantages as intensively produced crops, that is, protected environment, pest and disease control, weed elimination and the correct growing media. Plants raised in seed trays require more attention than outdoor crops and more skill is needed in sowing and management.

The trays for raising seedling trees can be either plastic or wooden, as long as they have adequate drainage. They should also be clean to ensure no disease is carried to newly emerging seedlings. If boxes need to be sterilized they can be dipped in formaldehyde, but it is important to ensure they are thoroughly dried and aired after sterilization as the fumes are toxic to plant growth.

The seed compost should be an open mixture to assist drainage and the following is recommended for a cubic metre (cubic yard):

2 parts sterilized loam
1 part sphagnum peat
1 part sand
1 kg (2 lb 4 oz) single superphosphate
300 g (10·5 oz) ground chalk

Compost should be evenly firmed throughout the box to give an even seed bed.

The seed sowing is governed by the same rules as in outdoor seed beds, that is, evenly spaced and thinly sown to avoid 'damping-off'. After sowing, the seed is covered with compost to about the same depth as the seeds' diameter unless it is a light-responsive plant, such as *Rhododendron*, when no covering is given.

Seed trays are placed in a well-ventilated glasshouse to encourage germination. In some cases bottom heat of 15 °C (60 °F) may be given to speed up the process. Germination normally occurs after a few weeks; once seedlings emerge they should not be exposed to cold draughts or excess heat which would result in flagging.

Transplanting or pricking out takes place as soon as the seedlings can be easily handled. This should be done with care, especially with expensive or rare plants, as damage can easily occur with careless handling. Plants can either be pricked out into trays or containers for growing on. The seedlings can then be treated as normal container plants when established (see Part 4).

8

Vegetative propagation systems

So far we have dealt with the propagation of crops from seeds, but now we turn to asexual or vegetative propagation systems. Vegetative propagation is probably the most widely practised form of propagation among general nurserymen.

Propagation from cuttings is indeed extensively practised and therefore, in the following chapters, we will deal with the rooting of cuttings under mist, under polythene with bottom heat, under low polythene tunnels, in double-glazed cold frames and in heated cutting bins. We will also deal with root cuttings, with hardwood cuttings both in heat and without heat, and with rootstock production from cuttings. However, cuttings are by no means the only method of vegetative propagation open to the nurseryman and for this reason we will also cover the production of rootstocks by stooling and by layering and also cover the production of other crops by various methods of layering. Then, of course, there is also budding and grafting which are used to produce a wide range of trees and various shrubs.

TOOLS

To be successful with vegetative propagation, whether by cuttings, grafting, or whatever method, it is essential to have the correct knives and secateurs, and it is also important to care for them correctly. It will be as well here, therefore, to say a few words on the selection and care of knives and secateurs.

Knives

Use the correct knife for the job, for example, a budding knife with a spatula on the handle or blade for budding, and a heavy grafting knife for field grafting. Use a lighter grafting knife for bench grafting. Grafting knives should have straight rather than curved blades.

Many nurserymen use a budding knife for taking cuttings. This is generally satisfactory but it may be better to invest in a light, straight-bladed knife purely for the purpose of propagation from cuttings (see Plate 1).

Buy the best-quality knives available as these will then serve you for a great many years and, being made from good-quality steel, the blades will retain their cutting edge for much longer than cheap knives before the need to resharpen. Cheap knives are made from soft steel and the blades very quickly become blunt and therefore need more frequent sharpening. This results in the blades being worn away in a comparatively short period of time. Never buy a knife with a stainless-steel blade as it is virtually impossible to get it really sharp.

When buying knives ensure that the blade is firmly set in the handle and does not move about—if you buy top quality this is no problem. With cheaper knives very often the blades have a habit of becoming loose after they have been used for some time.

Having bought good-quality knives you should take great care of them. For instance, avoid dropping them; using them with a sawing action; chipping the blades; and twisting when cutting, which can distort the blade. Always clean knives after use and oil sparingly occasionally. It is a good idea to have your name on all your knives to minimize the risk of loss.

Now we come on to sharpening knives, starting with those with straight blades. Firstly clean the blade to ensure there is no grit on it. Then clean off the oil stone, again to ensure there is no grit on this. Grit can seriously damage the cutting edge of the blade. Then apply a little oil to the stone and on no account flood it with oil. Now you must check the side or sides on which the knife is to be sharpened. Many horticultural knives are single-edged—that is, they are only sharpened on one side of the blade. One should always stick to this same edge when sharpening and on no account grind off the other side. Other knives may be double-edged, that is, sharpened on both sides of the blade. In this case always sharpen on both sides.

When sharpening, ensure that the complete length of the blade is in contact with the stone and then slightly raise the back edge. Now push the knife up the stone (away from you), holding the handle in one hand, with the fingers of the other hand applying pressure to the blade. When the blade reaches the end of the stone lift it up and off the stone and reposition it at the other end. Repeat this as often as necessary to obtain a really sharp edge. It sounds a slow procedure when described in this way, but in fact it is just the opposite. Remove the 'wire' on a leather strop after sharpening (some people refer to 'wire' as burs). These are small particles of metal adhering to the edge of the blade and unless removed result in a blunting effect.

Finally clean the blade and the handle, and be sure to remove any plant sap from the blade. This can be removed with methylated spirits. If you have a knife with a curved blade (for instance, a pruning knife) then you will need to sharpen it on a curved stone. Use the technique described above, but reposition the knife to ensure that the entire edge is sharpened.

Secateurs

Secateurs are essential to the nurseryman—for instance, for preparing hardwood cuttings, for preparing rootstocks during field grafting, for stooling and layering, for pruning, and so on. Again buy the best available to ensure they are made of top-quality steel which will withstand regular sharpening.

We would suggest that you avoid the anvil type as these have the annoying habit of crushing stems during use. Instead go for the parrot-bill type which cut with a slicing action. It would be best to buy a type that can be dismantled as it is then easy to sharpen the blade when required. Simply remove the central pin or bolt so that the secateurs can be taken apart.

Before sharpening, again clean the blade and also the oil stone. Now sharpen with sweeping strokes along the blade, using this time a small oil stone. Generally there is only one blade to sharpen and again make sure you sharpen it on the side that was originally sharpened in the factory. Finally remove any 'wire' or burs on a leather strop, clean all parts, reassemble and lightly oil the pivot.

You are now ready to propagate. Do not forget that if you are working in the field take along a small pocket oil stone for touching up the blades of knives as required.

9

Mist and polythene

Mist propagation, which involves automatically spraying cuttings intermittently with a fine mist-like spray of water, evolved in the 1950s and revolutionized the rooting of cuttings of all kinds of plants. Today most nurseries producing hardy plants have a mist-propagation unit and very often this is the main method of rooting cuttings. However, the rooting of cuttings under polythene with bottom heat is also now becoming widely used, especially for winter and autumn propagation. There is no doubt that mist propagation has enabled growers to root hitherto difficult subjects with comparative ease and to speed up the rooting of the more easy subjects.

Setting up a mist unit

A mist unit can be set up in a glasshouse, in walk-in polythene tunnels or in frames, but most nurserymen prefer to have a mist unit in a conventional glasshouse as there is better control over ventilation.

Traditionally the mist unit is set up on strong benches, which can be constructed of such materials as railway sleepers, concrete building-blocks, galvanized angle iron or some similar strong material. A suitable width for each bench is 1·2 m (4 ft) – wider benches make it difficult to reach the cuttings in the centre. It is essential to have a porous base to allow excess water to drain away. We have used welded-steel mesh covered with heavy black polythene sheeting with holes in for drainage.

There is no need to install the mist unit on benches. One of our units is installed above concrete pads at floor level. The pads are heated from below by means of hot-water pipes (underfloor heating) and the trays of cuttings stand directly on the concrete. Concrete pads are also sometimes heated by means of electric warming cables embedded in them.

The layout of the jets, which spray the cuttings with water, is very important. The jets, or mist heads as they are also called, should all be at the same level. They may either be suspended from the roof of the glasshouse above the benches, or be attached to stand-pipes which are fixed to the bench.

There are various types of jet or mist head available, most of which produce a circular spray pattern, but some of the more expensive types produce a rectangular pattern. A conventional mist head is shown in Fig. 10.

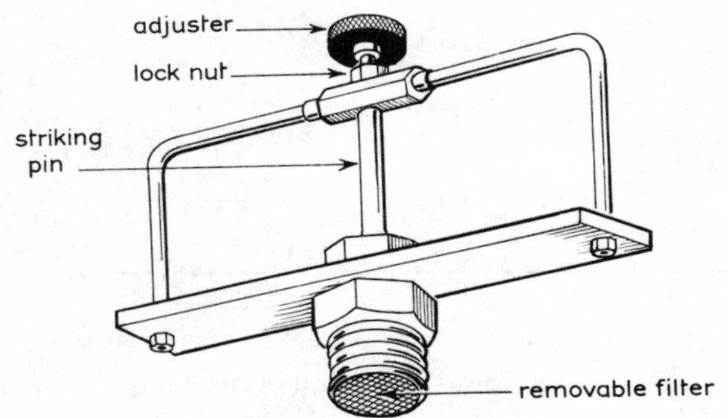

Fig. 10 A conventional mist-propagation jet which produces a circular spray pattern

The mist heads should preferably run in a single line down the centre of each bench – a staggered layout is wasteful of water. Mist heads which are too large for the bench are also wasteful of water as the spray pattern will extend considerably beyond the edges of the benches. The jets must be placed so that there are no dry corners on the bench and for the same reason the spray patterns must overlap. Different types of spray pattern are shown in Fig. 11.

One way to check water distribution over each bench is to place petri dishes over the bench at regular intervals, set the mist unit in operation, and then measure the amount of water in each dish. If the unit is well set up there should be an equal amount of water in each dish.

Let us now consider water in general. There must of course be an unfailing supply – it should always be available and if necessary there should be some form of emergency supply. The water supply must be clean and uncontaminated. Most nurseries use the mains supply and to ensure sufficient pressure at the mist heads it is often

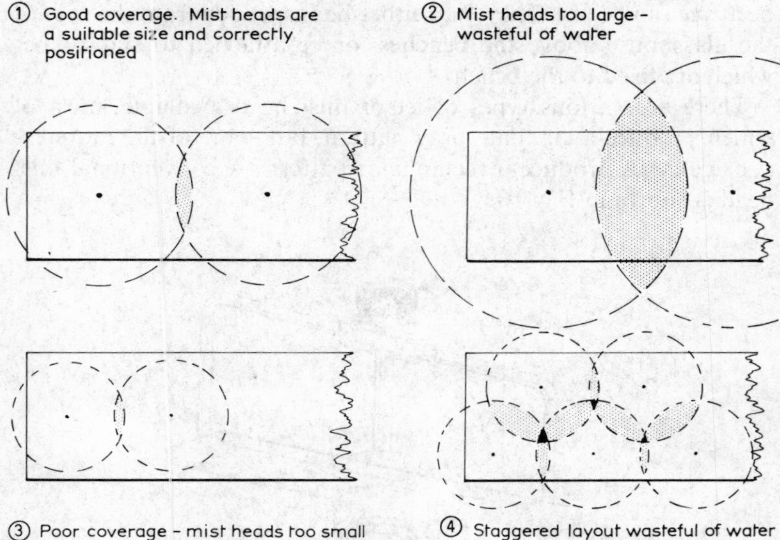

Fig. 11 Overhead spray patterns on a mist bench

necessary to install a pressure tank and pump. This will also ensure consistent pressure.

Alkalinity is one of the main problems with a mist unit. The effects of alkaline water are:

1 Deposits of calcium on the cuttings, which are difficult to remove, unsightly, and which inhibit new growth.
2 A build-up of alkalinity in the compost, which inhibits root growth and causes problems with slow-rooting plants especially.

In a hard-water area one could overcome the problem of alkalinity by using rainwater, or by installing water-treatment apparatus which removes dissolved salts from the water before it is applied to the cuttings. The ideal pH for the water is 5·5 to 6·5.

If a mist unit is set up on benches, then bottom heat can be provided by means of soil-warming cables. These can be laid in sand or gravel on the bench – a 50 mm (2 in) layer of sand or gravel then the cables, then another 50 mm deep layer of sand or gravel. Lay the cable in straight lines running the length of the bench, looped at each end, and with each loop at the same level. There should be a minimum space of 50 mm between each loop. One should aim for

135 w/m² (15 w/sq ft) and this will ensure a temperature of 21 °C (70 °F) under any conditions. The soil-warming cables are controlled by means of a rod-type thermostat placed 50 mm (2 in) above the cables and across the bed – just below the surface of the bed. A 450 mm (18 in) rod thermostat is very often used.

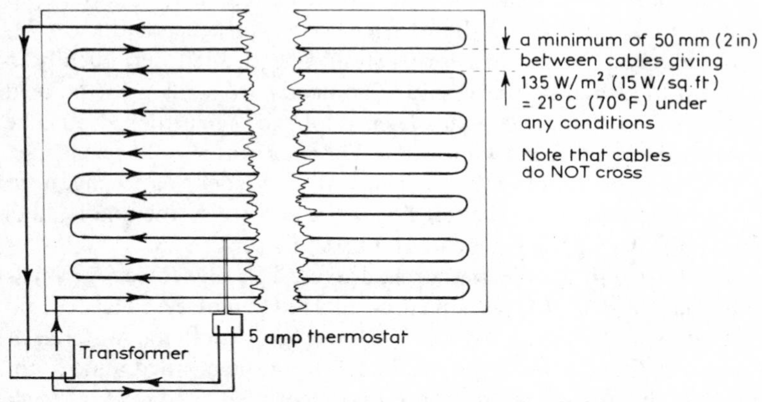

Fig. 12 Layout of heating cables

The frequency of operation of misting is controlled by a madistat placed between the cuttings. This is popularly called an 'electronic leaf'; that is, a moisture-sensitive element, which dries out at the same rate as the cuttings. So when the leaves of the cuttings are dry, the surface of the madistat is also dry and it therefore activates the mist.

It is necessary to position the madistat carefully on the bench, for if too close to a mist head it may collect too much water and then the mist may not operate as frequently as necessary to keep the leaves of the cuttings moist. If too far away from a mist head it may not be adequately moistened each time the jets operate and therefore the mist may come on too frequently, and the cuttings will receive too much water, resulting in a saturated compost.

The madistat should be at a similar height to the tops of the cuttings, or maybe slightly higher. Generally one needs to move the madistat around on the bench until it is in a suitable position. At all costs one should avoid run-off of water from the foliage as this results in a saturated compost. Each burst of mist should result in a thin layer of moisture on the leaves of the cuttings. (It is sometimes useful, if the cuttings dry out too quickly and more frequent misting is required, to tilt the 'leaf' slightly so that it dries out more quickly, resulting in more frequent bursts of mist.)

Routine maintenance of a mist unit

To function properly a mist unit should be regularly checked over and maintained. Ensure the nozzles on the mist heads do not become blocked. Metal mist heads should be cleaned periodically in concentrated hydrochloric acid. The heads are soaked in the acid until all the calcium scale has been removed. Then they should be washed thoroughly in plain water. The madistat should be cleaned periodically by rubbing the surface with fine emery paper, again to remove calcium scale. Do not finger the surface of the madistat as this can leave a greasy deposit and upset its sensitivity.

The mist unit should be checked over each day to see that it is working properly. At the same time all dead and diseased leaves and cuttings should be removed. The cuttings should be watered if necessary. Once a week the madistat should be cleaned and, if applicable, the mist-unit pump should be reprimed. The weekly check should include removal of any weeds, empty boxes and other containers, dead plants and so on, from the house.

In the winter the mist can be switched off at 5 p.m. and turned on again at 7.30 a.m. whenever it is considered necessary.

Conditions provided by a mist unit

A mist unit automatically provides the optimum conditions for rooting cuttings – warm bottoms and cool tops. It gives protection to the cuttings at all times and therefore results in quicker rooting. It ensures the successful rooting of difficult subjects and generally results in better-quality plants for potting off or lining out. One can operate a mist unit with semi-skilled labour – even newcomers to the profession can prepare cuttings and place them under mist.

The aim of misting is to keep the leaves of cuttings cool; this, coupled with high atmospheric humidity, maintains turgor pressure in the leaves and so prevents them wilting. Turgid cuttings root more quickly and more successfully than cuttings which are allowed to wilt. Water loss from the leaves is reduced by the cooling effect of the evaporating water film on the surface of the leaves, and so the cuttings do not wilt. We must remember that newly prepared cuttings have no roots and therefore they are very prone to water stress unless placed under optimum conditions, such as provided by a mist unit. To prevent water stress in the cuttings the vapour pressure inside and outside of the leaves should ideally reach the same level. This can be achieved with a mist unit.

Between bursts of mist, there are often long periods during which leaves are drying off and this can result in severe water stress in the cuttings, resulting in reduced rooting. This is one of the disadvantages of mist over bottom heat and polythene. With a polythene covering the high atmospheric humidity is constant, whereas with mist it is variable. So under polythene there is less stress on the cuttings and in fact one achieves better rooting during the winter period. However, mist cools the leaves of cuttings but under polythene, in the summer, the leaves are subject to high temperatures, again resulting in poorer rooting. To sum up, the ideal system is to root cuttings under mist in the spring and summer, and to root autumn and winter cuttings under polythene with bottom heat.

Not so very long ago it was considered unwise to shade cuttings under mist for fear of reducing photosynthesis, thereby inhibiting rooting, but recently there has been new thinking on the subject of shading. Obviously excessive shading will limit photosynthesis, thereby resulting in a shortage of carbohydrates necessary for root formation. There are no stored reserves of carbohydrates in cuttings.

With a certain amount of shading, sufficient to reduce leaf scorch, the cuttings will produce sufficient carbohydrates to ensure successful rooting. A very high light-intensity will, in fact, result in an excessive build-up of carbohydrates within the cuttings, which it has been found inhibits rooting.

The optimum amount of shading is 20 per cent from spring to autumn. Green shading netting is often used, which is suspended over the cuttings. In the future we will, perhaps, see the advent of light-modulated shading, which must be the ultimate in the shading of cuttings.

Good ventilation in the mist house is necessary to prevent high air temperatures, which lead to excessive extension growth of cuttings. This uses up carbohydrates in the cuttings at the expense of root production. The heat is needed at the base of the cuttings, not in the atmosphere, and therefore a basal temperature of 21 °C (70 °F) is generally recommended.

There can be a deterioration of cuttings under mist due to loss of nutrients by leaching. This can be overcome by the use of nutrients in the mist or slow-release fertilizers in the compost. Both techniques are being researched at present so there are no firm recommendations that can be made.

We have already stated that there should be no run-off from the leaves of the cuttings. Apart from saturating the compost and lowering the soil temperature, it also causes nutrient leaching. Cuttings should not be left under mist once they have rooted as this can result in rapid deterioration. They should be weaned off and then potted off to prevent any check to growth.

A cropping programme for a mist unit

A mist unit, to be economically viable, should ideally be used all the year round. It is possible to obtain six to eight crops per year from a unit – an average of two to six weeks' rooting. Generally the peak rooting period is May, June and July, which puts great pressure on

Table 5 Mist-propagation programme

	Type of cutting	*Rooting period*	*Examples*
A	Evergreens, difficult rooting (semi-ripe)	Approximately 8 weeks	*Rhododendron*, *Mahonia*, *Ilex*, *Garrya*
B	Conifers, easy rooting (semi-ripe)	Approximately 8 weeks	*Chamaecyparis*, *Thuya*, × *Cupressocyparis*
C	Softwoods, forced stock plants	Approximately 4 weeks	*Acer*, *Azalea*, *Syringa*
D	Softwoods, normal method	Approximately 4 weeks	Shrubs, climbers, alpines, herbaceous, etc.
E	Conifers, dwarf, if not grafted (semi-ripe)	Approximately 8 weeks	*Picea*
F	Evergreens, easy rooting (semi-ripe)	Approximately 8 weeks	*Viburnum*, *Skimmia*, *Choisya*
G	Conifers, difficult rooting (semi-ripe)	Approximately 8 weeks	*Juniperus*, *Taxus*

the mist unit and on the nursery staff. One should therefore aim to reduce this peak. For instance, where possible use other means of propagation; or force stock plants so that you obtain earlier cuttings —for example, subjects like *Forsythia*, *Acer palmatum*, deciduous *Azalea*, *Caryopteris*, *Ceratostigma* and *Clematis* can be forced in tunnels or under glass. Deciduous material can be rooted in the period May to September, while evergreen subjects can be rooted in the autumn and early winter.

Do not root hairy- or woolly-leaved subjects under mist as they dislike continuously wet foliage and the hairs collect too much water, with the result that heavy losses can occur.

Each nursery will probably have its own mist-propagation programme for the year, but we can recommend the programme given in Table 5 and Fig. 13.

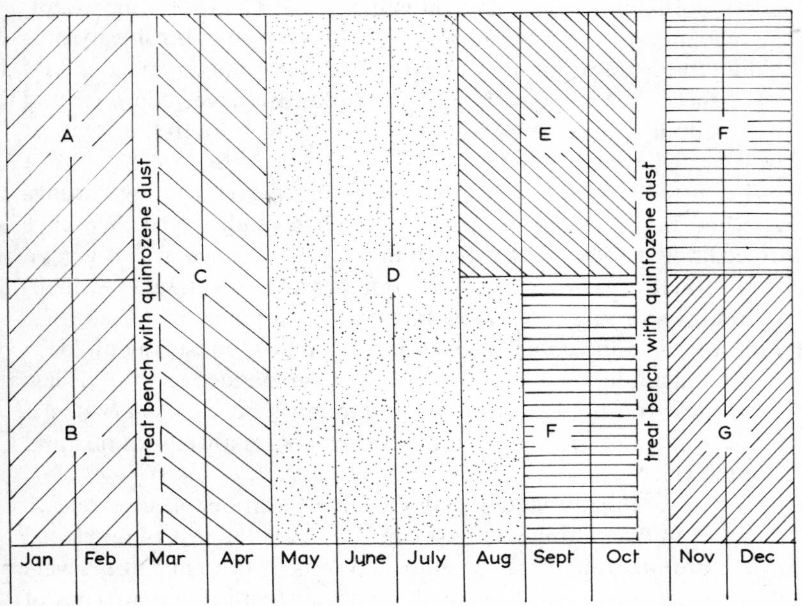

Fig. 13 Mist-propagation programme

Containers for cuttings

Containers for propagation are discussed in Chapter 20, and readers should therefore refer to that chapter for more detailed information. Containers in a mist unit, whether seed trays or the various types of unit containers, need a well-drained base, such as sand or gravel, to minimize risk of an over-wet rooting medium. Some of the newer propagation blocks like rockwool and foam plastic need less drainage than peat blocks and pots. In fact, we have found that many of the peat blocks can become too wet under mist. There must be a good moisture/air relationship in the rooting medium and to achieve this there must be adequate contact between the propagation unit and the base on which it stands. Propagation units need higher bottom heat to compensate for loss of heat caused by evaporation of moisture from the unit's surface.

Composts for cuttings

A suitable moisture/air relationship in the compost is important for good results under mist. The moisture content can, to some extent, be regulated by the mist supply but it is easier to control it by providing the correct amount of drainage, both in the compost and on the bench. The relationship between the drainage, compost and water supply is important if good moisture/air ratio in the compost is to be achieved.

The usual type of compost to use under mist for rooting cuttings is 50:50 moist sphagnum peat and coarse sand or grit. We have exceedingly good results with 6 mm (0·25 in) crushed grit: it gives a well-aerated, well-drained compost which encourages a high-percentage rooting and substantial root development in the cuttings. For autumn and winter propagation a compost consisting of 25:75 moist sphagnum peat and grit can be recommended as it holds less moisture. Another compost which is often used by nurserymen is 50:50 sphagnum peat and Perlite which creates a well-drained and aerated warm compost.

We have already stated that the incorporation of slow-release fertilizer in the cutting compost can overcome the loss of nutrients. There are no really firm recommendations at present but growers may care to experiment in small-scale trials with different types of fertilizer at varying rates.

Preparation and insertion of cuttings

Cuttings under mist should have a high leaf/stem ratio to encourage quicker and better rooting: leafy cuttings result in more photosynthesis and hence better rooting. Generally, larger cuttings are used than for other systems of propagation.

Cuttings are prepared in the conventional way in other respects: that is, they are nodal and have the lower leaves removed cleanly. Leaves of some subjects can be stripped cleanly between the finger and thumb, but other subjects will need the leaves cut off to avoid bark tearing which can result in rotting of the cuttings. Some subjects will need wounding at the base of the cutting, that is, removing cleanly a thin slice of bark or wood. For example, conifers such as *Juniperus*, need only light wounding—a shallow 25 mm (1 in) long cut no deeper than the cambial layers under the bark. Other subjects (including *Rhododendron*, *Ilex* and *Elaeagnus*) need a heavy wound—the removal of a 25 mm long thin slice of wood. This wounding results in a higher survival rate of the cuttings after propagation.

To encourage quicker rooting and a more substantial root system it is usual to treat the bases of all cuttings with a root-promoting hormone. IBA (indolebutyric acid) is generally used and the powder form is generally preferred. Captan can be mixed with this to prevent rotting at the base of the cuttings. There are various strengths of hormone rooting powders, for treating softwood, semi-ripe and hardwood cuttings.

Some nurserymen use liquid preparations of IBA. There is the 'long-dip' method whereby the cuttings (the lower 25 mm (1 in) stand in the dilute solution for 24 hours. The concentration of IBA can vary from 20 ppm for easy-rooting cuttings, to 200 ppm for those which are considered more difficult to root. The solution can be made up by dissolving IBA in a small amount of ethyl alcohol and then adding water to bulk it up. Then there is the 'quick-dip' method which is often used for difficult hardwood cuttings. A concentrated solution of IBA is used in this instance, and can vary from 500 ppm to 4,000 ppm IBA. The chemical is dissolved in ethyl alcohol. The cut surface only of the cutting is dipped in the solution and is removed immediately.

To prevent diseases such as *Botrytis* from attacking the cuttings, they can be completely dipped in a solution of benomyl prior to hormone treatment.

The rooting medium should not be made too firm in the container and the cuttings should not be firmed in too much, as a fairly loose rooting medium ensures good aeration. The compost should be just firm enough to support the cuttings. The cuttings can be settled in by hand watering once on the mist bench. As soon as the cuttings have been inserted they should be placed under mist so that they have no chance to wilt.

Aftercare of cuttings

On the mist bench, cuttings are prone to attack by *Botrytis* so spray them about once a fortnight with a solution of benomyl. Remove dead leaves and cuttings regularly. Ventilate the house freely to keep the atmosphere cool.

Once the cuttings have rooted, when the roots are at least 25 mm (1 in) long, they should be weaned off the mist. Ideally the mist should be gradually reduced until it is stopped completely, but this is not generally possible owing to unrooted cuttings being on the bench. Instead the rooted cuttings can be transferred to a bench in a heated propagation house, to become acclimatized to the normal atmosphere, and then moved out to polythene walk-in tunnels or shaded cold frames.

Of course, once the rooted cuttings have been weaned off, they must be potted off; otherwise, if they are rooted in a medium with no nutrients, they will starve. It is essential to avoid a check to growth at this stage of production.

It may be found that some cuttings have produced excess callus tissue and little or no roots. Excess callusing can be due to the fact that rooting conditions are not right: perhaps the basal temperature was too high, the rooting medium was not right, or the cuttings were not taken at the optimum time of year. Callus is a healing tissue and is completely separate from rooting. An excess can, in fact, inhibit the rooting that should occur before much callus is formed.

Finally, remember to allow time in the propagation programme to treat the benches with quintozene dust (see Fig. 13) to control the disease *Rhizoctonia* which causes a black rot at the base of the cuttings.

BOTTOM HEAT AND POLYTHENE

Cuttings of many subjects can be rooted with the aid of bottom heat and polythene sheeting. Although some growers use this system all the year round we have found that it is most satisfactory for propagation during the autumn and winter, with mist propagation for the spring and summer.

Construction

Generally, this system is set up on a strong bench in a propagation house. The bench should be capable of supporting sand or shingle and must allow for the drainage of surplus water. Soil-warming cables are laid, preferably on a sand base, and are then covered with a further layer of sand. These should of course be thermostatically controlled and a base temperature of 21–24 °C (70–75 °F) should be the aim.

A more up-to-date system is to have heated concrete beds at floor level in the propagation house. Generally these are heated by means of hot-water pipes bedded in the concrete. A small oil-fired boiler could be installed in the propagation house. For this system one should, of course, seek the advice of specialist heating engineers, and a reputable firm should be sought to ensure there is no trouble in the equipment, once installed, as this could mean having to break up the concrete to reach any faulty pipes!

A selection of subjects

We have already stated that many subjects respond to this method of propagation and the following list gives some of the main types of plant material. We have given the optimum periods for the propagation of each plant and readers will notice that some are propagated in the spring and summer. Some growers may prefer in fact to root these particular subjects under mist instead of polythene, and just use polythene for autumn/winter propagation.

Azalea, deciduous (April)
Azalea, evergreen (July–August)
Berberis (September–October)
Camellia (August)
Chamaecyparis (October–February)
Cotinus (June)
Cotoneaster (July–August)
× *Cupressocyparis* (October–February)
Cupressus (October–February)
Elaeagnus (December–March)
Garrya (February)
Ilex (October–February)
Juniperus (January–February)
Magnolia (April–July)
Mahonia (October)
Pieris (July)
Pittosporum (October)
Rhododendron, dwarf species/cultivars (February)
Rhododendron, hardy hybrids (October)
Spiraea (July–August)
Thuja (October)
Viburnum (April–May or July–August)

Preparation and insertion of cuttings

Cuttings are prepared in the normal way for the particular subject, most of them being ordinary nodal cuttings but *Mahonia*, for instance, is generally propagated from leaf-bud cuttings (see Plates 2 and 3). *Camellia* can also be propagated from leaf-bud cuttings. Some of the thin-stemmed *Berberis*, like the *thunbergii* cultivars, are propagated from mallet cuttings.

The term 'mallet cuttings' needs an explanation. The propagation material consists of lateral shoots produced in the current year but if these were taken as ordinary nodal cuttings they would probably die before rooting occurred owing to rapid depletion of food reserves in the cuttings. To prevent this, these thin shoots are removed from the stock plants with a portion of older wood at the base—about 12 mm (0·5 in) in length. This older wood is cut just above the base of the lateral shoot and about 12 mm below it. The food reserves in this portion of wood then tide the cutting over until it has rooted.

It is advisable to immerse all cuttings in a solution of captan before insertion, to prevent losses from fungal diseases; then they can, if required, be treated with an IBA rooting powder. The cuttings are generally inserted in the normal way in seed trays of cutting compost, although for some subjects which resent root disturbance, such as *Elaeagnus*, unit containers would be preferable (see Chapter 20).

Aftercare of cuttings

The trays of cuttings, after being watered in, are placed on the heated benches or heated concrete beds and covered with 19 μm (75 gauge) polythene sheeting. This can be laid directly on the cuttings, and the edges tucked under the seed trays to ensure high humidity within.

It is sensible to apply light shading to the glasshouse to prevent the cuttings becoming scorched by direct rays from the sun. This is important, even with autumn propagation and certainly for late winter/spring cuttings. It is, of course, absolutely essential during the summer and at this period a plastic-mesh shading material should be suspended over the benches or beds. The idea of shading is not only to prevent scorch, but to reduce high leaf temperatures in the cuttings.

The cuttings should be inspected regularly—at least every seven days. Any dead leaves should be removed together with any dead or dying cuttings. The batches of cuttings could be sprayed with a solution of captan or benomyl to reduce the incidence of disease. The polythene should be turned before replacing it so that the cuttings do not become saturated as a result of excess condensation.

Once the cuttings have rooted they should be gradully weaned off by slitting the polythene sheeting. This slitting can be gradually increased until the cuttings are subjected to full air, at which stage the heat should either be turned off or the trays of cuttings moved off the benches.

The cuttings could be transferred to a large polythene tunnel to await potting off.

A COMPARISON BETWEEN BOTTOM HEAT AND POLYTHENE AND MIST

It is interesting to compare bottom heat and polythene with mist propagation. Firstly it is often cheaper to install than mist, especially if suitable benches exist in the propagation house. Under polythene there is no leaching as can be the case with mist and there is no fear of over-wet compost, which can result in heavy losses among cuttings.

Probably more care and attention is needed with polythene, especially in relation to hygiene, shading and weaning. There can be difficulties in summer with polythene, owing to high temperatures, which can reduce turgidity in the cuttings.

There is no doubt in our minds that the polythene/bottom-heat technique is better for autumn/winter propagation and mist is superior for spring/summer cuttings.

There is higher humidity under polythene than under mist and this humidity is constant, whereas under mist it is irregular, being higher after the cuttings have been misted and lower as the cuttings dry off.

Cuttings of some subjects may be slower to root under polythene than under mist but on the other hand there is the advantage that cuttings are often far better rooted when removed from under polythene. It is therefore up to the nurseryman to decide which technique he is going to use—as we have already stated, the ideal system is to have bottom heat and polythene for autumn/winter propagation, and mist for spring/summer propagation.

10

Low polythene tunnels and frames

A wide range of evergreen shrubs, and some deciduous subjects like *Berberis thunbergii* cultivars, can be easily rooted from semi-mature cuttings under low polythene tunnels outside, to provide well-rooted liners within one year from propagation. It is mainly the lower-value subjects that are raised by this method, which represents a low-risk, low-cost form of propagation. Also, especially important from a management point of view, the system does not require highly skilled labour to achieve excellent results and high-percentage rooting.

Choosing the site

The tunnels can be constructed on any well-drained piece of ground which is reasonably fertile and free from the pernicious perennial weeds. Choose a sunny aspect but ensure the site is really well sheltered from winds to prevent tunnels being damaged or lifted during high winds and gales.

Ideally the site should be sterilized with dazomet to control weed seeds in the crop of cuttings and to eliminate soil-borne diseases. Deep ploughing, prior to dazomet application, would also be beneficial, to break up any hard cultivation pans and ensure good drainage.

Construction

We use 38 μm (150 gauge) white (opaque) polythene and find that a width of 2 m (6 ft 6 in) is ideal. The polythene is supported on wire hoops which we form ourselves from rolls of heavy-gauge galvanized wire.

The ideal length of wire to form a hoop is 2·4 m (8 ft) as this allows a hoop 1 m (3 ft 3 in) wide to be formed, complete with stems of 300 mm (1 ft) to insert into the ground and eyelets at the top of the stems to secure the tying material. It is easy enough to form a template to construct the hoops—we partially knock nails into a wooden bench to form the outline of the hoop (and eyelets) and then bend the length of wire around this template.

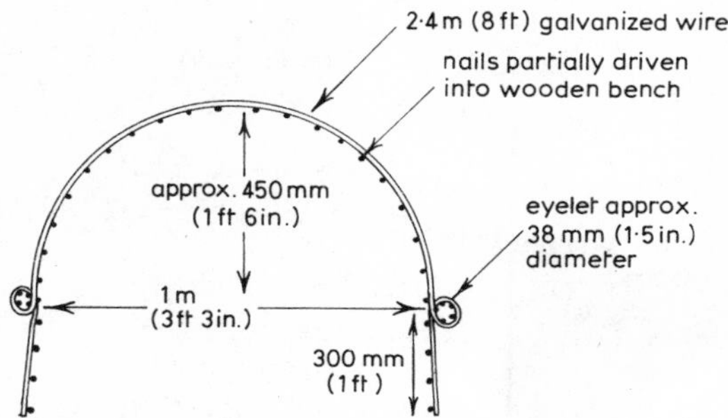

Fig. 14 Template used to form wire hoops for low-polythene-tunnel construction

We construct beds 1 m (3 ft 3 in) wide for the cuttings and, of course, they can be of any length desired. First of all parallel lines are put down to mark the edges of the beds and to keep them straight. Cutting compost, equal parts sphagnum peat and coarse sand, is laid 75 mm (3 in) deep over the soil to form the beds. It is not firmed, as loose compost facilitates insertion of the cuttings. The cutting compost is then topped with a 25 mm (1 in) deep layer of coarse sand or crushed gravel. We feel this gives better drainage around the cuttings and also better aeration.

Once the beds have been made, the wire hoops are pushed in about 1 m (3 ft 3 in) apart down the bed, ensuring the stems are well down in the soil and the eyelets are at soil level. If the stems are too short, or are not inserted to their full depth, there is a chance the hoops will keel over or come out of the ground. At each end of the bed we use double hoops spaced 150 mm (6 in) apart and tied together at the top, as these provide greater strength when the polythene is pulled tight. Single hoops at the ends just keel over when the polythene cover is stretched tight.

Once the hoops are in place the polythene can be placed over them or, alternatively, you may prefer to fill the bed first with cuttings and then put the polythene cover on. In this instance try not to leave any cuttings for too long before covering them as they will transpire and wilt. If the polythene is put on correctly it is quite easy to lift it up on either side and tie it loosely at the top, to gain access to the beds to insert cuttings and indeed for general maintenance.

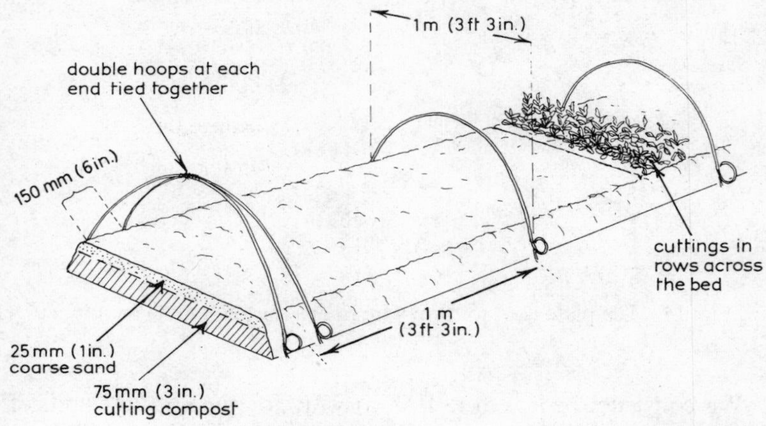

Fig. 15 Low-polythene-tunnel construction

The ends of the polythene can be secured in two ways. We prefer to bury the ends in the soil about 300 mm (1 ft) deep. The alternative is to insert a stout wooden stake at each end and to tie the polythene to it.

The polythene is held down over the hoops with binder twine (the polypropylene type is best as this does not rot), securing each end of the twine to the eyelets in the hoops at ground level. Ensure that the polythene is stretched reasonably tight over the hoops but not so tight that the hoops are pulled over.

In a very windy situation it would be advisable to bury the edges of the polythene in the soil once the bed has been filled with cuttings.

Conditions provided

The conditions provided by this type of low tunnel are a fairly humid atmosphere, well-drained rooting medium and freedom from desiccating winds. There is, of course, very little frost protection but this is not important as all the subjects are really hardy. Provided the cuttings are quickly covered with polythene after insertion they will not wilt and the humid atmosphere keeps them turgid.

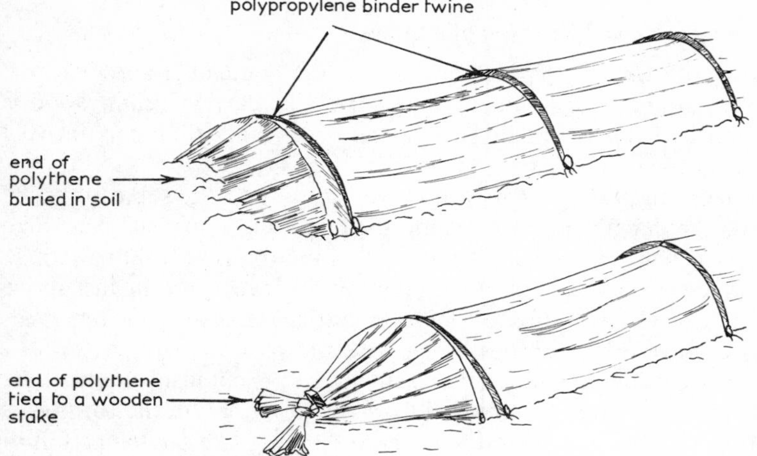

Fig. 16 Securing the polythene on low tunnels

Subjects rooted from cuttings

We are constantly adding to the range of subjects that can be rooted under low polythene tunnels and our advice is to try as many different shrubs as possible, to assess their response to rooting in these conditions. The following list of shrubs includes those that we have successfully rooted under low tunnels, a great many of which have resulted in 80–100 per cent rooting. The majority are easy-rooting evergreen shrubs but there are some deciduous subjects also and we have indicated these.

Aucuba japonica and cultivars; *Berberis* species and cultivars, including deciduous kinds like *B. thunbergii*; *Cassinia retorta*; *Cistus* species; *Escallonia* species and cultivars; *Griselinia littoralis*; *Hebe*; *Hypericum calycinum* and other species; *Helichrysum plicatum*; *Laurus nobilis*; *Lavandula* species and cultivars; *Ligustrum* species; *Lonicera pileata*; *Olearia* × *scilloniensis*; *Olearia stellulata*; *Osmanthus heterophyllus*; *Ozothamnus ledifolius*; *Potentilla* species and cultivars (deciduous); *Prunus laurocerasus* and cultivars; *Prunus lusitanica*; *Rosmarinus* species and cultivars; *Rubus* species including *R. calycinoides* and *R. tricolor*; *Ruta graveolens*; *Santolina* species; *Senecio* 'Sunshine' (syn. *Senecio greyi*) and *S. monroi*; *Skimmia japonica* and cultivars; *Viburnum tinus* and cultivars; and *Vinca major* and *V. minor* cultivars.

Preparation and insertion of cuttings

The cuttings are prepared and inserted in September and October. They are really classified as semi-ripe — the current year's wood is used, and this is ripe or hard at the base while still comparatively soft at the tip.

The length of cuttings will vary according to the subject but the average length is 75–100 mm (3–4 in). Vigorous subjects, like *Prunus laurocerasus*, can be up to 150 mm (6 in) in length. With *P. laurocerasus* we usually cut out the soft tip of each cutting just above a node. The soft tips of *Berberis* cuttings can also be removed. With most other cuttings the tips are allowed to remain.

The cuttings are nodal, that is, the bases are cut just below a node. The leaves should be removed from the lower half of the cuttings — these are easily pulled off with many subjects like *Santolina*, but in other cases they need to be cut off to prevent bark tearing as, for example, with the evergreen *Prunus*. The bases of the cuttings are dipped in a hormone rooting powder containing 0·8 per cent IBA.

We mentioned earlier that it is advisable not to firm the cutting compost as this facilitates insertion. To speed up this operation the cuttings are simply pushed into the compost thus eliminating the use of dibbers, which slow down insertion considerably. Insert the cuttings up to the lower leaves. We insert the cuttings in rows across the bed, the rows being spaced about 75 mm (3 in) apart. The distance between the cuttings in the rows will vary according to the subject — the leaves should not be touching as then there will be good air circulation around the cuttings — but the average spacing is something like 50–75 mm (2–3 in). Very slim cuttings like *Cassinia* could be spaced even closer together, but do ensure there is ample space between cuttings for good air circulation otherwise you may experience losses due to rotting. The cuttings can, in fact, be kept in neat straight lines across the bed by using a 1 m (3 ft 3 in) narrow stick or board up to which the cuttings are stuck. This will also provide the width between the rows if it is about 75 mm (3 in) wide. This has worked well with many nursery workers.

After insertion the cuttings should be heavily watered in, to firm them. Each batch of cuttings should, of course, be clearly labelled with a plastic label, using a waterproof pen. Include the source of the cutting material, the full name of the subject and the propagation date.

Aftercare of cuttings

It is advisable throughout the autumn, winter and following spring to check the cuttings occasionally and to water them, if necessary. However, we find that it is rarely necessary to water in the autumn and winter as the compost remains nicely moist. It is a mistake to keep the compost too wet as this can lead to losses owing to rotting.

While you are checking for water requirements take the opportunity to remove any dead cuttings or dead foliage to minimize the risk of *Botrytis* developing. This can spread very rapidly under the humid conditions in the tunnels, and may result in further losses of cuttings. Generally speaking we have very little trouble from this disease, simply because we maintain hygienic conditions in the beds. If there should be any trouble then spray the cuttings with benomyl systemic fungicide.

Removal of polythene

The polythene is removed in the spring but the timing is critical. Do not be in too much of a hurry to remove it, as cold spring winds can rapidly desiccate the cuttings, as we found to our cost on one occasion! Generally it is safe to remove it in May, once the weather starts warming up. It could be removed gradually, that is, start by lifting up the sides a little to gradually acclimatize the cuttings to the outside conditions. After a few days it can be removed completely.

Once the polythene is removed the cuttings will need regular watering and also some hand weeding may be required, especially if the ground was not treated with dazomet the previous year.

The cuttings should be allowed to remain in the beds until the following autumn. In fact it is in the spring that they really start to form a substantial root system. During the growing season they will make a substantial amount of top growth so that by the autumn one will be lifting good-quality liners.

Lifting

The liners are lifted in the autumn with a fork and there are various methods of growing them on. For example, some subjects could be rolled (see Chapter 20), especially the ground-cover types like *Hypericum calycinum*, *Rubus* species and *Vinca*. Other subjects can be potted or containerized, or some of the more vigorous subjects which are often used for hedging, for example *Ligustrum* and *Prunus laurocerasus*, could be lined out direct in the field to grow on.

TUNNELS VERSUS MIST AND HEATED BENCH

It can be seen, then, that raising shrubs under low polythene tunnels represents one of the cheapest forms of propagation. There is very little point in raising these easy-rooting subjects in a mist-propagation unit or on a heated bench with polythene. It is far better to use the heated propagation facilities for the more difficult subjects as it is uneconomical to root easy evergreens and deciduous shrubs in these expensive-to-run conditions.

Admittedly rooting would be speeded up under heated conditions but when rooting cuttings in heat they have to be hardened off in walk-in tunnels or cold frames, again taking up valuable covered space.

DOUBLE-GLAZED FRAMES

Another economical method of raising shrubs from cuttings is in double-glazed cold frames. These are normal Dutch-light frames but they are insulated with 38 μm (150 gauge) clear polythene. Our method is to fix a sheet of polythene to a light timber framework slightly smaller than a Dutch light so that it can be fitted into the frame above the cuttings and just below the glass. These polythene 'lights' can be supported on strips of timber running the length of the frame, along the front and back.

The frames are prepared by placing a 100 mm (4 in) deep layer of cutting compost in the base and as for low-tunnel work this should not be firmed as it is then easier to insert the cuttings.

Propagation programme

Such a system can be used for shrub propagation at various times of the year. For example, in September and October one can root all those subjects listed under low-tunnel propagation, that is, the easy-rooting evergreens and some deciduous subjects.

We have found that *Ilex* species and cultivars root well when inserted at this period. Cotoneasters are another subject that come to mind and there is also a wide range of 'scale' conifers that respond well to this system. × *Cupressocyparis leylandii* roots especially well in double-glazed frames, as do *Cryptomeria*, *Chamaecyparis lawsoniana* cultivars, *Taxus* cultivars and *Thuja* species and cultivars.

The rooted cuttings of shrubs inserted in September and October can be lifted in late spring, but it is best to wait until June before lifting rooted conifer cuttings. Again the growing-on method depends on the particular subject. For example, the conifers could be containerized and grown on in walk-in tunnels and placed out on the container beds in the second season. Other shrubs could be containerized or rolled and perhaps given tunnel protection until established. The more vigorous subjects could be lined out direct in the field.

During April one could insert *Juniperus* cuttings in the frame where they will root within about 12 weeks at which stage they can be lifted and containerized, and grown on in polythene tunnels.

In the months of June and July a wide range of semi-ripe shrub cuttings may be rooted in the double-glazed frames. Examples include *Clematis*; *Cotoneaster*; heathers; *Hedera*; deciduous shrubs like *Philadelphus*; and viburnums, such as *V. davidii*. By the autumn these can be lifted, potted and overwintered in a walk-in tunnel.

Maintenance of the frame

During the winter additional protection should ideally be given—especially for conifers—during hard frosts by covering the lights with matting or hessian.

Shading is very important during bright sunshine in the spring, summer and autumn, and the rays of the sun must not be allowed to come in contact with the polythene otherwise the cuttings may be badly scorched. Use a proprietary shading material and spray, or 'paint', this on to the glass when required.

Before the cuttings are lifted it is a good idea to gradually acclimatize them to cooler conditions, firstly by removing the polythene lights and then by gradually increasing the amount of ventilation by raising the Dutch glass lights.

Generally watering is not needed as humid conditions are maintained in the frame, but nevertheless do check regularly. It is also necessary to remove any dead cuttings or foliage on a regular basis.

Advantages of double-glazed frames

To summarize, then, what are the advantages of this system over mist, heated bench and polythene and low polythene tunnels? As with tunnels, it represents a very economical method of propagating shrubs—especially the low-value kinds but also the more valuable subjects like conifers.

If one can root these plants without heat then it is really uneconomical to use mist or heated bench space. Frames can be constructed far more cheaply than a mist unit or maybe even a heated bench—and of course they cost nothing to 'run'. Far less maintenance is required in frames, as the cuttings will not rapidly dry out and they can be left to their own devices for several weeks at a stretch.

One needs to keep a closer eye on subjects under mist or on heated benches—particularly to ensure the cuttings do not become excessively wet or suffer from an over-humid atmosphere. More cuttings can be inserted in the frames than in the equivalent space on a bench, for in the latter case the cuttings are generally inserted in trays or unit containers whereas, with the frame system the cuttings are inserted direct into the bed of the frame, giving a similar spacing to that recommended for low-tunnel work.

IMPROVING WINTER ROOTING

One of the problems of rooting cuttings is the loss due to *Pythium* and *Phytophthora*. Researchers have been carrying out trials to find effective systemic fungicides to reduce losses due to diseases, especially during the winter. Many growers are now treating cuttings with furalaxyl three days after cutting-insertion. Cuttings are drenched at a rate of 0·25 g/l. (0·08 oz/0·2 gal) using a 500 ml (0·1 gal) drench for a standard seed tray. Not only does this chemical reduce plant losses, but in some species it has resulted in a reduction in rooting time, especially in the winter and early spring.

11

Root cuttings in cold frames

The propagation of trees and shrubs, perennials and alpines from root cuttings is a particularly attractive proposition, for saleable plants can be obtained in as little as 12–18 months depending on the subject. Furthermore, the cost of propagation falls at the lower end of the scale and comparatively unskilled labour can be used for the preparation and insertion of the cuttings. With many subjects the percentage rooting can be as high as 95–100 per cent. This applies to such plants as *Rhus*, *Aralia*, *Eryngium* and *Papaver orientale*.

Stock plants

Ideally, a supply of young vigorous stock plants should be maintained for the production of root cuttings. Young plants will provide a good quantity of young roots. As soon as there is any sign of deterioration in the stock plants, or if they become too large, then they should be replaced with new stock. Ideally, the plants should be dug up in order to remove propagation material but, with trees and shrubs, this becomes difficult and labour intensive as the plants get larger.

We would advocate planting stock plants in land which has been prepared by the incorporation of a large quantity of cutting compost (equal parts peat and sand) as this encourages vigorous root activity. This treatment is certainly desirable if you intend planting in fairly heavy soil. With light sandy soils the addition of cutting compost is not really necessary although the addition of peat to conserve moisture during dry weather would be beneficial. With trees and shrubs the peat and sand mix could be placed in a deep band on either side of the row so that the plants root into it. A depth of 300 mm (1 ft) would be ideal, with a similar width. Keep stock plants well irrigated in dry weather, again to encourage maximum root growth.

Suitable subjects

We have been successful with a wide range of subjects from root cuttings as indicated in the following lists – while these lists are reasonably comprehensive they are not complete, but they do contain a range of material likely to be found on the average nursery producing hardy stock.

1 Trees and shrubs: *Aesculus*, particularly *A. parviflora*; *Ailanthus altissima*; *Amelanchier*; *Aralia chinensis*; *Calycanthus*; *Campsis*; *Caragana*; *Catalpa bignonioides*; *Ceanothus*; *Celastrus*; *Chaenomeles*; *Halesia*; *Hypericum*; *Paulownia tomentosa*; *Populus tremula*; *Prunus padus*; *Rhus copallina*; *Rhus glabra*; *Rhus typhina*; *Robinia*; *Rubus* and *Sambucus*.
2 Hardy perennials and alpines: *Anchusa*; *Arabis*; *Asclepias*; *Crambe cordifolia*; *Dicentra spectabilis*; *Echinops*; *Eryngium*; *Incarvillea*; *Morisia monantha*; *Oenothera*; *Papáver orientale*; *Phlox paniculata*; *Primula denticulata*; *Pulsatilla vulgaris*; *Romneya coulteri*; *Saponaria ocymoides*; *Statice*; *Stokesia laevis*; *Symphytum*; *Trollius europaeus* and *Verbascum*.

Frame preparation

Cold frames for root-cutting propagation should be sited in a warm, sheltered, sunny situation and the existing soil must be very well drained. Excessively wet conditions can result in heavy losses of cuttings due to rotting. A frame is very easily prepared: a layer of cutting compost (equal parts peat and coarse sand) should be placed in the base of the frame, about 100 mm (4 in) deep and lightly firmed.

It is preferable, before laying this rooting mix, to dig over the soil in the frame, especially if it is compacted, as the plants will in fact root into this – many subjects propagated by this method have very deep fleshy roots.

Collection and preparation of cuttings

The time of year to carry out propagation by root cuttings is from November to January when the plants are dormant. If possible dig up the entire plant carefully with a fork and gently shake the soil away from the roots.

The thickness of roots will vary according to the subject: wherever possible try to select roots of about pencil thickness, or slightly thicker for those subjects which have very thick roots, like *Rhus* and *Eryngium*. Other plants, such as *Phlox paniculata*, have thin roots, in which case simply pick the most substantial for propagation. Do not completely strip the plants of roots but leave a reasonable quantity to enable the plants to re-establish quickly. Certainly leave as much fibrous root as possible.

Replant the stock plants immediately you have finished collecting to prevent the roots drying out. If you are taking roots from a large tree or shrub which cannot be lifted then simply scrape soil away from around the plant to expose the roots; after collection return the soil and firm the plant in thoroughly with the heels.

Preparation of cuttings in the propagation area is reasonably simple. Let us first deal with the preparation of thick-rooted subjects. The roots are cut into 50 mm (2 in) long sections, using a sharp knife or very sharp secateurs—the former is preferred. In order to ensure the cuttings are inserted the right way up, it is usual to make a slanting cut at the 'distal' end (the bottom) and a flat cut at the 'proximal' end (the top). The top of a root cutting is always the part that was nearest to the stem of the stock plant. With thin-rooted subjects the roots are simply cut into 50 mm (2 in) sections—there is no need to worry about the tops and the bottoms.

After preparation, the root cuttings can be lightly dusted with captan fungicide to help prevent rotting off. Shake them up in a bag containing a little of the fungicide.

The cuttings can be inserted direct into the peat/sand bed in the frame. Thick root cuttings are inserted vertically; they can be pushed into the cutting compost so that their tops are just below the surface; space them about 75 mm (3 in) apart each way. Thin root cuttings are laid on the surface of the compost, horizontally, and covered with a 12 mm (0·5 in) layer of the same compost. If you prefer, the thin-rooted subjects could be inserted in seed trays, and these stood down in the frame.

It should be mentioned that some of the subjects listed could give a higher percentage 'take' if rooted in boxes in a heated propagation house—these include *Ceanothus*, *Halesia*, *Romneya* (individually in pots) and *Verbascum*.

Aftercare of cuttings

Root cuttings should not be allowed to dry out at any time but on the other hand they must not be allowed to become excessively wet. So they should be covered with frame lights over the winter, these being removed in May. Watering may be required over the winter—

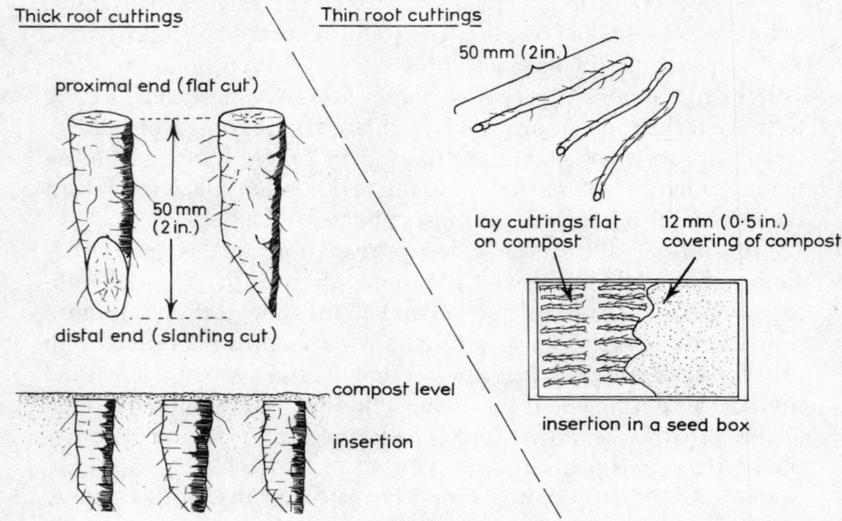

Fig. 17 Preparation of root cuttings

this will certainly be the case if you have some subjects in a heated glasshouse.

On favourable occasions ventilate the frames to prevent an over-moist stale atmosphere. Water and hand weed as necessary in summer.

Lifting rooted cuttings

Root cuttings which have been inserted direct in beds in a cold frame should be left where they are until the following autumn, by which time they should have formed a substantial root system. They should be lifted with a fork and you may find that the roots of some have gone down quite a long way. Once lifted, the plants can be incorporated into the normal container or field-production systems.

Root cuttings in boxes should be moved on as soon as they have formed a satisfactory root system – but do not be in too much of a hurry to lift, as root cuttings, especially those in warm conditions, produce top growth before they start to root. Once the roots show through the bottom of the boxes then the plants can be lifted and containerized and then hardened off in tunnels, if raised in heat.

12

Hardwood cuttings without heat

Hardwood cuttings are prepared from the current season's wood which is well ripened or hard. Therefore, the usual time of year for this method of propagation is between November and February. It can be a particularly economical way to raise trees and shrubs, for many subjects will root in the open ground or in cold frames. Also, the cuttings are quick and easy to prepare and insert and the whole operation can be carried out by unskilled labour or young trainees. There is minimal risk of failure if suitable rooting conditions are provided and many subjects quickly give saleable plants.

HARDWOOD CUTTINGS IN THE OPEN GROUND

Choice of subjects

This method is used for those subjects which root easily and are able to stand up to the inclement weather, which is often with us in the early spring. Examples of plants that we raise in the open are as follows: black currants; gooseberries; *Ligustrum*; *Lonicera nitida*; *Populus*; red currants; *Rosa multiflora* (for rootstocks); *Rosa rugosa* (for rootstocks) and *Salix*. Note that many of these subjects are often required in large quantities, such as rose rootstocks, and hedging material like *Ligustrum* and *Lonicera nitida*, and therefore a cheap method of production is essential.

Selection and preparation of site

The success of rooting hardwoods in the open ground depends on careful selection of site and also on the part of the country in which the nursery is located. Generally speaking, the method is more successful in areas which have mild winters, as fewer losses then occur.

A site that is well sheltered from cold searing winds is very much recommended, to prevent the cuttings from becoming desiccated and the new shoots from becoming scorched or even killed. Try to avoid a frost pocket as too many frosts can result in upheaval of the cuttings as the ground thaws out. This can inhibit rooting and ideally the cuttings should be refirmed if they are partially lifted out of the ground.

It is vital that the soil is really well drained—on a wet site there can be many losses among the cuttings due to rotting. A lighter soil is really recommended, such as sandy types and the lighter loams, which are generally better drained than heavy clays.

If there is no alternative to using a rather wet site then coarse sand placed under the cuttings will help to prevent losses, but this is then increasing the cost of production, which the system is designed to keep to the minimum. It may be better in this case to root the cuttings under Dutch-light frames where conditions should be drier.

A sheltered aspect will ensure that the ground warms up quickly in the spring and also that it dries out by the time lining out commences. A south-facing site is therefore desirable.

Adequate preparation of the land is necessary and preferably this should be carried out in the previous autumn. The site must be free from perennial weeds as these are difficult to control among the cuttings when they are in the process of rooting. Carry out deep ploughing, and ensure any hard cultivation pan is well broken up to ensure free drainage and unhampered root activity.

Just before the cuttings are lined out the land should be thoroughly harrowed to create a fine tilth—this is especially important if lining out by planting machine. Also, for this operation the site should be as level as possible to ensure a consistent planting depth. Any bumps and hollows will make machine planting extremely difficult.

Preparation of cuttings

The cuttings are collected from a stock hedge which has been pruned hard to give a good crop of strong vigorous wood. The annual pruning is, in fact, carried out during removal of the cutting material.

Do not remove cuttings at leaf fall for then the plants have a large quantity of abcissic acid, which it is thought inhibits rooting. It is therefore important to wait until a few weeks after leaf fall before collecting material. In fact it is usual to wait for a quiet period on the nursery in which to prepare the cuttings.

Cuttings are prepared with secateurs and the wood is cut into lengths of about 200–250 mm (8–9 in). Discard the top part of each shoot as this may still be rather soft. When preparing the cuttings cut cleanly just below a node at the base and just above a node at the top. The cuttings of some subjects should have the lower buds removed by cutting or rubbing them out. This is to ensure they do not produce growth from below ground level. It applies to red currants, gooseberries, white currants, and rose species to be used as rootstocks. All except the top three to four buds should be removed. The subjects mentioned generally do not need hormone treatment as they root easily but if it is felt that they should be treated then dip the bases of the cuttings in a hormone rooting powder formulated for hardwoods — one containing 0·8 per cent IBA.

We grade the cuttings for thickness — they can generally be sorted out into two or three different sizes. As a point of interest some of the subjects will yield quite thick cuttings: maybe up to 12 mm (0·5 in) in diameter with things like *Salix* and *Populus*. We would not suggest making cuttings any thicker than this. Other subjects produce thinner wood — particularly currants, gooseberries, roses and so on, and in this instance one should use only the thickest material, as very thin cuttings will have low food reserves and they could die before rooting has taken place.

It is not usually possible to line out the cuttings immediately after preparation as the ground is too wet, especially for machine planting, and so the cuttings are stored as outlined below until the ground is in a suitable state for lining them out in the early spring.

Tie the cuttings into bundles of 25, using polypropylene string, as this does not rot like ordinary string or twine. It is important to ensure the bases of the cuttings are all level in each bundle for the method of storage that we use. Each bundle should contain only one grade of cuttings. Do ensure all the cuttings are bundled the right way up — with some subjects the dormant buds are rather indistinct and so one should try to ensure the cuttings are kept the right way up at all stages of preparation. If some cuttings in a bundle are upside down then there is a very real chance that they will be lined out the wrong way up.

Label each bundle with a plastic tag label attached to the top tie of the bundle — each bundle has two ties, one at the top and another near the base. The information on the label consists of the name of the subject, the date the cuttings were taken and the grade.

Heeling in cuttings

We generally find it is necessary to store the cuttings until soil conditions improve in the early spring. The cuttings can be held in a heeling-in bin situated in a cold, but sheltered, north-facing aspect. In such a situation the cuttings are not subjected to cold drying winds and, being cool and shaded, they will not come into growth prior to lining out. However, they may start to produce roots, or maybe just form callus tissue.

The heeling-in material can be coarse sand to ensure free drainage around the cuttings or peat could also be used, although this may get very wet in heavy rain. The heeling-in bin should in fact be sited in a well-drained position. The sand or peat can be retained by forming a framework with timber, about 150 mm (6 in) in height, so making a raised bed.

The bundles of cuttings are stood in trenches to about half their depth and the heeling-in material worked well between them and moderately firmed. Ensure the labels are not buried, keep each subject separate from the next and keep all the grades separated. This will ensure quick and accurate extraction of material at lining-out time. A lot of time can be wasted sorting out bundles of cuttings if they have not been heeled in in a logical way.

Lining out cuttings

This should be carried out just as soon as the ground is workable in the spring. If you delay lining out for too long then the cuttings will start to produce top growth and this is very easily damaged or knocked off, especially when machine planting. We have already mentioned the final preparation of the land prior to lining out.

The cuttings can either be lined out by hand or by planting machine. For further details of machine planting refer to Chapter 27. Hand planting simply involves making a V-shaped trench with a spade, using a line to maintain straight rows. The back of the trench should be straight so that the cuttings can be stood upright in the trench. Hardwood cuttings are inserted to about half to two-thirds of their depth in the soil. Space the cuttings about 150 mm (6 in) apart in the rows, the distance between rows depending on the system being used (see Chapter 27).

It is important that the cuttings are well firmed in and this should be done by treading if hand planting. In fact, we have often found it necessary to firm in cuttings by treading even after machine planting. So the lining-out process, even when done by hand, can be a team effort. One member of the team can be taking out the trench or spade nick, another can be placing the cuttings in the nick, and a third member can follow along behind firming. Ideally there should be a fourth member supplying the planters with material. This will almost certainly be necessary when machine planting.

Aftercare of cuttings

Hardwood cuttings in the field will remain where they are until the following autumn, by which time they should have formed a substantial root system. However, in the meantime there will be weed control and irrigation to attend to. One is generally wary about recommending the use of residual herbicides among hardwood cuttings, as they could impede rooting. However, to keep annual weed growth under control there is no reason why paraquat should not be used provided a spray guard is fitted to the spray lance. This will control weeds between the rows, so all that remains is to hoe off weeds between the actual cuttings. It really does pay to keep weeds under control as cuttings can quickly become choked with weed growth and the young top growth may simply be smothered before it has a chance to develop.

Irrigation is vital in dry weather for if the soil is allowed to dry out then rooting will be adversely affected and root initials may even shrivel and die. With due care and attention there should be every chance of a very high rooting percentage with hardwood material. If the site is well sheltered from cold drying winds the young growth will grow away unchecked. If, on the other hand, the site is very exposed then the young top growth could be killed and this invariably results in loss of cuttings.

Treatment when rooted

We have said that the cuttings will be well rooted by the following autumn, at which time they can be lifted and incorporated into the main production system, that is, lined out in the field to grow to saleable stage or containerized. We should add that with many of the low-value subjects which are rooted from hardwoods—like hedging material and willows and poplars—the usual way to grow them on is in the field.

Lift the cuttings carefully, either by machine or by hand (see

Chapter 32). Before planting or containerizing, the material should again be graded out for quality and size. The amount of top growth made by this time will depend on the vigour of the subject, but things like *Salix* and *Populus* could well have made at least 1 m (3 ft 3 in) of growth by this time.

HARDWOOD CUTTINGS IN COLD FRAMES

There is no doubt that many subjects are best rooted in cold frames to protect the cuttings from excessively wet conditions and cold drying winds experienced in the winter. Many of the subjects we root in frames have pithy or hollow stems and such material is more prone to rotting than plants with very firm, solid wood. Typical hardwoods that we regularly root in frames are as follows: *Buddleia*; *Cornus*—the shrubby dogwoods; *Deutzia*; *Diervilla*; *Forsythia*; *Hypericum*; *Ligustrum*—particularly the choicer less-hardy species; *Lonicera*—the choicer, ornamental flowering species; *Philadelphus*; *Ribes*; *Sambucus*; *Spiraea*; *Symphoricarpus*; *Tamarix*; *Viburnum* and *Weigela*.

Frame preparation

The frame should be located on a well-drained piece of land which is sheltered from cold drying winds and preferably with a warm southerly aspect. The existing soil should be reasonably fertile and must be well broken up by deep digging. A bed of cutting compost (equal parts of peat and coarse sand or grit) is made up in the bottom of the frame to a depth of 100–150 mm (4–6 in). This should be only moderately firmed to facilitate insertion of the cuttings. Once the bed has been prepared, put the frame lights on to prevent the bed becoming too wet prior to insertion of the cuttings. The compost should be moist but not over-wet.

Preparation and insertion of cuttings

Again, cuttings should be prepared from well-ripened or hardened current-year's wood as described earlier in this chapter. Preparation is again carried out with secateurs, and the bottom cut should be made just below a node and the top cut just above a node. With all of the ornamental subjects the buds are left intact as we want growth to be produced from below ground level to give bushy shrubs. The length of cut will vary according to the subject as some, like *Cornus*, may have very long internodes, while others do not have this characteristic. Those with long internodes may only have three nodes per cutting.

Try to aim for an average length of 150 mm (6 in), and use only the strongest, thickest wood as this has a greater survival rate than thin material. The cuttings may be treated with a hormone rooting powder formulated for hardwoods, that is, 0·8 per cent IBA (indole-butyric acid).

As batches of cuttings are prepared they should be inserted in the cold frame. Provided the compost has been only moderately firmed it is possible to push the cuttings in without the use of a dibber (this only slows down the operation and therefore is not recommended), so push in the cuttings to about half to two-thirds of their depth, firming in with the fingers if necessary. However, even this operation may not be necessary if the compost is of the right degree of firmness.

The cuttings can be inserted in rows running from the front to the back of the frame, spacing the rows about 75 mm (3 in) apart with the cuttings about 50 mm (2 in) apart in the rows. The batches of cuttings, and therefore the labelling, should run from left to right. We find it best to separate species of the same genus so that there is no chance of mixing species (or cultivars) when it comes to lifting. For example, the different kinds of *Forsythia*, and many other subjects, look very much alike as cuttings and are very easily mixed, if not well separated, with cuttings of other genera.

Using a waterproof pen label each batch of cuttings clearly with plastic or wooden labels, including the plant name, date of propagation and the source of the material, and then replace the lights.

Aftercare of cuttings

Check the cuttings regularly to see if watering is required and also to remove any dead material, although this should be minimal if the cuttings are not kept too wet. By about May the frame lights can be removed completely and watering will be necessary throughout the spring and summer.

By the following autumn the cuttings will be well rooted and will have made a good amount of top growth, the length depending on the species. The rooted cuttings should now be lifted with a digging fork – remember that most will have rooted into the soil below the cutting bed so dig fairly deeply. When lifted they are graded out for size and quality. They can then either be containerized or lined out in the field to grow on to saleable stage.

Generally, ornamental shrubs benefit from being pruned in the liner stage to encourage growths to break from the base, which result in well-branched or bushy plants. This can either be done at the lifting stage or once the plants have been lined out or containerized. Generally the top growth can be pruned back by approximately half its length.

Many of these subjects, such as the vigorous *Buddleia*, *Cornus*, *Philadelphus*, *Sambucus*, *Weigela*, and so on, should make saleable plants in about 12 months from lining out or containerizing.

13

Hardwood cuttings in heat

During January and February a range of hardwood cuttings of climbers, trees and shrubs can be rooted on a heated bench in the propagation house. As with hardwoods in the open and in frames, the preparation of the cuttings is straightforward and the percentage take is high — in the region of 80–85 per cent.

We prepare two types of cuttings — straightforward nodal types for the majority of subjects and eye cuttings mainly for the fruiting vines.

Subjects rooted from hardwoods

1 Eye cuttings: *Vitis* 'Brant'; *Vitis pulchra*; *Vitis vinifera* cultivars like 'Black Hamburg', 'Buckland Sweetwater' and 'Purpurea'.

2 Conventional cuttings: *Actinidia kolomikta*; *Akebia trifoliata*; *Ampelopsis aconitifolia*; *Azara serrata*; *Bignonia capreolata*; *Celastrus orbiculatus*; *Coronilla emerus*; *Cytisus battandieri*; *Ficus carica*; *Fuchsia magellanica*; *Hoheria lyallii* and *H. sexstylosa*; *Holbelia coriacea*; *Hymenanthera crassifolia*; *Lonicera* × *purpusii*; *Metasequoia glyptostroboides*; *Parthenocissus henryana*; *Parthenocissus thompsonii*; *Periploca graeca*; *Polygonum baldschuanicum*; *Sinofranchetia chinensis*; *Solanum crispum* 'Autumnale'; *Vitis coignetiae*; *Vitis davidii*; and *Wisteria sinensis* and *floribunda* cultivars.

Rooting conditions

The cuttings are rooted on a heated bench in a propagation house and are given a bottom-heat temperature in the region of 21 °C (70 °F). The air temperature in the house is about 18 °C (65 °F) and the cuttings are fully exposed to the glasshouse atmosphere, that is, they are not covered with polythene or subjected to mist.

The time the cuttings take to root depends on the subject, but things like *Metasequoia* and *Taxodium* may take about eight weeks, although some of the vines and other subjects will have formed a good root system in a much shorter period of time.

Compost and containers

We use a standard compost for all our cuttings, this being equal parts sphagnum peat and crushed grit or coarse sand.

There is a wide range of containers one can use. For the eye cuttings of vines we generally prefer to use unit containers of various types in plastic or peat and insert one cutting per unit. This, of course, minimizes root disturbance when it comes to potting off the rooted cuttings.

The longer conventional hardwood cuttings need deeper containers and most of ours go into 125 mm (5 in) plastic pots as these hold a reasonable depth of compost to support the cuttings. We insert approximately 10 cuttings per pot – round the edge and in the centre.

We also use the larger plastic unit containers for some of our hardwoods; the 60 mm (2·5 in) square type generally provides sufficient depth for the shorter cuttings. Also 60 mm pots can be used, inserting one cutting per pot.

Preparation and insertion

The cutting material should come from healthy stock plants and must be well-ripened wood formed in the previous growing season. The cuttings are prepared with secateurs and it is essential that these are really sharp and not of the anvil type, which are inclined to crush stems instead of cutting them cleanly. All cuttings are treated with a hormone rooting powder containing 0·8 per cent IBA.

Eye cuttings are prepared by cutting the stems into 25–35 mm (1–1·5 in) lengths making the top cut just above a node, the bottom being internodal. One bud is left at the top of the cutting, the opposite bud being carefully cut out. Conventional hardwood cuttings have an average length of 150–200 mm (6–8 in) and as they are nodal cuttings, prepare them by cutting just above a bud at the top and immediately below a bud at the base. All the buds are left intact. The number of nodes each type of cutting carries will vary, for some subjects have widely spaced nodes and therefore may only have buds at the top and bottom of the cutting, while other types may have several more.

As soon as the cuttings have been prepared they should be inserted in the appropriate containers. The eye cuttings are inserted vertically and to such a depth that the bud at the top is at compost level. They can simply be pushed into the compost. The longer hardwoods are also pushed into the compost to about a third to half their length, depending on the depth of the containers. Do not overcrowd them – if using 125 mm (5 in) pots then about 10 cuttings per pot will be adequate.

When the cuttings have been inserted water them in to settle the compost around them and then stand the containers on the heated bench. Keep the cuttings moist but not wet, or they may rot.

Subsequent treatment

You will notice that top growth is very often quickly produced due to the air temperature in the glasshouse but do not be led into thinking that a good root system has been formed at this stage. The cuttings will probably be starting to root but will need several more weeks, according to the subject, before they are ready for potting off.

Once the cuttings are well rooted, which will be in the spring for the majority of subjects, they can be potted off. The size of pot will vary according to the vigour of the root system of each subject. Once the rooted cuttings have been potted they can be transferred to a polythene tunnel or cold frames to harden off.

The type of material we have been discussing is generally sold in containers and, therefore, as soon as the young plants have filled their initial pots with roots they can go into their final containers. Generally 150 mm (6 in) polythene bags are used, but for some of the more choice or valuable species then rigid containers would be more suitable. Once containerized the plants can be stood on the container beds and the climbers should be given a 1 m (3 ft 3 in) bamboo cane for support. Regular tying-in is essential with climbers otherwise they will become hopelessly entangled.

The length of time needed to make saleable plants will vary according to the species, but the more vigorous subjects will make good-size specimens in 18 months from propagation, while the less-vigorous species may take about 24 months. *Metasequoia* and *Taxodium* are generally sold as three-year-old plants and they are often container grown. If they were field grown they might make deep roots which would cause lifting problems. This is especially so with *Taxodium*.

14

The heated cutting bin

In recent years new techniques have been developed by research stations for rooting hardwood cuttings of ornamental trees and rootstocks and one of these developments has been the heated cutting bin. This method of production can be easily fitted into the winter propagation programme and replaces layering and stooling, which are the traditional production techniques for many species.

Construction and operation of bins

Bins should be constructed in a cool, insulated building, for example a north-facing stone barn, as this will ensure cuttings have the minimum bud development and are not exposed to draughts which can cause the rooting medium to dry out and the cuttings to be desiccated.

Bins need to be of the dimensions 1·2 m (4 ft) wide and up to 1 m (3 ft 3 in) high so that they hold long woody cuttings. An area of 1·2 m × 1·2 m (4 ft × 4 ft) will hold up to 5,000 cuttings.

The bin is constructed from insulating blocks to ensure that heat is retained in the rooting area. It is important to maintain a well-drained rooting medium for successful callusing of cuttings and therefore floor blocks must have drainage gaps between them.

Once the blocks have been placed in position the heating cables can be laid out on the floor. The aim of these warming wires is to give basal heat to the cuttings. It is critical to the success of the bin that temperatures are controlled. Various alternatives for sensing the temperature can be used, but a cheap, flexible resistance thermometer, with the sensor constructed from standard PVC-covered tinned-copper wire, is preferred by many growers. Once the cables have been laid out a welded-steel-mesh screen is laid above to protect them and facilitate compost removal.

Finally, the rooting medium is placed in the bin; normally a peat: sand medium (50:50) is used, but some growers have had better results by using one part peat and two parts polystyrene granules as well as a 5 °C (41 °F) rise in the rooting environment resulting in a heat input saving. This medium is also lighter, making it easier to handle and improving aeration.

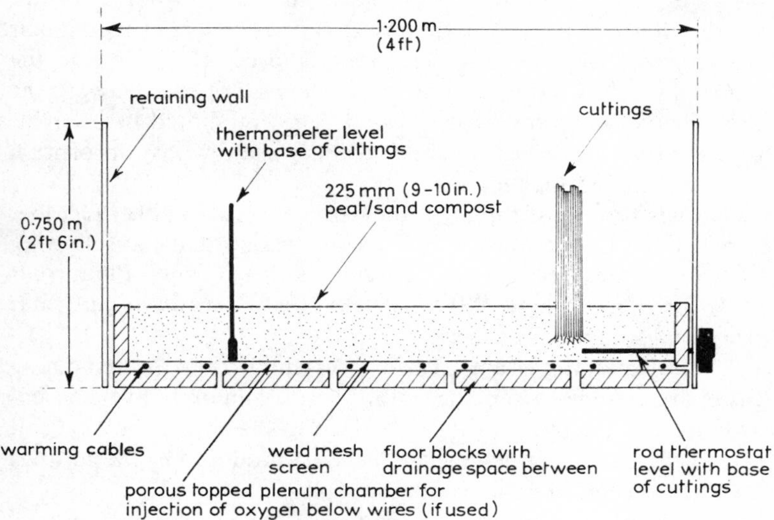

Fig. 18 Hardwood cutting bin

Subjects rooted in heated bins

The range of plants rooted by this technique is constantly increasing; the following have been successfully rooted in heated bins:

1 Ornamental species: *Acer campestre*; *Corylus avellana*; *Laburnum anagyroides* 'Vossii'; *Platanus* × *hispanica*; *Pterocarya fraxinifolia*; *Sorbus intermedia*; *Tilia cordata*; *Tilia* × *europaea* and *Ulmus glabra*.
2 Fruit rootstocks: *Malus*: M27, MM106, MM111, M26; Plum: 'Myrobalan B', 'St Julian A', 'Brompton'; *Prunus* (cherry): 'Colt'; *Pyrus*: Quince A, Quince C.

Success in rooting is governed by collecting the cuttings at the correct time, applying the right hormone and giving the cuttings the right basal temperature in the bin.

Collection and preparation of cuttings

Cuttings are collected from stock hedges which are grown at a minimum spacing of 300 mm × 2 m (1 ft × 6 ft 6 in) (see Chapter 16). The material selected must be from one-year-old vigorous, healthy shoots. Cuttings are removed during the winter with a pair of secateurs. Select pencil-thick shoots and cut them close to the previous year's wood to include the swollen shoot base between the one-year-old and two-year-old wood. The cut should be at right-angles to the long axis of the shoot as this will allow easy absorption of the rooting hormone.

Cuttings root most rapidly if they are collected in either October or mid-February to March. It is recommended that the following are taken in October when 50 per cent leaf drop occurs: Plum root-stocks 'Brompton' and 'Myrobalan'; *Prunus cerasifera* cultivars; *Prunus padus*; and *Tilia* species.

If October cuttings are used it is essential that the remaining leaves are stripped from the cuttings to maintain a hygienic environment in the bin. Cuttings obtained in the spring must be collected before they start leafing as all energy produced by the cuttings must be concentrated on producing roots.

After collecting, cuttings are treated with a rooting hormone by dipping their bases in a solution containing indolebutyric acid (IBA). The auxin is normally mixed with an alcohol. Pure alcohol is expensive and methyl-alcohol or methylated spirits are cheaper and give just as good a result. The hormone mixture is normally prepared by a chemist; a concentration of 2,500 ppm is normally used for most species, but a rate of 5,000 ppm is recommended for the plum rootstock 'Brompton' and 1,000 ppm for the cherry rootstock 'Colt'. If pre-formed roots have already occurred then no IBA treatment is required.

Cuttings are dipped for five seconds. Hold them upright, tap them on the bench so that the base of all the cuttings is level, then dip in 12 mm (0·5 in) of the IBA solution. Excess liquid is shaken off and they are allowed to dry for 30 minutes before insertion.

Uniform rooting is governed by all cuttings being dipped to the same depth and duration. Absorption of hormone is governed by the moisture content of the cutting and the angle at which the cutting is dried. Best absorption is obtained by collecting material a few hours before dipping in hormone as the extra water stress in the cuttings will mean more absorption of rooting hormone. An alternative to an IBA mix is to dip the cuttings in 50 per cent ethyl alcohol and then into a commercial rooting powder formulation.

Cutting insertion

The aim of the rooting bin is to promote root development quickly and this is achieved by applying warmth to the base of the cuttings. Rooting potential increases with rising temperature, the optimum for most species being 21 °C (70 °F). Two to three weeks of bottom heat should be adequate to initiate root development in most species.

All material should be placed at the same depth in the heated bin. This should be the same as the level of a rod thermostat or sensor: about 25 mm (1 in) above the heating wires.

Bins should be checked for watering at regular intervals to ensure the compost is kept adequately moist; drying out will result in dehydration and eventual death of the cuttings.

Three weeks before planting the heating is switched off to allow the cuttings to harden off. At the same time it is still important that material is not induced into early leaf, prior to planting, as this will hinder establishment.

The only other management procedure that needs to be carried out is to ensure the bin is not infested by rodents which may be attracted to the warm basal environment during winter months.

Lifting

As soon as soil conditions are suitable for planting, the cuttings are lifted from the bin. Care is important, both to preserve the cutting and to ensure the heating cables are not damaged.

Some growers have experienced losses at the planting stage in the late winter and this can be overcome by ensuring the soil is in the correct condition for planting and even backfilling the planting trench with old bin compost. It is important that soil conditions are neither too wet nor dry as losses will result.

Hardwood cuttings of rootstocks, if grown satisfactorily, can be budded during the growing season or allowed to grow on for one full season before being grafted or budded.

Routine maintenance of bins

For successful propagation hygiene is important. The rooting medium in the bins should be changed every year; if left for a number of seasons the texture will slowly break down and result in impaired drainage.

Compost can be easily removed from the bin without damaging the heating cables if the cables are connected to the underside of a protective grid which can also be lifted to allow disinfection. The bins should be thoroughly washed down with a sterilant, such as formaldehyde, before any fresh growing medium is placed in them.

Oxygen injection

The amount of oxygen in a rooting medium will affect the rooting potential of the plant material; with this in mind some growers have, in the past, introduced oxygen injection into their bins to encourage rooting. Oxygen pipes (12 mm/0·5 in diameter) are placed under the heating cables with welded-steel mesh separating them to prevent the weight of the compost causing the cables to rest on the oxygen pipes and severing them. The oxygen pipe has holes in it at 150 mm (6 in) spacings and gas is injected into the growing area every three days for a five-second burst. In some years this has resulted in better callusing and rooting of hardwood cuttings, but in other years little benefit has been apparent.

With this advance in technology we now have a method of producing a wide range of ornamental plants and rootstocks from hardwood cuttings, with more plants being produced in a shorter time than by using more traditional techniques.

15

Layering

SIMPLE LAYERING

The propagation of plants by layering, that is, rooting shoots while they are still attached to the mother plant, was once very widely practised by nurserymen before the advent of sophisticated facilities. Nowadays layering is not so popular because of the other ways in which it is possible to propagate plants that hitherto proved difficult, if not impossible, to raise by any other means.

However, one should on no account dismiss layering as a method of propagation on the modern nursery for it is useful for increasing those species which are still difficult, or even very slow, to root from cuttings. Also it is a good method when only a few plants of a particular species are required and of course this applies very much to the smaller nurseryman.

A great advantage of layering, apart from the fact that it is an easy method of propagation and cheap, is that it enables one to produce large saleable plants quickly—they are rooted in the first year and in the second year they are grown on to saleable size. This is an especially attractive proposition for high-value shrubs like *Hamamelis* and *Magnolia*. However, there are a few shrubs, mainly *Magnolia* and *Rhododendron*, which need about 18 months to form a good root system; nevertheless, large plants are still quickly obtained.

It is mainly trees and shrubs which are propagated by layering, and on page 134 we give a fairly comprehensive list of those that we regularly produce by simple layering.

The mother plants

It is essential to encourage vigorous growth in the mother plants to ensure a succession of strong young shoots for annual layering. This can only be achieved by soil conditions that are ideal for the purpose.

Firstly, one must choose a well-drained piece of land on which to establish the layer beds. It must also be fertile and free of perennial weeds. The texture of the soil can be improved, especially if the land is heavy, by the incorporation of peat and coarse sand. It would also be beneficial to incorporate peat into a light sandy soil during initial preparations for planting so as to improve the moisture-holding capacity. Also, ensure the nutrient status is satisfactory and, if necessary, apply a fertilizer containing a suitable balance of nitrogen, phosphorus and potash.

The mother plants are planted in rows, which are spaced at least 3 m (10 ft) apart. The mother plants should be spaced 2–2·5 m (6 ft 6 in–8 ft 3 in) apart in the rows. All this space around the plants is necessary for pegging down the shoots and it can be seen, therefore, that layering takes up quite a lot of ground. This is another reason why it is not so popular today and why it is best reserved for those subjects that may be difficult to propagate by other means.

The mother plants should be allowed to become established for two to three years before layering commences on an annual basis. The mother plants will then remain productive for many years before they need replacing—provided, that is, they are properly maintained.

The annual programme for simple layering

Simple layering is generally carried out in spring—during the period March to June. Basically the idea is to peg down strong, young shoots which were produced in the previous year, so that they root into the soil. They are arched over and pegged down all around the mother plant. While these are rooting, a new crop of shoots will be produced by the mother plant and these are used for pegging down in the following year. So a succession of one-year-old shoots is maintained.

Before pegging down, the shoots must be wounded to interrupt the flow of sap, to encourage rooting at that point on the shoot. Each stem should be wounded approximately 300 mm (1 ft) from its tip. There are various ways of wounding. The shoot may be sharply twisted, using both hands, so as to damage the tissue. Or a tongue may be cut in the stem by drawing a sharp knife half way through the stem for a length of about 35–50 mm (1·5–2 in). When the shoot is pegged down ensure that this tongue remains open.

The wounded shoots should be pegged down into well-loosened soil using galvanized wire pegs in the shape of a hairpin. Make sure

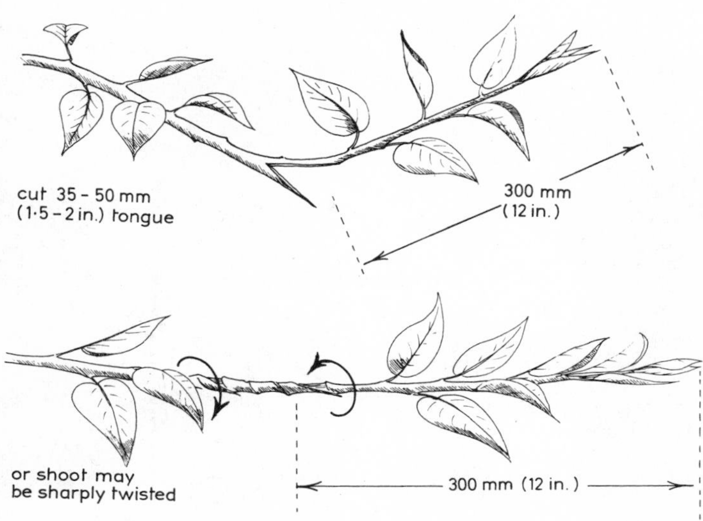

Fig. 19 Simple layering—wounding shoots

they are in close contact with the soil. They should be pegged where the wound was made. The layers should be spaced out evenly all around the mother plants, about 150 mm (6 in) apart. When the shoots or layers have been pegged down, tie them in an upright position to short canes, using raffia. This ensures straight stems in the resulting young plants. Next, the pegged parts of the shoots are covered with 75–100 mm (3–4 in) of soil. Use fine soil for this purpose, which can be obtained from between the rows. The idea of this soil covering is to prevent the layers drying out, as this would seriously inhibit rooting.

Throughout the spring and summer the layer beds must be kept moist, by irrigating if the weather is dry. The beds must also be kept free from weeds and this is best achieved by hand weeding as residual herbicides could affect rooting of the layers.

Generally, the rooted layers can be lifted in the autumn, once the plants are dormant, although very often we delay lifting until the following spring. The majority of subjects will be well rooted in one growing season but, as we have said before, *Magnolia* and *Rhododendron* are best left down for 18 months, so these can be lifted in the second autumn from layering.

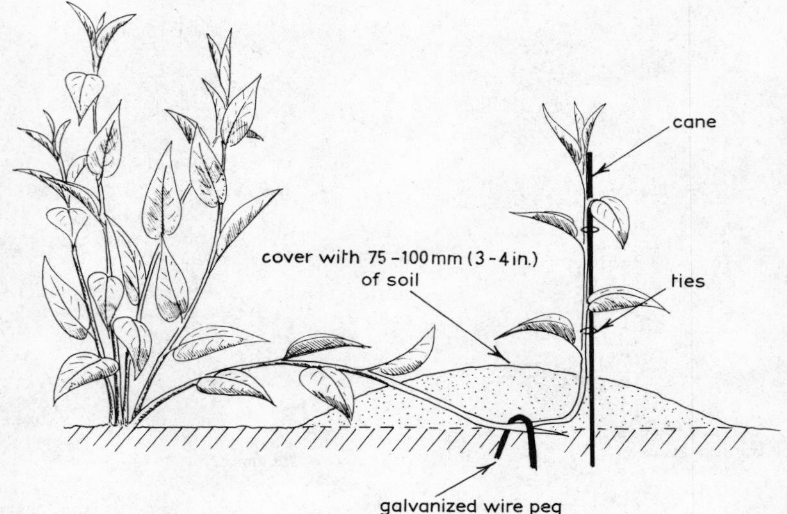

Fig. 20 Simple layering – pegging down a shoot

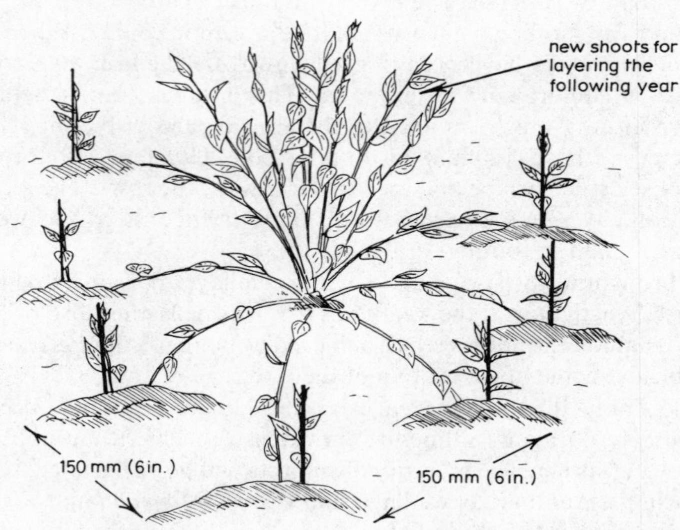

Fig. 21 A layered mother plant

When lifting, the soil covering should be carefully drawn away into the space between the rows. Then the canes and ties should be removed and the rooted layers carefully lifted with a fork. They should then be cut away as close as possible to the rooted part of the shoot and the remaining portion of shoot cut out as close as possible to the mother plant.

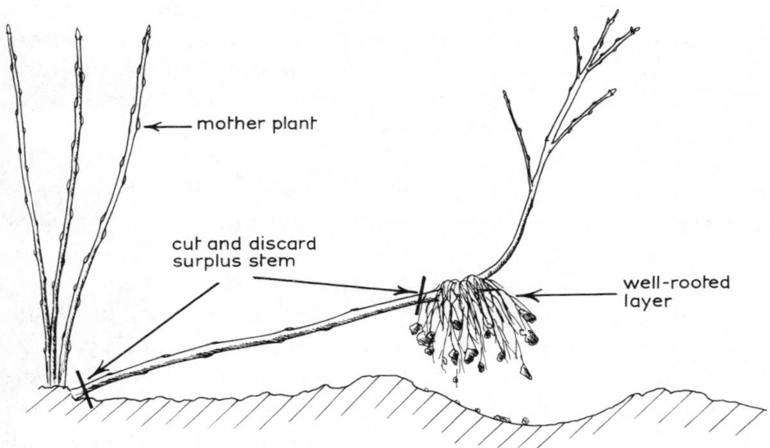

Fig. 22 Simple layering – lifting a rooted layer

Do ensure the roots of the layers do not dry out while lifting – all lifted layers should be kept covered with polythene or hessian prior to containerizing or planting out.

Once all the rooted layers have been lifted you will be left with the current year's crop of new shoots ready for layering again. It is best to prune out all the weakest shoots, leaving only the strongest for pegging down. Also, any unrooted layers should be completely removed at the same time. Just prior to layering it is necessary to feed the mother plants by applying a balanced compound fertilizer to supply the major elements of nitrogen, phosphorus and potash. This should be applied as a top dressing and pricked into the soil.

Growing on rooted layers

As most subjects that are propagated by layering are choice shrubs and trees it is probably best to containerize the rooted layers into

150 mm (6 in) containers. They can then be placed under polythene or shade tunnels to become well established. The rooted layers could also be bedded out in a sheltered area if containerization is not desired.

Subjects for layering

We regularly propagate the following trees and shrubs by simple layering: *Cornus controversa*; *Corylus avellana* 'Contorta'; *Corylus colurna*; *Corylus maxima* 'Purpurea'; *Cercidiphyllum japonicum*; *Hamamelis* × *intermedia* cultivars; *Hamamelis japonica* cultivars; *Hamamelis mollis* and cultivars; *Magnolia liliiflora* 'Nigra'; *Magnolia* × *proctoriana*; *Magnolia salicifolia*; *Magnolia sieboldii*; *Magnolia* × *soulangiana* and cultivars; *Magnolia stellata* and cultivars; *Parrotia persica*; *Prunus glandulosa* 'Plena'; *Prunus glandulosa* 'Sinensis'; *Prunus tenella* 'Fire Hill'; *Stachyurus praecox*; *Stephanandra tanakae*; *Syringa microphylla* 'Superba'; *Syringa vulgaris* cultivars; *Tilia cordata* 'Rancho'; *Tilia* × *euchlora*; *Tilia* × *europaea*; *Viburnum plicatum* cultivars. We should mention *Rhododendron* separately for although many nurserymen propagate the hardy hybrids by cuttings nowadays (or by bench grafting if some cultivars prove difficult from cuttings), layering is a very good method for this genus provided the layers are left down for 18 months. The deciduous azaleas can also be layered if the other method of propagation (softwood cuttings) should prove difficult.

FRENCH LAYERING

This is a modified version of simple layering, the difference being that the shoots are pegged down along their entire length and the buds develop into upright shoots all along the stems. Many more plants can therefore be obtained from each shoot – in simple layering each stem yields only the one plant.

The mother plants

For details of planting and spacing of the mother plants readers should refer to the section on simple layering (on page 129) as the details are the same.

The annual programme for French layering

Early in the new year – about January – the shoots produced in the previous year are pegged down horizontally (not arched) for their entire length and should be in close contact with the soil. In the spring the buds along the length of each shoot will break and form upright shoots. When these shoots are 50 mm (2 in) in length they should be covered with soil so that only the extreme tips are showing above soil level. Use very fine soil from between the rows. This can be fined down with a rotary cultivator.

When the shoots have made further growth they can again be earthed up with fine soil. Sometimes a third earthing can be given, if necessary, to ensure the horizontal shoots are covered with about 150 mm (6 in) of soil. The final earthing up should, in any case, be completed by early summer.

As with simple layering the beds must be kept moist at all times to ensure rooting, and weed control should be carried out by hand.

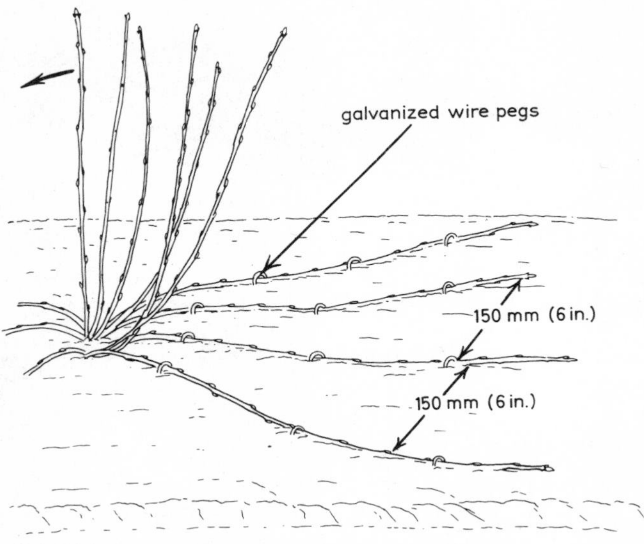

Fig. 23 Pegging down shoots for French layering

Again, lifting can be carried out in the autumn or the following spring after removing the soil covering. Lift with a fork and cut away each of the original stems as close as possible to the mother plant. There should be a good number of rooted shoots on each of the original stems and each should be removed as close to the rooted area as possible.

If any of the original stems did not root they should be cut away as there will be a new crop of shoots for layering. Again cut out the weakest of these and leave only the strongest for pinning down. Just prior to layering apply a compound fertilizer, as recommended for simple layering. The growing on of the rooted layers is the same as for simple layering.

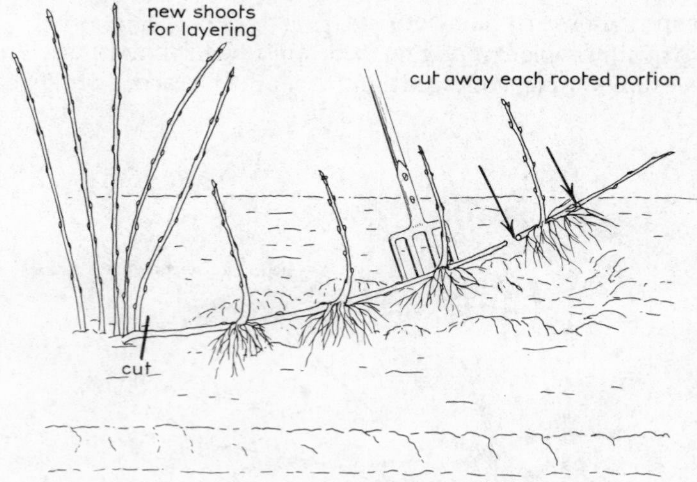

Fig. 24 Lifting French layers

Subjects for French layering

Each year we French layer quite a range of trees and shrubs which often prove difficult to propagate by other methods so we have listed them below. Neither this list, nor the one in the section on simple layering, is exhaustive, but indicates a representative range of plant material that responds well to this method of propagation.

Acer cappodocicum 'Rubrum'; *Acer saccharinum* 'Laciniatum'; *Alnus cordata*; *Alnus incana* 'Aurea'; *Carpinus betulus* 'Fastigiata'; *Carpinus betulus* 'Purpurea'; *Chimonanthus praecox* and *C.p.* 'Lutea'; *Corylus colurna*; *Corylus avellana* 'Aurea'; *Corylopsis pauciflora*; *Corylopsis willmottiae*; *Cotinus coggygria* and cultivars; *Euonymus europaeus* 'Red Cascade'; *Fothergilla monticola*; *Halesia carolina*; *Hydrangea paniculata*; *Hydrangea quercifolia*; *Styrax japonica*; *Tilia platyphyllos* 'Rubra'; *Viburnum* × *bodnantense*; *Viburnum farreri*.

16

Rootstocks

Modern fruit trees and ornamental trees are often made up of two parts: a rootstock, which is a plant upon which another has been superimposed, and a scion, the part which forms the tree head with the desired characteristics.

There are many reasons for using a rootstock to raise a plant but they can be summarized as follows:

1 The rootstock will have a desirable root system, whereas the scion, which has often been bred specifically for fruit or flower production, may have a poor root system.
2 The rootstock will tolerate unfavourable conditions, such as wet or heavy soils.
3 Resistance to pests and diseases may be a characteristic of the rootstock, a factor that is illustrated in the production of vines. American vines are resistant to damage by the nematode *Phylloxera* while French vines are prone to damage; therefore in France the rootstock is of American origin.
4 The rootstock may be 'cold hardy' as illustrated in America where grapefruits are worked on to lime roots.
5 One of the major factors is that the rootstock can influence the habit of the scion; this is because dwarfing rootstocks have a greater ratio of phloem to xylem than vigorous rootstocks. The result is that at the graft union a greater disarrangement of tissue occurs with dwarf stocks and this acts as a stranglehold, restricting liquid passage. This affects the ultimate size of the plant, nutrient uptake, cropping capacity and time of cropping.

TYPES OF ROOTSTOCKS

Rootstocks can be divided into two groups as itemized below.

Seedling rootstocks

These were used for apple production, but now can only be found in cider-apple production where 'Tremlett's Bitter' is used as it gives even growth as well as being simple and economical to raise. The main disadvantage of seedling rootstocks is their genetic variation which often results in variability in growth performance.

Clonal rootstocks

These are raised vegetatively with the advantage that each plant is exactly the same genetically and the breeder can preserve special characteristics so that the grower has a known standard and controlled performance. The disadvantage of clonal material is that, with virus-tested material, it takes a long time before the grower obtains rootstocks bred at the research station.

The commercial production of rootstocks is primarily governed by the requirements of the fruit industry, the trend in fruit production being towards smaller trees, which makes picking and spraying easier, and closer spacing between trees. This means that most new rootstocks being produced are dwarfer than those traditionally grown.

The grower is also demanding quick-cropping, virus-cleared, plant material and this has resulted in research stations releasing virus-tested rootstocks (EMLA rootstocks).

Virus-tested rootstocks

Most work on virus-testing has been concerned with apples. The main virus diseases are Rubbery Wood, severely affecting apple 'Lord Lambourne'; Flat Limb, again on 'Lord Lambourne'; Apple Mosaic and Chat Fruit.

To obtain virus-tested material the researcher firstly has to recognize the virus and study its properties. Therapy measures are then taken, normally by giving the rootstock heat treatment at 40 °C (104 °F) for three to four weeks. At this temperature virus cells reproduce at a slower rate than plant cells and growth tips contain less virus than normal. Meristem cuttings can then be taken from the growth tips and grown on; finally this material is indexed for virus by graft inoculation on to an indicator plant. If this gives a clean bill of health then clean material can be bulked up for distribution.

The job of the research station is to 'clean-up' existing rootstocks as well as develop new types, but before this material can reach the grower it has to be bulked up and this is carried out by the Nuclear Stock Association (Fruit Trees) Ltd, who produce Special Stock Certificated Plants for the commercial raiser in the British Isles.

The Nuclear Stock Association (Fruit Trees) Ltd

This association was started in 1966 to obtain rootstocks and mother trees from the researchers and then bulk them up under the Special Stock Certification Scheme. The rootstocks are then released to the commercial trade which, normally, takes about four years from receiving to release.

This non-profit-making organization will officially inspect proposed raising sites to ensure they meet the required regulations concerning isolation, freedom from nematodes and freedom from certain earth-borne diseases. Once a site has been approved, EMLA material may be purchased through the NSA and raised under the Special Stock Certification regulations. The certification is based on pedigree of stock, isolation, periodic inspections during the growing season and retests for viruses. It is the special stock material which is released to growers for raising fruit and ornamental trees.

CLASSIFICATION OF ROOTSTOCKS

Rootstocks are classified under vigour as indicated in the following:

1 APPLES

Very dwarf:

M8—used as an interstock for very dwarf trees in the United States of America.

M27—gives a tree height of 1·5 m (4 ft 6 in). Liable to Plant Breeders Rights.

Dwarfing:

M9—'Jaune de Metz' has poor anchorage and brittle roots and therefore needs staking all its life. Used for bush trees, cordons and dwarf pyramids. Improved form is M9A (available as EMLA).

Semi-dwarf:

M7—well-anchored rootstock which is quick growing, but liable to sucker.

M106—similar to M7 but does not sucker, good rootstock on light soils (available as EMLA).

M4—'Holstein Doucin'. A quick-growing tree is produced in early life, although it has a poor root system. Not normally grown in Britain.

Vigorous:

M2—'Doucin'. A common rootstock for bush-tree production, with a well-anchored root system and vigorous on stool-beds.

M104—well-anchored tree produced, roots easily on the stool-beds.

M111—now replacing M2 and grows well from hardwood cuttings (available as EMLA).

M1—'English Broadleaf'. Only used where heavy clay soils are a problem.

Very vigorous:

M25—propagates readily, but susceptible to woolly aphis (available as EMLA).

M16—'Ketzier Ideal'. Susceptible to woolly aphis, produces a well-rooted tree.

Crab C—very vigorous rootstock, but difficult to root from stooling.

M109—sensitive to waterlogged conditions, propagates readily.

2 PEARS

Pears or *Pyrus* are normally worked on to Quince, *Cydonia oblonga*, as pear on pear produces a very large tree that is slow to fruit and produces small green pears. It is also difficult to propagate pear vegetatively in the nursery. The following rootstocks are therefore used:

Semi-dwarf:

Malling Quince C—induces an early, heavy-cropping tree; it is a useful rootstock where shy-cropping varieties need to be produced (available from EMLA).

Semi-vigorous:

Malling Quince A—principal commercial rootstock which is highly productive in the nursery (available from EMLA).

Malling Quince B—now rarely grown, almost identical to Quince A.

3 CHERRY

Dwarf:

'Colt'—*(Prunus avium × Prunus pseudocerasus)*. 50 per cent dwarfer than normal cherry rootstocks, resistant to bacterial canker and Cherry Replant Disease. Covered by Plant Breeders Rights.

Vigorous:

Malling F12/1—produces a well-rooted tree and is the common rootstock for cherry production (available as EMLA).

4 PLUM

Dwarf:

'Pixy'—rootstock protected under Plant Breeders Rights.

Semi-dwarf:

'Brussels'—(syn. 'Varkenspium'). Easy to propagate, ideal rootstock for plum cultivar 'Victoria', although prone to suckering.

Common Mussel—widely compatible, used for plum and peach, both culinary and ornamental. Suckers, does not come readily from layering, although it roots from hardwood cuttings.

'Pershore'—good for small trees that crop early; costly to propagate due to difficulty in getting it to root.

Semi-vigorous:

Common plum—*(Prunus domestica)*. Varieties on this rootstock show a high degree of resistance to Silver-leaf Disease *(Stereum purpureum)*. It is incompatible with damson and plum 'Czar' and 'Marjories Seedling' as well as being prone to suckering.

'St Julien A'—compatible with all plums, roots well from hardwood cuttings and induces early cropping (available as EMLA).

Vigorous:

'Brompton'—compatible with all plums, also good for nectarine, peach and apricot. Suckers little and rather shy-rooting in layer beds. Roots readily from hardwood cuttings (available as EMLA).

'Myrobolan B'—may induce later cropping, but will eventually out-crop more conservative stocks. No good for peach tribe, damsons and bullaces, 'Oullins' or 'Compte D'Althanns'. Roots well when layered and comes readily from hardwood cuttings (available from EMLA).

'Marianna'—incompatible with plum cultivars 'Czar', 'President', 'Oullins', damsons and peaches. Produces few suckers and comes readily from hardwood cuttings.

'Damas C'—widely compatible, layers well and roots well from hardwood cuttings.

PLUM POX OR SHARKA DISEASE

Unless a pest or disease has been specific to the production cycle we have omitted it in the text, but such a serious problem as Plum Pox, concerning the raising of plum rootstocks, needs special attention.

This disease was first detected in 1966 on imported rootstocks although it has been widespread for the last 20 years in Central Europe. The virus disease is spread by aphids and even so-called resistant clones quickly become infected.

Leaf symptoms

Infected plants show a characteristic chlorotic leaf pattern during the spring and summer which is most noticeable on fully expanded leaves. The pale green diffuse rings and spots are easiest to see on dull days with transmitted light. They can be distinguished from Line Pattern plum disease by their hazy and watermark type outlines, as the latter disease has sharply bordered rings and lines.

Fruit symptoms

The first indication of Plum Pox on fruit is a significant drop of fruit seven to ten days before the normal date of maturity for that variety. Close inspection of the fruit may reveal symptoms such as uneven ripening, dark-coloured rings, lines or bands and pitting or grooving of the fruit surface.

These symptoms are most obvious on the orange or red-fruited varieties, e.g., 'Victoria'. Yellow or green fruits are not normally affected, although keeping qualities may be impaired.

Plants affected

Apart from plum, the virus also affects damsons, gages, apricots, peaches, nectarines and ornamental plums (cherries, ornamental cherries and almonds are not affected by the disease).

Similar symptoms are found on the other plants attacked by Plum Pox. The main exceptions are the symptoms on the leaf of peach, which appear early in the year as the young leaves expand. The leaf may be distorted, having a wavy edge and perhaps a slight twist.

The main problem with detecting this disease is that there is no way of telling whether imported rootstocks are infected when they arrive in the country during the dormant season.

How to avoid Plum Pox

1 Plant only certified trees.
2 Spray regularly against aphids. If the number of winged aphids is maintained at a low level the spread of infection is minimized. The problem is trying to persuade fruit growers to spray against aphids after the crop has been harvested, which many may say, justifiably, is uneconomic.
3 Inspect the orchard/nursery regularly.
4 Consult an adviser immediately you suspect Plum Pox.

Precautions against Plum Pox in your nursery

1 Separate stock of unknown origin from healthy stock.
2 Establish new propagation beds or hedges with Ministry certified SS/EMLA stock.
3 Keep control of crop hygiene.

Plum Pox detection

Plum Pox can appear in a period of a few days and regular inspections are therefore important. The traditional method of confirming the virus is to graft on to peach, but this takes 10 days before confirmation of the virus. However, methods have now been speeded up and confirmation can be given in five days. The new detection method has been developed by researchers and it is a serological one, involving the reaction of virus with a specific antibody. The virus-specific antibody has an enzyme attached, which can be detected by a change in colour when another substance is added.

If the disease is recorded on a nursery the following regulations apply:

1 Eradication by fire of diseased plants.

2 Susceptible species must be sold by the end of the calendar year and to non-commercial areas.
3 Young nursery stock budded with infected material must be destroyed.

ROOTSTOCK PRODUCTION

Rootstocks can be raised by various methods but normally, depending on the species or clone, they are grown on stoolbeds, by layering or from hardwood cuttings.

Stoolbed production

This is the oldest method of vegetative propagation and one of the most reliable, relying on the fact that if a young stem is placed in darkness it will produce adventitious roots. The major disadvantage of this system is that a lot of skilled handwork is required to obtain a high-quality crop.

The first consideration in planting a stoolbed is the soil; ideally it should be a light, sandy loam which will warm up quickly in the spring, be well drained and slightly acidic. Avoid placing stoolbeds in frost pockets and where perennial weed problems occur.

Planting of mother plants should take place in the autumn using high-quality, healthy material and planting in an upright position at a spacing of 1 m (3 ft 3 in) between rows and 350 mm (14 in) between plants; this gives adequate room for earthing up. After planting, the rootstocks are pruned to 600 mm (2 ft) above ground level.

During the following summer the mother plants are allowed to grow naturally to become established; a good crop is never obtained during the first year. In February or March the plants are cut back to 25 mm (1 in) above the soil to encourage side shoots to emerge.

CROP PRODUCTION

During the next year new shoots emerge which will be the first crop of rootstocks. In the spring the soil around the rootstocks is loosened to allow for earthing up. When the new shoots are 300 mm (1 ft) high they are stooled, that is, covered with soil to about one-third their height using a ridging plough. This is basically a blanching of the stems to induce roots (not to be confused with etiolation where shoots grow in darkness).

Shoots are stooled again when they are 350 mm (14 in) in height, followed by a final earthing up in late summer to give a 150–200 mm (6–8 in) high stool. In the British Isles soil is used for stooling, but materials such as sawdust are just as effective and have been used by some growers.

Between November and January the soil around the stooled plants is forked away. It is important that this is not carried out until the plants are fully dormant, to ensure that the plant material is not damaged.

One-year rooted cuttings are now removed from the mother plant. Cut as close to the original stool plant as possible, otherwise future growth will produce a spindly plant which is difficult to manage and which will produce inferior rooted cuttings. When removing cuttings use sharp secateurs, which will not crush the bark and destroy the lateral buds.

In the first year of production a stool will produce between one and five rooted cuttings, but the numbers of rooted shoots will increase as the stool becomes established. The stools should remain productive for about 15 years if well managed.

Rooted cuttings are normally graded into two sizes after removal, based on the diameter of the rootstock at the budding zone. Grades are: Grade I – 7–12 mm (0·2–0·4 in) diameter at the budding zone. Grade II – 5–7 mm (0·1–0·2 in) diameter at the budding zone. All other material is discarded.

Annual maintenance of the stoolbed should include weed control, irrigation when required, pest and disease control and fertilizer applications. Rooted cuttings should be planted out as soon as possible for growing on for tree production.

Layer beds

Prunus F12/1 rootstocks and occasionally mulberry and walnut can be produced by etiolation layering. Etiolation is where shoots are produced in darkness, resulting in etiolated, leafless branches and having the effect of distributing growth over a large number of shoots. This technique is only used on plants which will not root from stools as the system is costly when compared with stooling – more labour is involved and it is more difficult to mechanize.

Land preparation prior to planting includes the removal of perennial weeds and drainage improvements if necessary. Plants are planted in rows 1·7 m (5 ft 6 in) and 500–700 mm (20–27 in) be-

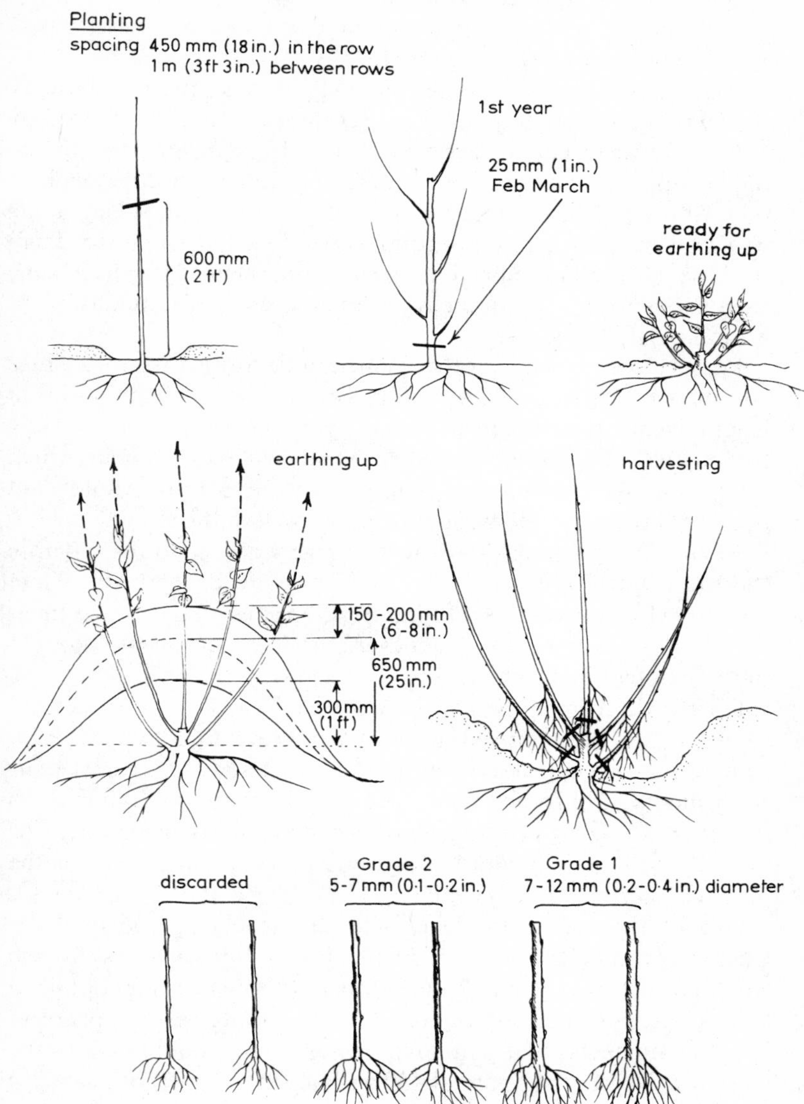

Fig. 25 Stoolbed production

tween plants in the row. The mother plants are planted at a 45° angle pointing south; if planted in the opposite direction the shoots tend to grow back towards sunlight.

Pegging down of the mother plant should take place in January or February, earlier pegging often resulting in pegs being lifted by frost. Any weak laterals are first removed and strong laterals are lightly tipped; a shallow trench is then prepared, wide enough to take all the branches without cramming any of them. When laying down the mother plant it is recommended that soil is removed from the base of the plant to prevent bowing of the stem. This ensures the stem lies horizontal, with the result of an even distribution of plant hormones along the stem.

Pegs for securing the mother plant can be formed from 10 gauge wire in a U shape, or sharpened pieces of wood, 200 mm (8 in) in length, ideally from *Castanea sativa*, Spanish chestnut, which rarely rots in the soil. Do not use green wood, willow or poplar which often root. Once the mother plant is pegged down, the whole plant is covered with fine soil before the buds swell in the spring.

In late spring young shoots will emerge with curled tops. Before the shoot uncurls it should be earthed up to a depth of 20 mm (0·7 in). This process of earthing up is repeated two or three times during the growing season, but never bury the one-year-old shoot to more than half its height.

During the winter the soil is removed from the layer bed and rooted shoots are removed, using sharp secateurs. Shoots with no roots are again pegged down to produce material for the next year. If all shoots have rooted then leave one shoot every 300 mm (1 ft) for the next year's layering. All harvested shoots are graded for budding and grafting and the layering process is repeated for the next year's production.

One of the major problems with raising cherry rootstocks is Cherry Replant Disease caused by the fungus *Thieloaviopsis basicola* which can drastically reduce the number of rooted cuttings obtained from a layer bed. To prevent this disease becoming a serious problem it is recommended that you apply benomyl as a soil drench to the layer beds in May at a rate of 150 g/90 m (5 oz/295 ft) of row.

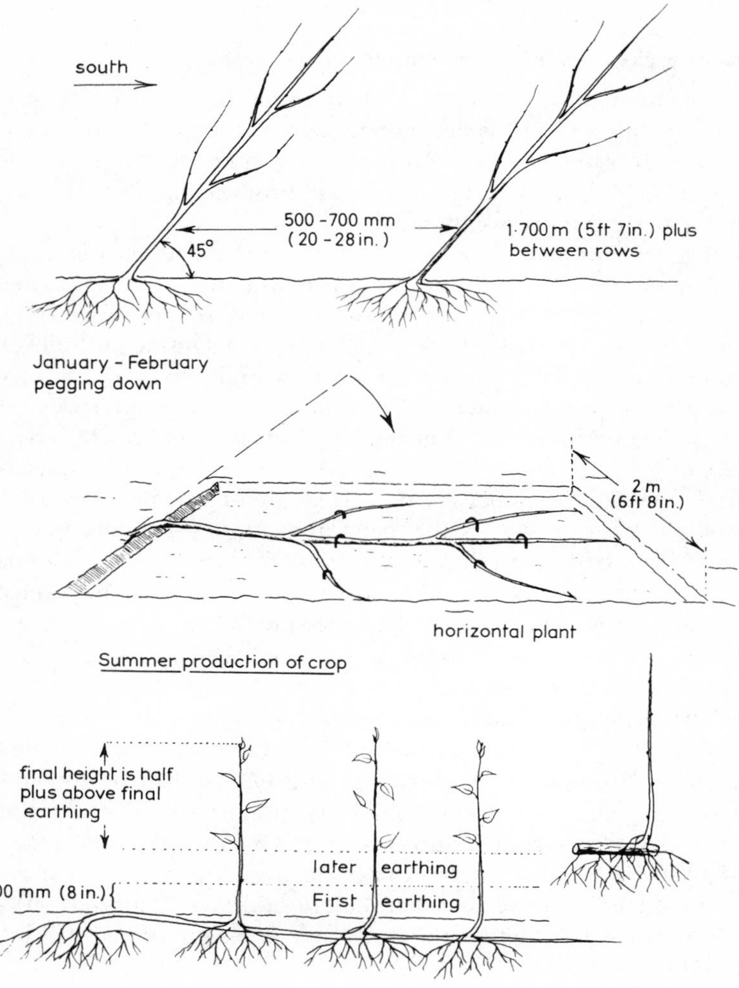

Fig. 26 Etiolation method of layering

ESTABLISHING CUTTING-HEDGES

Rootstocks from hardwood cuttings

As mentioned in Chapter 14 rootstocks can be produced in heated cutting bins and this is becoming the most accepted technique for rooting rootstocks. The important factor in raising by this method is establishing stock hedges which will produce vigorous one-year-old material for propagation.

The mother plants are planted during the winter at a minimum spacing of 300 mm (1 ft) × 2 m (6 ft 6 in) between rows. This material should be one- or two-year rooted material of good quality and, once planted, shortened back to 600 mm (2 ft). During the following summer it should be allowed to grow naturally to establish a root system and produce laterals. These laterals are pruned back in the second winter to two to four buds and subsequent growth is again left to grow naturally during the summer. In the third winter the first crop of cuttings may be harvested, although only a few will be suitable, with the rest of the material again being pruned back to two to four buds to produce a framework for future cutting material.

Once a framework has been constructed, cuttings can be taken on a yearly basis. After cuttings have been removed, coarse feathered shoots are pruned back to two to four buds while small shoots are cut back to one or two buds.

The technique of taking cuttings is discussed in Chapter 14.

Apart from rooting rootstocks in heated bins, certain rootstocks such as 'Brompton', 'Myrobalan', and Quince can be rooted in specially constructed frames outdoors. Frames can be constructed of railway sleepers on the north side of a building to make a frame 450 mm (18 in) high. In the base of the frame 75 mm (3 in) of sand is placed to improve drainage before adding 450 mm (18 in) of 50:50 coarse peat and sand. A 2·4 m^2 (8 ft square) bed will hold 20,000 cuttings.

Propagation can take place from mid-October and a 0·5 per cent IBA in ethyl-alcohol rooting hormone is used. Good callusing occurs after one month in the frame and rooting should soon follow. Rooting will be slower than in a heated bin but material should be ready for planting in April.

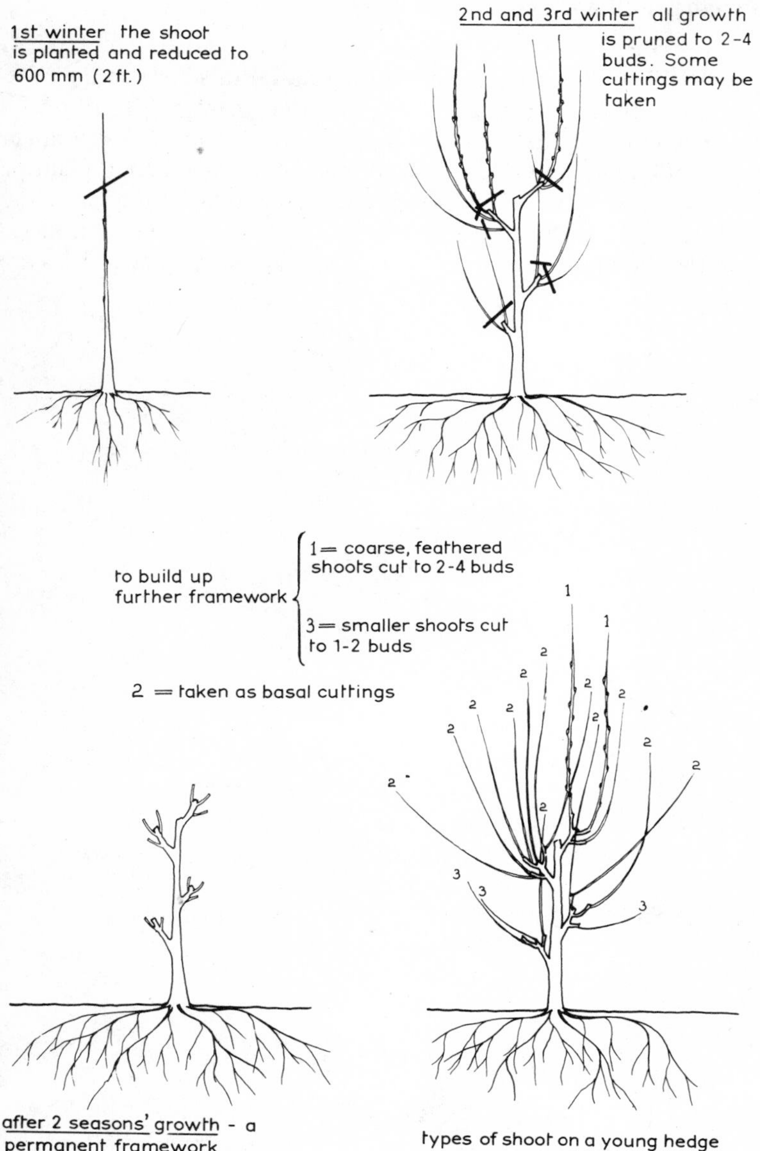

Fig. 27 Establishing cutting-hedges

Planting until working

It is important that the rootstocks are established before budding or grafting. If budding is the normal method of raising then the rootstocks are worked during the summer after planting. If grafting is preferred the rootstocks are allowed to grow during the first summer and grafted the following spring. It must be stressed that at planting time the rootstock has far more stem growth than root growth and this situation needs to be reversed to produce good trees and therefore the establishment period is important if high-quality trees are required.

17

Grafting

When grafting, one forms a new plant out of portions of two other plants. One plant provides the root system for the new plant and is correctly called the rootstock and another plant provides the top growth (the stems and leaves) and is known as the scion. In grafting, the scion is fixed to the rootstock so that eventually the two join together and form a permanent union. For this to happen, stock and scion must be what is known as 'compatible' otherwise the tissues of rootstock and scion will not unite.

It is usual, therefore, to graft scions of cultivars on to a closely related rootstock. Generally the rootstock is the common counterpart of the scion, usually the common species. For instance, if we want to graft hardy hybrid rhododendrons then we use the common *Rhododendron ponticum*, the wild species. As another example, cultivars of *Chamaecyparis* are grafted on to rootstocks of the wild *Chamaecyparis lawsoniana*.

However, success is not achieved simply by using the appropriate rootstock. One must become very skilled in knife work so that cuts on scion and stock match exactly. This means that the cambium layers (the green tissue just beneath the bark) of stock and scion are in intimate contact to ensure that a union takes place. Cambium is meristematic tissue and it is this tissue which unites stock and scion: the cambium layers actually fuse together during cell division.

In budding, which is really a form of grafting, we see that a single growth bud forms the scion, whereas in other methods of grafting a portion of stem or shoot, containing several growth buds, forms the scion. Budding is generally carried out in the summer, but the majority of grafting is done just before plants start into growth. The months of February and March are the usual times for carrying out grafting under glass and in the open ground. Grafting under glass is commonly referred to as 'bench' grafting, while open-ground grafting is popularly known as 'field' grafting.

Why graft?

Before we go on to discuss the various methods of grafting, perhaps we should ask ourselves why it is necessary to propagate plants by grafting rather than by other methods like cuttings, layering or seeds. There are, in fact, a number of very good reasons why nurserymen propagate certain subjects by grafting instead of using perhaps more simple methods. Far less grafting is done, nowadays, due to the fact that research has resulted in the ability to raise many more hitherto difficult subjects from cuttings. However, very much more grafting is done on the Continent, particularly in Holland, than in the UK. Grafting is particularly useful for raising plants (trees, shrubs and conifers) which still prove difficult to propagate in large numbers by any other means.

Many trees need to be grafted to ensure that they have a suitable root system – one that gives the desired growth rate and is suited to a particular soil. This is particularly important with fruit trees such as apples, pears, plums, cherries, peaches and the like. In apples, for instance, one may need to produce dwarf bush trees or trained forms like cordons, in which case one would need to graft the cultivars on to a dwarfing rootstock. Or, on the other hand, one may need to produce standards that will develop into large orchard-type trees, and here a very vigorous rootstock may well be required.

Grafting can also reduce the production time in a crop of trees or shrubs as, generally, grafted plants make larger plants in a shorter period of time than plants raised, say, from cuttings. Grafting also enables nurserymen to spread out the workload – much grafting is done in February or March which can be a fairly quiet time on many holdings.

In addition, grafting can induce vigour into weak-growing plants as very often the rootstock, the common counterpart of the cultivar being grafted, is far more vigorous in habit than the plant being propagated. This is not always acceptable to some people, as rootstocks can alter the natural habit of the cultivars on them. For instance, dwarf conifers are often grafted because they are difficult to root from cuttings, and because they invariably take a considerable period of time to produce saleable plants on their own roots. However, the true character and habit of growth is frequently lost when dwarf conifers are grafted. Nevertheless, many commercially produced dwarf conifers are grafted, particularly in Holland where nurserymen graft a far wider range than we do in the UK.

Rootstocks for grafting

As we have listed a range of rootstocks which are used commercially, and examples of scions to put on them in Chapter 18, we will now discuss some of the grafts likely to be used on the modern nursery.

BENCH GRAFTING

We have already mentioned that this is carried out in heat under glass. The reason it is called 'bench grafting' is because the actual grafting is carried out on a bench in the potting shed or other suitable area. The grafts are then placed in heat to unite. It is generally carried out in the months of February and March, although some grafting takes place in October or November.

Typical subjects which are bench grafted include: *Acer japonicum* and *A. palmatum* cultivars; *Betula* cultivars; *Camellia* cultivars; *Cytisus* cultivars; *Fagus* cultivars; *Hibiscus* cultivars; *Hamamelis* cultivars; *Rhododendron* hybrids; miniature roses; and *Syringa* cultivars. Of course, a wide range of conifers are also bench grafted, including many dwarf cultivars and those that are difficult to root from cuttings like: *Chamaecyparis lawsoniana* 'Golden King', *C.l.* 'Lutea', *C.l.* 'Stewartii', *C.l.* 'Triomphe de Boskoop'; *C. obtusa* 'Tetragona Aurea'; *C. nootkatensis* 'Pendula'; *Cupressus glabra* 'Pyramidalis'; *C. macrocarpa* 'Lutea'; *Abies* cultivars; *Cedrus* cultivars; *Larix* cultivars; *Picea* cultivars; *Pinus* cultivars and *Taxus* cultivars.

The main bench grafts which are used commercially are the spliced side veneer, the veneer graft, the spliced side graft and the saddle graft.

However, we must first mention a few general points before we discuss each method in turn. It is essential to have a sharp knife to ensure really clean and accurate cuts. The bench should be clean to avoid getting dirt on the cuts, which can result in failures. Generally we use two-year-old rootstocks which are grown in 90 mm (3·5 in) pots. Eight weeks before grafting these stocks are taken into a heated glasshouse to induce new root growth. Generally they are plunged in peat and kept moist, but two weeks before grafting the watering is reduced and the stocks are kept moderately dry, to reduce the flow of sap. This is especially important with conifer stocks. Before grafting, the base of the stocks should be stripped free of foliage and all soil cleaned off with a clean rag. After grafting, the grafts are plunged in moist peat in a heated grafting case. The heat is provided by soil-warming cables, and a temperature of 21 °C (70 °F) should be maintained. The grafts should be plunged so that the scion faces upwards. We generally lay the grafts at an angle in the case. The grafting case is covered with a sheet of thin clear polythene to ensure high humidity within. The grafts should be checked over regularly and any dead material removed. Also, attend to watering as necessary and turn the polythene regularly to avoid excessive condensation building up.

Six weeks later the head of the rootstock can be reduced, if applicable, by about half its length and the remainder can be cut off just above the union within another six weeks, at the same time removing the tying material. The grafts should be gradually acclimatized to the normal glasshouse atmosphere and eventually transferred to a polythene tunnel after having been containerized into final containers. It is often the practice now to grow on conifers and other shrubs under polythene or netting structures to reduce production time.

Spliced side veneer graft

This is the graft which is generally preferred for conifers, and it can also be used for many other subjects. The head of the rootstock is left intact and one grafts as low as possible. The stock is prepared by making a short downward cut at an angle into the rootstock near soil level. Then a long cut, about 38 mm (1·5 in) in length, is made to meet the first cut so that a slice of wood can be removed. We now have a long cut with a shoulder at the base. Now the scion is prepared and this is generally about one-third the length of the rootstock. Use well-ripened healthy wood formed the previous year. First a 38 mm long cut is made on one side at the base, and then a very short cut is made on the opposite side at the base. The scion is now fitted on to the rootstock as shown in Fig. 28 and securely tied in with either rubber tying strips or 12 mm (0·5 in) wide clear polythene tape.

Veneer graft

This is also suitable for conifers and other subjects. Again leave the head on the rootstock and graft as low as possible. Make a 38 mm

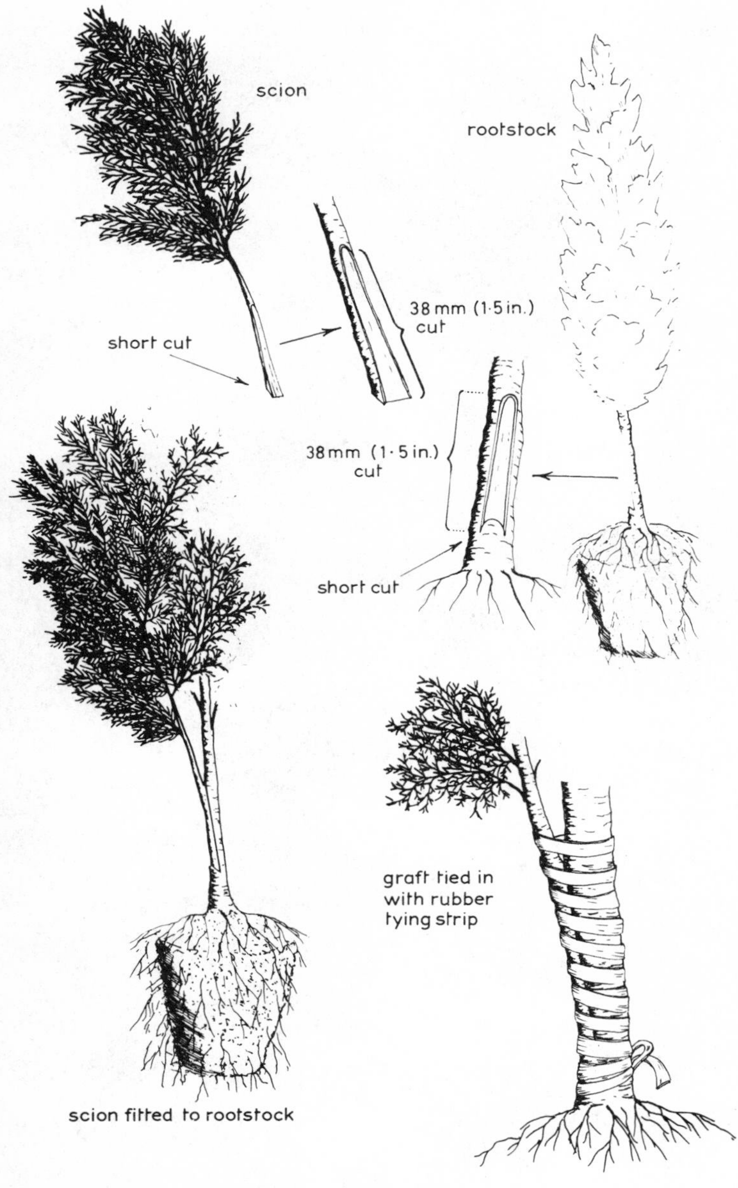

Fig. 28 Spliced side veneer graft (conifer)

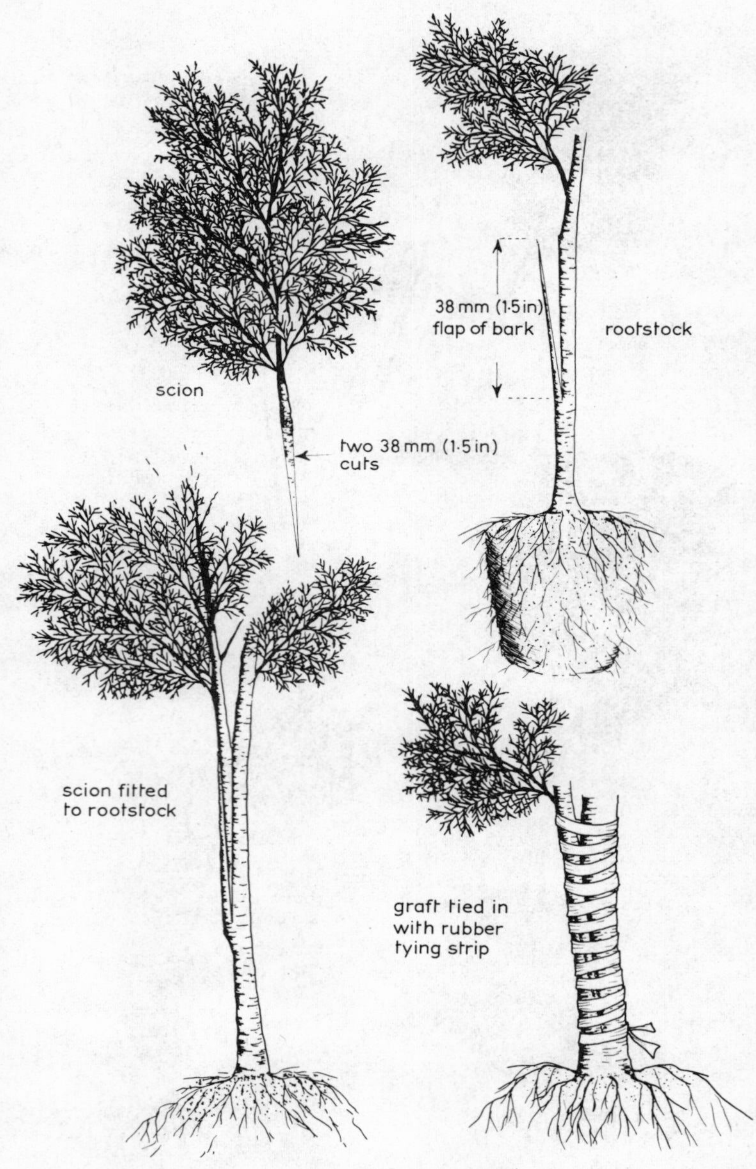

Fig. 29 Veneer graft (conifer)

(1·5 in) downward cut on one side of the stock to result in a flap of bark with the wood exposed behind. Making the scion about one-third the length of the stock, cut the base into a wedge shape by making two 38 mm cuts opposite each other. Now slip the scion behind the flap of bark and tie in securely, again either with rubber grafting strips or 12 mm (0·5 in) wide clear polythene tape.

Spliced side graft

This is often used for rhododendrons but can be used for other shrubs like *Hibiscus* and so on. The head of the rootstock is removed about 50 mm (2 in) above compost level. Then a short downward cut at an angle is made near the base of the stock, followed by a 38 mm (1·5 in) cut down to meet it.

The scion can be in the region of 100–150 mm (4–6 in) in length and in the case of rhododendrons ensure there is a plump bud at the top. The base of the scion is prepared by making a 38 mm (1·5 in) long cut on one side and a short cut on the other side to correspond with the cuts on the stock. Now join the two together and tie in securely.

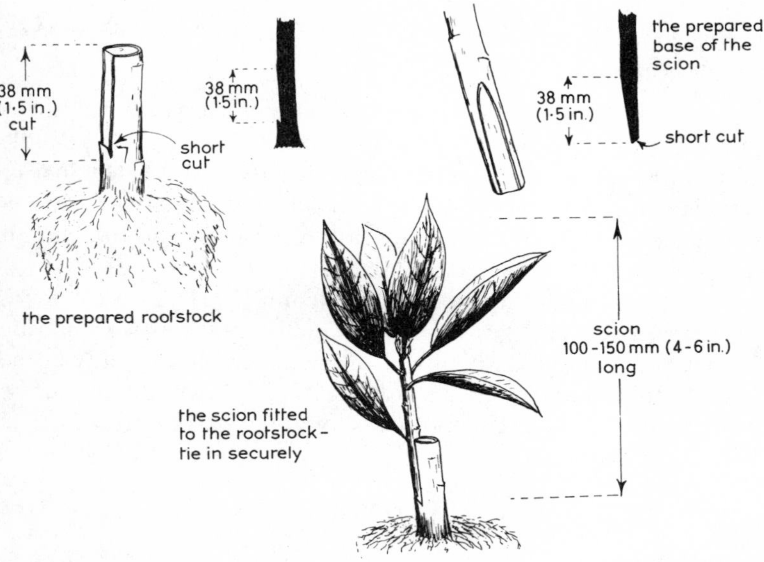

Fig. 30 Spliced side graft (*Rhododendron* hybrid)

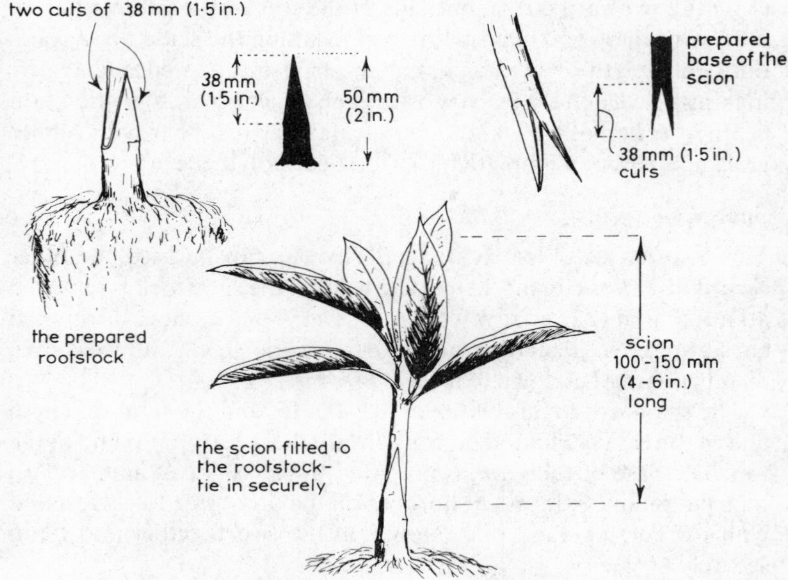

Fig. 31 Saddle graft (*Rhododendron* hybrid)

Saddle graft

This is used for rhododendrons, but many nurserymen nowadays prefer to use the spliced side graft instead. However, the saddle graft, although it takes longer to do, results in a greater area of cambial contact than with the spliced side and therefore there is a stronger union. Also, there is less risk of knocking off the scion if the grafts happen to be handled badly.

Firstly, the rootstock is beheaded 50 mm (2 in) above soil level. Then the top is cut into a wedge shape by making two opposite 38 mm (1·5 in) cuts. Two cuts of the same length are made in the scion to form an inverted V shape, the piece of wood in the centre being taken out. The scion now 'sits' on top of the rootstock and is securely tied in.

FIELD GRAFTING

This is done in February or March using two-year-old rootstocks which have been lined out for a year in the open ground. We generally use the whip and tongue graft and the method is normally used for the production of fruiting and ornamental trees, such as *Malus* and *Pyrus*, *Prunus*, *Sorbus* and the like. It is often used when buds—inserted in the previous summer—have failed to take, although it is also often done in its own right.

Scion wood should be healthy strong shoots formed in the previous year. The shoots should be cut into four-bud lengths, discarding the unripened tips and lower part. Cut the upper end of the scion just above a bud and the lower end 25 mm (1 in) below a bud. The latter is known as the 'stock bud'.

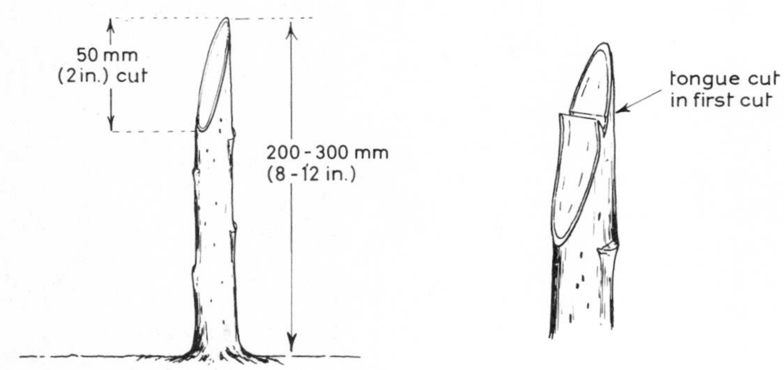

Fig. 32 Whip and tongue grafting apple—rootstock preparation

Now make a 50 mm (2 in) long slanting cut at the lower end of the scion; this should extend from one side of the scion through to the opposite side. The stock bud should now be midway along this cut but on the opposite side. Now make a short upward cut in the first cut to form a tongue.

The rootstock should be cut down to within 200–300 mm (8–12 in) of the ground and a 50 mm (2 in) long cut made at the top from one side to the other to correspond with the main cut on the scion. Again a tongue is formed, this time by making a downward cut.

Now join the scion to the stock, making sure the tongues interlock and that the cambium layers match all round. If the cuts do not match exactly, then make sure the cambium layers are in contact at least on one side.

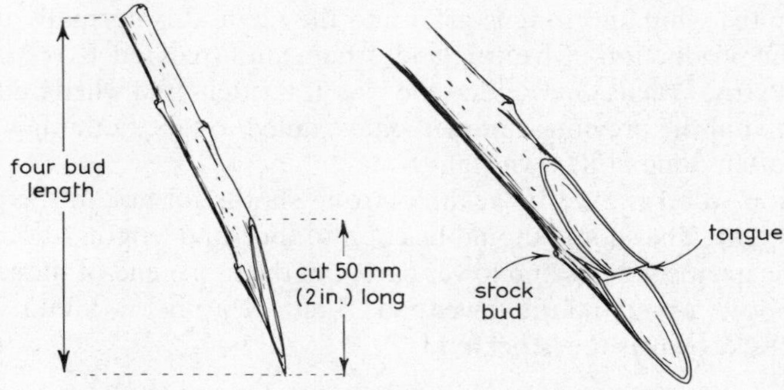

Fig. 33 Whip and tongue grafting apple—scion preparation

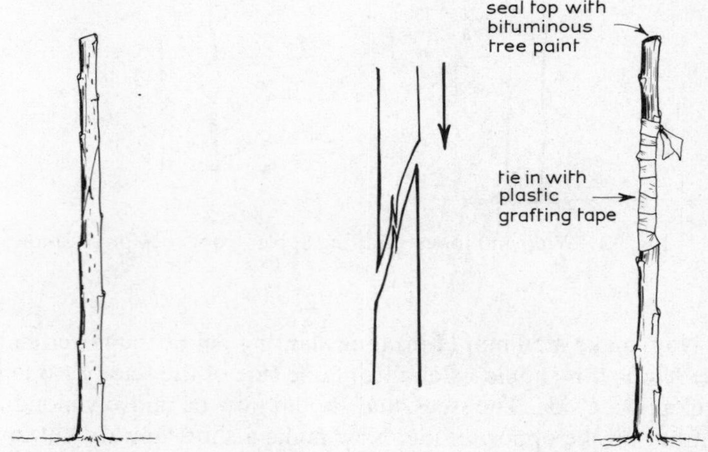

Fig. 34 Whip and tongue grafting apple—joining scion to rootstock

If the rootstock is thicker than the scion (as is invariably the case) then do not cut right through the stock but instead remove only a shallow slice of wood so that the cut is the same width as the cut on the scion. In this instance, to facilitate tying, remove a small portion of wood from the top of the stock on the opposite side to the main cut, so that you slope off the top of the stock.

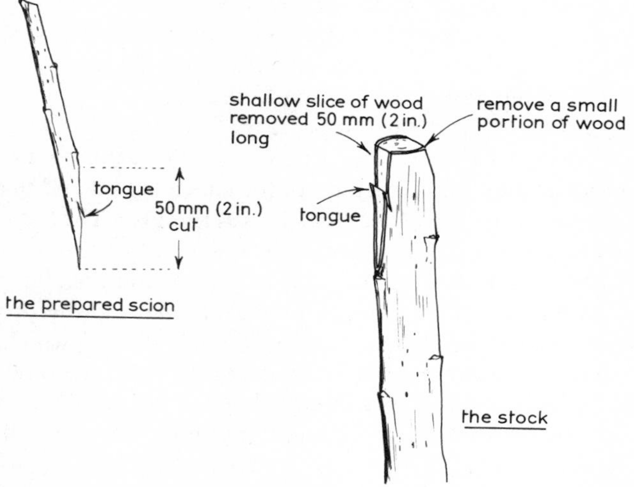

Fig. 35 Whip and tongue grafting apple—when rootstock is thicker than the scion

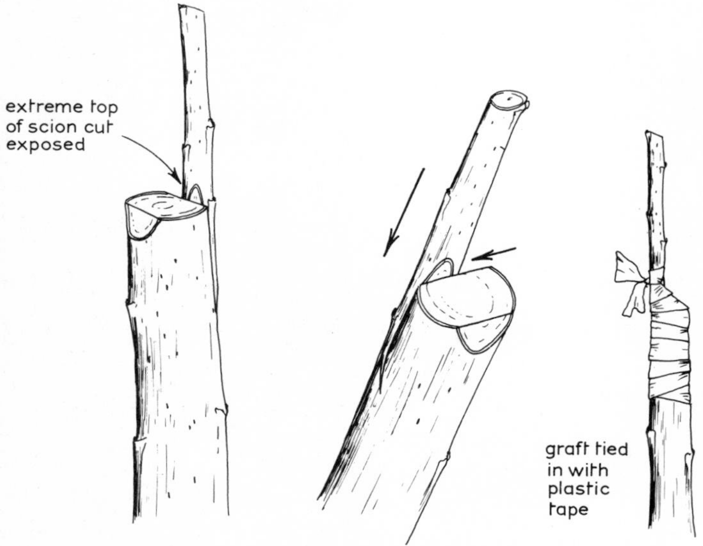

Fig. 36 Whip and tongue grafting apple—joining the scion to thick rootstock

When positioning the scion on the stock, ensure that a small portion of exposed wood (the extreme top of the scion cut) shows above the top of the stock – this ensures really close contact between the cambium layers at the top of the graft.

Now tie the graft firmly with plastic grafting tape, ensuring that each twist overlaps the previous one to prevent water entering it. Make sure that the complete length of the cuts is sealed and that the tape is taken over the top of the stock to seal this also. The top of the scion may be given a dab of bituminous tree paint to seal it.

Allow about 12 weeks for the grafts to unite, and then cut away the tape. At this stage the scions should be making vigorous growth. Some scions may have made a double leading shoot, in which case the strongest and straightest should be left intact and the other one cut back by about half. If any lateral shoots have developed these should also be cut back by about half. Any shoots produced by the rootstock should be rubbed out while they are still soft.

From now on one will start tree training and this is fully discussed in Chapter 30.

18

Budding

The term 'budding' is used to describe a form of grafting where the scion consists of a single bud instead of a shoot as in other types of grafting. Budding should take place when the vascular cambium cells are capable of dividing. This will vary with species, for example *Prunus* can be budded early in the year, while *Malus* are best budded later in the season.

Budding is preferred as one can obtain economy of scion material and the method is a quick and simple way of raising large numbers of plants which are difficult to produce by other means. There are four main methods of budding: T budding; inverted T budding; chip budding; and budding gun.

T BUDDING

T budding is carried out when the rootstock rind will lift easily, which is normally between July and September. A period soon after a rainy spell or irrigation is best as it is then that the bark of the rootstock lifts more easily.

Budding must be done with a sharp, clean budding knife and normally work is carried out in teams consisting of a budder and a tier.

Preparing the budstick

Ideally, the budstick should be cut as near to the time of budding as possible. However, if circumstances do not permit this, then sticks can be stored for a short period in a bucket of water in a cool place and for the long-term in a cold store. Budsticks should consist of current or previous season's growth, 300 mm (1 ft) to 450 mm (18 in) in length. To obtain this, disregard developing buds at the growth tip and more mature basal buds. On the remaining section leaves are removed to leave short petioles. Budsticks should then be bundled and clearly labelled until budding commences.

Preparing the rootstock

Rootstocks should be trimmed to give a clean leg up to and above budding height. Budding height recommendations are constantly changing, but most growers will bud at 300 mm (1 ft) as this reduces the chance of *Phytophthora cactorum*, or Collar Rot, infecting more susceptible scions by splashes from the soil.

A clean, smooth spot is selected on the stem and with the budding knife a cut 40 mm (1·5 in) long is made, just deep enough to penetrate the bark. At the top of this cut another cut is made, 13 mm (0·5 in) in length, at right angles to the original. This produces the T shape (see Fig. 37). The bark on either side of the longer cut can now be lifted back.

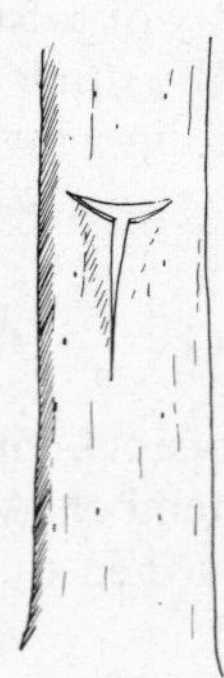

Fig. 37 T budding—T cut on rootstock

Taking the bud

A healthy bud is selected and cut from the budstick by starting the cut 13 mm (0·5 in) below the bud.

When the bud has been removed it has been the practice in the past to remove the shield of wood at the back of the bud. However, it is now recommended that the wood shield is left as there is no economic importance in shield removal, and leaving the wood saves time. It is important not to finger the back of the bud as grease is transferred from the finger to the bud, so forming a barrier between the bud and rootstock.

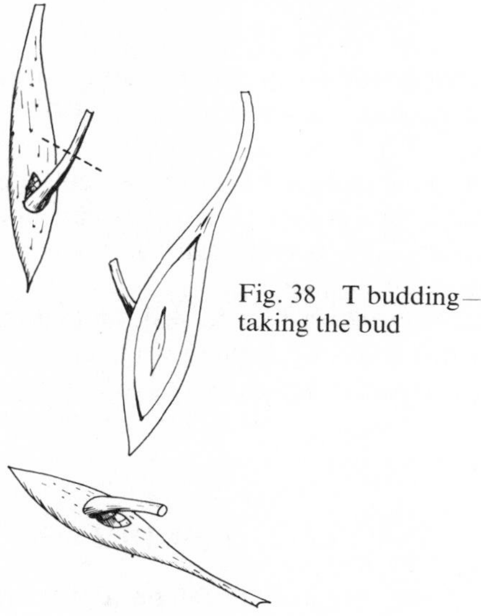

Fig. 38 T budding—taking the bud

Inserting the bud

The bud 'shield' is inserted into the top of the T cut and pushed down. Any part of the 'shield' which is left protruding from the cut should then be trimmed off with the knife.

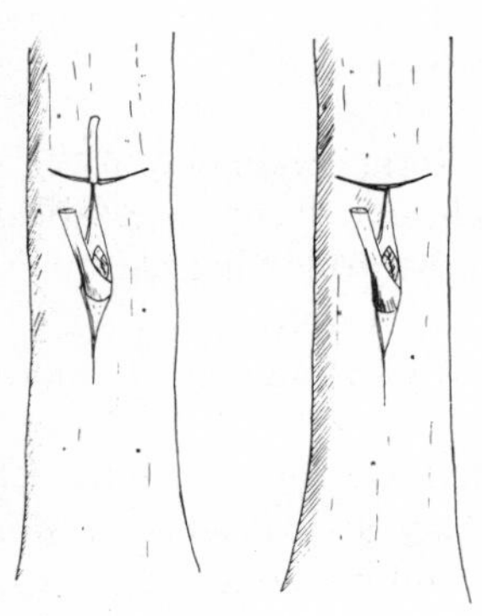

Fig. 39 T budding—inserting and trimming the bud

Tying

There are many types of tying materials on the market. The material selected should be soft, flexible and capable of holding the bud firmly in place.

Materials vary from soft raffia, clear and coloured polythene to rubber ties. Whichever is selected it must be remembered that checking of the ties after 'take' is important. Too much pressure on the bud can result in a lower take.

It is no longer normal practice to seal the tied-in bud. The only time this can be justified is when there is a likelihood of attack from red bud borer, *Thomasiniana oculiperda*, which lays its eggs under the bark of budded plants. Control can be obtained by sealing tied buds with petroleum jelly.

INVERTED T BUDDING

Inverted T budding originated among citrus and rubber-tree growers where it is a normal technique. The method has been adopted by some growers when budding on to *Malus* rootstock M26. The normal T budding produced variable growth of maidens, but by reversing the method so that the horizontal rootstock cut is below the vertical cut, and also by taking the bud cuts in reverse, they have noted a better result. Growth starts earlier, water does not enter the incision as easily and the flow of nutrients down the rootstock to the bud is not interfered with.

One disadvantage is that it is slower than conventional T budding, especially to a skilled budder who has to adapt to a new method.

CHIP BUDDING

It is believed that this method of budding originated in the Angyo nursery district of Japan, and the technique has now established itself as the main means of budding for the following reasons:

1 Cambium contact with the bud is instant, resulting in more 'takes' as all buds should grow away strongly and a good union should form before winter.
2 It is quicker than T budding as there are fewer hand movements.
3 A reduction in union canker, *Nectria galligena*, as normally spores colonize behind the lifted rind in T-budded plants.

4 Maiden growth in the following spring is more uniform and vigorous.

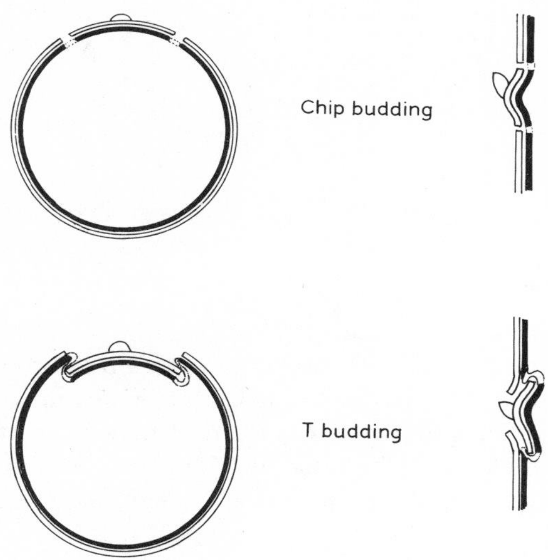

Fig. 40 Chip budding and T budding, showing cambial contact

Preparing the budstick

As with T budding, the material collected should be healthy and true to type. Leaves must be removed to leave a short petiole and, again, immature buds are removed. The budstick is then prepared as for T budding.

Preparing the rootstock

Initial preparation is the same as for T budding, except for the cutting of the rootstock. The first cut is made at an angle of 20° into the stem to a depth of 3 mm (0·125 in) to produce an acute lip. The second cut is made 40 mm (1·5 in) above this cut and an inverted U-shaped cut is made down to the original.

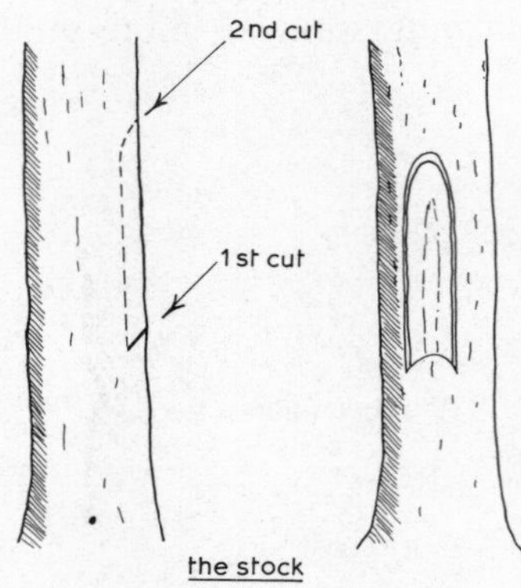

Fig. 41 Chip budding—preparing the rootstock

Chip bud preparation

The budstick is held so that the base faces the budder and the bud is removed by making cuts similar to those on the rootstock. The bud can then be removed by lifting it between the thumb and knife blade and then it is transferred to the rootstock where the lip in the rootstock should firmly hold the bud. The aim, as in grafting, is to match the cambium of scion and stock to induce quick callusing.

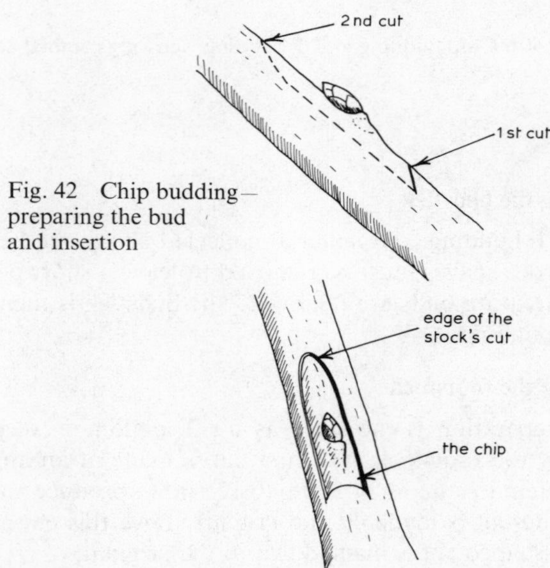

Fig. 42 Chip budding—preparing the bud and insertion

Tying

A chip bud is more exposed than a T bud and therefore tying is more critical and many nurserymen will use two tiers to one budder. Most growers will use 25 mm (1 in) polythene tape or degradable rubber strips. Polythene is preferred by many; this is cut into a 150–225 mm (6–9 in) strip and, once slightly stretched, it can be placed over the lower lip of the rootstock cut and secured by passing it around the stem and trapping the end.

The bud is tied in by overlapping the polythene over the bud; the tape can then be tied off above the top rootstock cut. The maximum tying pressure should be below and above the bud. If tight over the bud it can induce the bud to become 'sleepy' due to the pressure; it is often advisable with large buds to keep them exposed to avoid this problem.

Chip budding is now considered to be superior to T budding for the production of *Malus*, *Pyrus* and *Prunus* species, as well as many other ornamental species including *Tilia platyphyllos* 'Rubra', *Ulmus* species, and *Acer platanoides* 'Crimson King'.

Success has also been achieved by using chip budding under glasshouse conditions on *Acer*, *Betula*, *Fagus*, *Fraxinus* and *Hamamelis*, instead of bench grafting.

BUDDING GUN

The budding gun was developed in 1973 with the aim of speeding up the budding process in rose production, especially where unskilled labour was the only source of budders. The original prototype has now been replaced by an improved model and some rose growers are using it in trials in the commercial situation.

The advantages of using a budding gun are that firstly, it is quick, secondly it can be used by unskilled budders, thirdly rose budsticks do not need to have their spines removed, fourthly buds are never touched by hand and finally, the budding position is more comfortable.

The main disadvantage is that large rootstocks may overwhelm the smaller bud which is taken by the gun.

Method of budding

The gun works on a corer element which needs to be sharp; this cuts through the rind of the budstick and by a scooping action extracts the dormant bud. Once the bud is secured in the corer, the gun trigger is released and this results in the corer retracting into the gun body, the cutting edges closing to a point at the front of the gun. The cutting edges are then pushed through the rind of the rootstock, the trigger is pressed and the blades open the rind; and the plunger deposits the bud into the opened rind. When the gun is withdrawn the rind automatically closes, holding the bud in position.

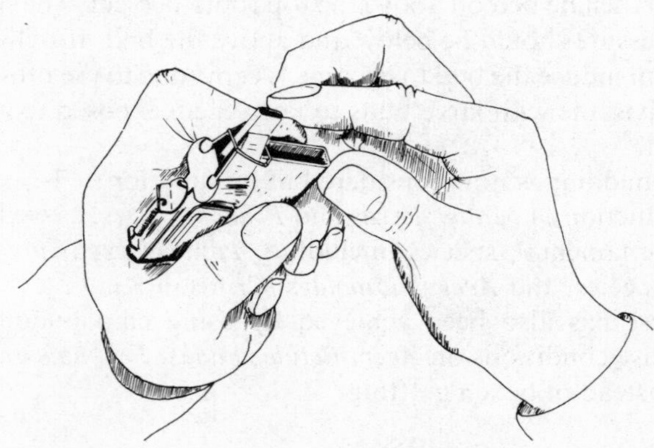

Fig. 43 The budding gun

The traditional rubber ties are too big for tying and masking tape has been used successfully as have smaller rubber ties.

The budding gun has been used for bench 'budding' roses, and then plunging them into peat in a glasshouse. Once buds have 'taken' the roses are field planted. If this system is adopted it could alter our production systems and remove the need for field budding.

NICOLIN BUDDING

Double-shield budding is occasionally used where stock/scion incompatibility exists to such a degree that it will eventually result in the union breaking apart. The Nicolin method is named after its inventor. Two pieces of budwood are used in the budding process.

The normal T cut is made in the rootstock and the bud is prepared for the intermediate scion, except that the bud is also removed leaving just a shield of wood which is inserted in the T cut. A normal bud is prepared from the required scion and inserted on top of the intermediate wood shield. Tying is then carried out in the normal way.

MANAGEMENT OF BUDDED PLANTS

The rate of development of the budded plant will be influenced by the fertility of the soil, establishment of the rootstock, elimination of competition and the microclimate, while the uniformity of budded trees will be governed by the soil preparation, evenness of rootstock establishment, season and technique of budding as well as the health of both stock and scion.

Bud ties should be checked after four or five weeks, especially with chip-budded material, and they should be removed once a well-established union has occurred between rootstock and scion (unless a degradable material is used). This can be done by taking a sharp knife and cutting the tie at the back of the bud.

Heavy fertilizer programmes immediately after budding are not recommended as this will produce sappy, vigorous growth in the rootstock resulting in a depressed bud union. Fertilizer should be applied in late winter after the rootstock has been headed back as this will encourage maiden growth.

Care should be taken with the application of residual herbicides after budding. It is often advisable to reduce the rate of spray chemical after budding as some retard growth and consequently affect bud take.

BUDDING AND GRAFTING STOCKS

In previous chapters we have mentioned the clonal rootstocks used in fruit and ornamental-tree production. Table 6 gives the rootstocks used for other commonly grown ornamentals.

Table 6 Rootstocks for common ornamentals

Bud or scion	*Rootstock*
Acer japonicum cvs.	*Acer palmatum*
Acer negundo cvs.	*Acer negundo*
Acer palmatum cvs.	*Acer palmatum*
Acer platanoides cvs.	*Acer platanoides*
Acer pseudoplatanus cvs.	*Acer pseudoplatanus*
Aesculus × carnea 'Briotii'	*Aesculus hippocastanum*
Alnus spp. and cvs.	*Alnus glutinosa*
Arbutus andrachnoides	*Arbutus unedo*
Betula spp. and cvs.	*Betula pendula* *Betula pubescens*
Camellia japonica cvs.	*Camellia japonica*
Camellia reticulata cvs.	*Camellia japonica*
Clematis cvs.	*Clematis vitalba*
Corylus avellana 'Contorta'	*Corylus avellana*
Corylus avellana 'Pendula'	*Corylus avellana*
Cotoneaster spp. and cvs.	*Cotoneaster frigida* *Cotoneaster bullata*
Crataegus spp. and cvs.	*Crataegus monogyna*
Cytisus battandieri	*Laburnum anagyroides*
Cytisus × kewensis	*Laburnum anagyroides*
Cytisus praecox	*Laburnum anagyroides*
Cytisus scoparius cvs.	*Laburnum anagyroides*
Daphne mezereum cvs.	*Daphne mezereum*
Daphne petraea	*Daphne laureola*
Fagus sylvatica cvs.	*Fagus sylvatica*
Hamamelis japonica cvs.	*Hamamelis virginiana*
Hamamelis mollis cvs.	*Distylium racemosum*
Ilex aquifolium cvs.	*Ilex aquifolium*
Juglans spp. and cvs.	*Juglans regia*
+ *Laburnocytisus adamii*	*Laburnum anagyroides*
Laburnum × watereri 'Vossii'	*Laburnum anagyroides*
Magnolia grandiflora	*Magnolia kobus*
Magnolia stellata	*Magnolia kobus*
Pittosporum dallii	*Pittosporum tenuifolium*
Pittosporum eugenioides	*Pittosporum tenuifolium*
Pittosporum tenuifolium cvs.	*Pittosporum tenuifolium*
Pittosporum undulatum	*Pittosporum tenuifolium*
Rhaphiolepsis × delacourii	*Crataegus monogyna*
Rhododendron hybrids	*Rhododendron ponticum* *Rhododendron* 'Cunninghams White'
Robinia hispida	*Robinia pseudoacacia*
Robinia pseudoacacia cvs.	*Robinia pseudoacacia*
Sorbus spp. and cvs.	*Crateagus monogyna* *Sorbus ancuporia*

Table 6—*continued*

Syringa cvs.	*Syringa vulgaris*
	Ligustrum vulgare
Viburnum × *burkwoodii*	*Viburnum lantana*
Viburnum carlesii	*Viburnum lantana*
Wisteria sinensis cvs.	*Wisteria sinensis*
CONIFERS	
Chamaecyparis cvs.	*Chamaecyparis lawsoniana*
Cupressus spp. and cvs.	*Cupressus macrocarpa*
Juniperus chinensis cvs.	*Juniperus chinensis*
Juniperus virginiana cvs.	*Juniperus virginiana*
Picea pungens glauca and cvs.	*Picea pungens*

Note: Many species and cultivars in the above list can also be propagated on their own roots, budding or grafting being an alternative to this production method.

19

Future trends in propagation

Technology is constantly developing new techniques for producing plants. In the previous chapters we have mentioned up-to-date methods being adopted by growers, and we would now like to look into the future, at the techniques we will possibly be adopting in years to come.

TISSUE CULTURE

Tissue culture is the isolation and growing of a small portion of plant tissue in sterile conditions on a carefully controlled nutrient medium in a sealed container such as a tube or flask. This technique is not new, as highly specialized propagation by tissue culture has been carried out since the 1960s and the production of virus-free plant material by meristem cuttings has been used for many years.

The important factor with this method of propagation is absolute sterility, as the plant material used has no epidermal layer for protection against bacterial and fungal spores.

Tissue cultures can be from various parts of the plant, such as meristems, pollen, embryos, callus and isolated cells. To ensure successful production the tissue material requires the normal growth elements in the form of mineral salts. Oxygen and hydrogen are supplied in the form of water and gas, while carbon is added in the organic form as sugar. Other materials required are amino acids, B vitamins and growth hormones. The medium used to support the plant tissue is agar. If the culture is submerged then aeration can be provided by shaking the flask in a reciprocating or rotating machine.

The main advantages of using tissue culture are, firstly, the rapid multiplication of slow-growing or difficult-rooting subjects (e.g., over a two-year period up to 20,000 plants can be produced from one original plant). Secondly, disease-free plants can be maintained and reproduced and, thirdly, plants can be delivered all the year round and economically. The hygienic growing conditions also mean it is far easier to export such material.

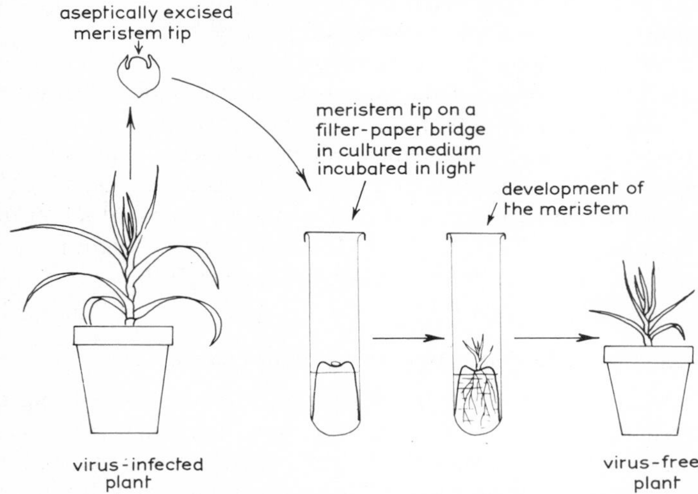

Fig. 44 Meristem propagation

No serious problems have been experienced in establishing plants in the soil, although care in transplanting is important.

Propagation facilities

For a grower to propagate by this technique he needs expensive special equipment, and this has resulted in specialist producers who have the capital and skill to make tissue culture a commercial proposition.

Glassware and culture vessels should be made of borosilicate glass, as soda glass is toxic to the young plants; storage of this equipment must be in dust-proof cupboards and facilities need to be made available for sterilizing glassware.

Sterilizing is normally done in an autoclave, which is similar to a pressure cooker in operation, that is, materials are sterilized by being heated by steam at a pressure of 103 kg/a (1,516 lb/sq in) at 121 °C (250 °F) for 10 minutes.

Scalpels, scissors and forceps are used to make tissue 'cuttings'. All such equipment is made of stainless steel or nickel plated and again must be kept sterilized, normally by flame sterilization using a spirit or gas micro-burner.

Cuttings are usually taken and prepared either in specially built laboratories or, on a smaller scale, on hooded benches.

The idea of the hood is to maintain a hygienic environment and reduce the possibility of fungal spores entering and infecting the plant tissues. Planning is important when preparing plants as the shortest time possible is ideal for plant and media exposure when tissues are being prepared. Prepared plant tissues are placed in an incubator for growing on. Cultures should be grown at a constant temperature, ideally 25 °C (77 °F) for most subjects. Light is not so critical and often incubators are lit by only a single fluorescent tube, giving a low light-intensity.

Propagation of deciduous trees using tissue culture

As new rootstocks for fruit production are constantly being developed, tissue culture permits the annual production of many thousands of plants from a single stem, whereas using conventional means one would be able to produce at most only a few dozen. This method therefore means rapid production and distribution of new rootstocks, cultivars and hybrids, especially those which resist conventional asexual means of propagation.

Tissue culture of woody subjects was difficult until the discovery of a phenolic constituent in the sap of apple trees, phloridzin, and one of its breakdown products, phloroglucinol, which promotes the growth and rooting of apple-shoot cultures *in vitro* (artificial conditions).

Flasks of tissues, nutrients, cytokinins (responsible for cell differentiation) and agar are grown in well-illuminated growing rooms where the tips produce small branches; these branches are excised and transferred singly to a fresh medium, containing no cytokinin, where rooting is induced. When rooted, plants are large enough to handle. They are potted off and placed in humid propagation boxes for about two weeks to establish; once this is achieved they are grown on in a normal glasshouse.

A number of nurseries are now building tissue-culture units and feel that tissue culture is another arm to propagation which is of value to the commercial grower.

Growers tend to use the Murashige and Skoog nutrient media and plants which are readily produced by this method include *Hosta*, using dormant eyes from the base of the plant and growing the tissues on at 20 °C (68 °F) for a 16-hour day; plants such as *Gypso-*

phila and *Chrysanthemum* can also be produced commercially by this technique.

EMBRYO PROPAGATION

Embryo propagation is a useful technique used for plants with complicated seed dormancies such as fruit-tree seeds, *Camellia*, *Ilex*, *Paeony*, *Viburnum* and *Tilia*. This method can also be used for viability testing in normal seed raising.

Firstly, the pericarp of the seed is removed and often this means soaking the seed beforehand. Once removed the seed is chipped and left to soak for 24 hours until fully imbibed, when the testa can be removed. The seed is now soaked for a further two or three hours so that the embryo can be easily removed. It is important that the embryo is not damaged at removal and this is achieved by gently squeezing the seed to loosen the food-storage tissue and then carefully pulling away the endosperm, taking great care not to damage the radicle or leaves.

The naked embryo is then placed on moist filter paper in a covered dish. It is important that the filter paper is kept moist and this can be achieved by passing a wick from the filter paper to a water source. Embryos should not be overcrowded as this will encourage disease spread; the recommended spacing is 20 mm (0·75 in).

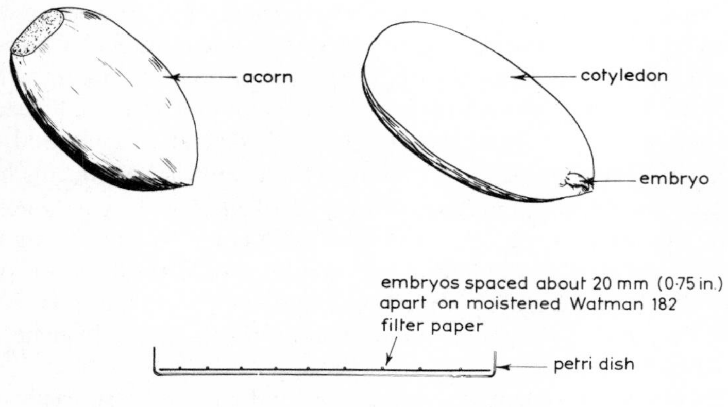

Fig. 45 Embryo propagation

Covered dishes are placed in an incubator at 20 °C (68 °F) with eight hours of light in a 24-hour period at 1,200 lux. Within three to four days, growth should have occurred, although daily checks are important to remove any embryos infected by mould; these should be removed straight away along with dead embryos which will look black and dry. If moulds develop to serious proportions then the filter paper should be changed, although this is not good practice as embryos may be damaged on moving.

After 14 days seedlings should be ready to be pricked out into containers of seedling compost. Potted seedlings should be placed in a humid environment until the first leaves are established, and they can then be moved into a polythene tunnel for a couple of months before going outside.

NUTRIENT FILM TECHNIQUES

In recent years we have seen the beginning of a revolution in glasshouse crops as growers moved away from traditional growing systems to the use of hydroponics and nutrient film. This technique has many advantages over other methods, including maximum water economy, better disease control, lower fertilizer requirements, optimum plant growth resulting in increased yields, and a saving in capital investment and labour input. The advantages to short-life crops are enormous and it is now worth looking at the potential of this technique to the ornamental plant producer.

The big problem occurs with hardy nursery stock. Research has shown us that the existing equipment, nutrients and knowledge will allow us to grow hardy plants in this system and conifers have been produced in eight months from unrooted cuttings, compared with similar container-grown plants with an age of two and a half years.

Two major problems are put forward against this method of production. Firstly, disease spread in the channels – again this has proved to be an unnecessary worry. *Phytophthora* will spread throughout the system, but will often only enter a plant through a root abrasion. This method of production should result in no root abrasions and therefore plants should show more resistance. Having said this, it is still important to maintain maximum hygiene to avoid such a problem.

The second problem is more serious and cannot be so easily ignored. Most plant losses will occur when plants are transplanted from the nutrient channels to the soil or normal growing media. The reason for this is the 'inter-phase' problem, that is, the difference in structure between the nutrient root-growing environment and the normal growing-media environment. This shock in different growing areas results in root death or roots being unable to adapt to the new growing environment. Because of this problem we feel nutrient film techniques have only a limited value to the hardy-nursery-stock producer, although in trials we have carried out we have found no serious problems in transplanting.

The main use of a nutrient film technique is in the production of stock plants, especially virus cleared, or those where forcing is required to obtain the right type of cutting at the right time. This method of production should also speed up the growth cycle which results in more cuttings being produced in a shorter period.

Growers, both in this country and abroad, have looked at the possibilities of producing saleable plants in various hydroponic systems, but in all cases the result has been sale resistance and poor establishment.

In this chapter we have looked at developments which may occur in nursery production. Some growers have already experimented with these techniques, some very successfully, others less so. It must be stressed that new techniques often change and develop, and before venturing into such a project it is important to obtain the most up-to-date information.

Part 4

CONTAINER-GROWING SYSTEMS

20

Containers

INTRODUCTION TO TYPES OF PRODUCTS

In recent years there has been a trend away from open-ground production to container production. One of the major factors which has governed this has been the opening of garden centres, with customers who require a product immediately for 'instant effect' planting at any time of the year.

Basically, the types of products we produce can be divided into three and it is worth mentioning them at this point before discussing container-growing systems.

Balled plants

Balled plants are grown in the field for marketing during the dormant season in a ball of soil which is wrapped in hessian. Normally the plants are broadleaf evergreens and conifers, but occasionally large trees are produced by this method.

Bare-root

Again a crop produced in the field, but sold without soil around the roots. Normally deciduous plants are sold in this way during the dormant season.

Container-grown

Any type of plant can be grown in a container in a standing area. The container will hold the whole root system which means that no root disturbance occurs at sale and therefore this product can be sold any time during the year. Compared to the two previous systems, producing a plant in a container means greater capital input, especially at the beginning of the cropping cycle, although returns are also often higher than for similar, field-grown plants.

When starting a container nursery the criteria which decides a suitable site will differ from those for field-grown nursery stock. A major requirement will be a supply of good water as a dry spell can soon induce stress in a containerized plant. The other major consideration is shelter; particularly as we are now using lighter growing media which can make plants unstable in windy conditions. Also, container-grown plants are not so cold resistant as their counterparts in the soil, and protection is required to get material through a severe winter.

CONTAINERS FOR PROPAGATION

The choice of containers for propagation (for example, rooting cuttings) consists of unit containers, boxes or trays, and pots. Boxes and pots are the conventional types, but in more recent years there has been a big swing towards unit containers—with this system each cutting is rooted in an individual unit and therefore root disturbance is minimized when potting off.

UNIT CONTAINERS

Propagation blocks

In recent years there has been increasing interest in the use of rooting blocks for the propagation of shrubs, trees and so on. The advantages of using these include potting off without root disturbance, quicker establishment of plants and often a better plant in a shorter period of time. There are some disadvantages however, for instance a larger area is needed for a given number of plants. For example, a seed tray will hold 28 blocks of 40 mm (approx. 1·5 in) each as opposed to 70 cuttings inserted direct in the tray in seven rows of ten.

With many blocks great care is needed with watering to avoid very wet or very dry conditions. Some blocks hold a lot of water; but, if allowed to dry out, are often very difficult to wet again. In addition, with this system it is essential to pot off cuttings as soon as they are rooted to prevent the roots from becoming tangled. Some blocks have no nutrients and this is another reason why cuttings should be potted off as soon as rooted. It is also important to remember that the blocks should be covered with 12 mm (0·5 in) of compost—the tops should not be above compost level.

There is a wide range of propagation blocks available to the nurseryman, and these are discussed below.

SYNTHETIC PROPAGATION BLOCKS

1 Foamed polyurethane: these are made of a flexible foam and originated in the USA. One of the problems is that they are difficult to wet.
2 Cellulose pulp fibres: these are cone-shaped blocks and have pre-formed holes. They are held together by synthetic adhesives. They become saturated very easily and have now lost favour among growers.
3 Mineral wool: also known as rockwool blocks. They are chemically inactive and are easily saturated with water. Rockwool blocks are discussed in detail in Chapter 21.
4 Phenolic foam: composed of crushed urea-formaldehyde foams. Look rather like cotton wool. They have various levels of pH and various water-holding capacities. They release nutrients over a long period once cuttings have rooted.
5 Vermiculite blocks: also known as micaceous mineral blocks, composed of silicate of aluminium and other silicates. They should be watered thoroughly before use and sand should be placed in the central hole to support the cutting.

COMPRESSED PEAT-BASED BLOCKS

These are very popular with nurserymen. There is 20–30 per cent air by volume in the rooting media:
1 Commercial ready-made blocks: composed of sphagnum peat with fertilizer added, some being held together with fine netting. There is a hole in the centre, which can be filled with sand to support the cutting; they may need to be soaked in water before use to expand them.
2 Commercial blocking composts: these are bought by the bag and the blocks are formed on the nursery with a blocking machine—there are hand-operated or automatic machines available. The composts consist of very fine sedge or sphagnum peat, which should be wetted really thoroughly before pressing out the blocks. Fill the holes with fine dry sand before inserting cuttings. Moss may form on the outside of the blocks but this does not affect rooting.

3 Normal peat products which can be blocked: for example, Irish moss peat can be blocked – it blocks well either with a hand-operated or automatic blocking machine. Remember that there is no fertilizer, so pot off as soon as rooted.

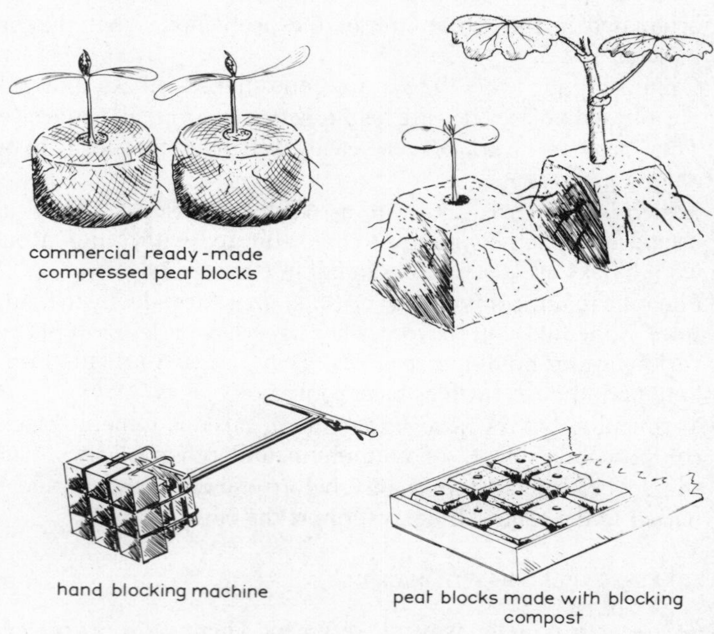

Fig. 46 Peat blocks for direct rooting

COMPOSTS WHICH CAN BE BLOCKED

Various potting composts can be blocked; for instance, peat-based types, peat and sand types and the loam-based John Innes composts. These all have fertilizers added and therefore potting off does not need to be carried out immediately the cuttings have rooted, although the roots must not become tangled.

WASTE PRODUCTS

There is inevitable interest in the use of waste products in rooting blocks. We have tried papier mâché blocks and these seem very promising. They do not dry out rapidly and cuttings are easily inserted – place sand in pre-formed holes. Newspaper should be finely ground down and then soaked in water for one hour. Blocks can then be moulded by hand (papier mâché will not pass through a blocking machine).

Compressed peat strips

These are commercial unit containers composed of compressed peat. The strips are divided into individual units and they are placed in a seed tray for support. They are then filled with cutting compost. When the cuttings have rooted, the strips are pulled apart and each unit is potted off with the rooted cutting.

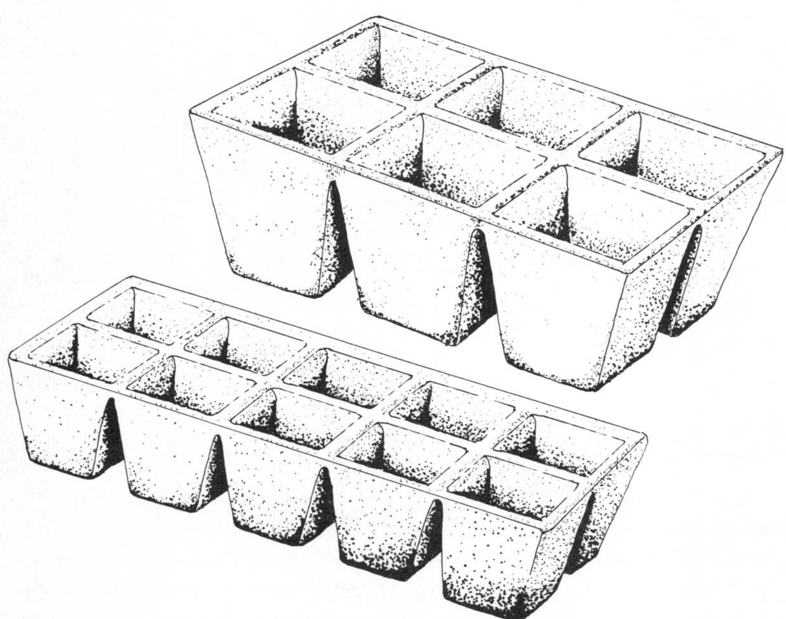

Fig. 47 Compressed peat strips

Plastic unit containers

Flimsy plastic unit containers, which are very popular for rooting cuttings, need the support of a rigid seed tray. All of them will fit standard-size seed trays, and each container is divided into a number of separate units: for example, 24, 40, 60 and so on. Fill them with cutting compost and then insert one cutting per unit as normal. Once rooted, the cuttings can be pushed out by applying pressure to the base of each unit.

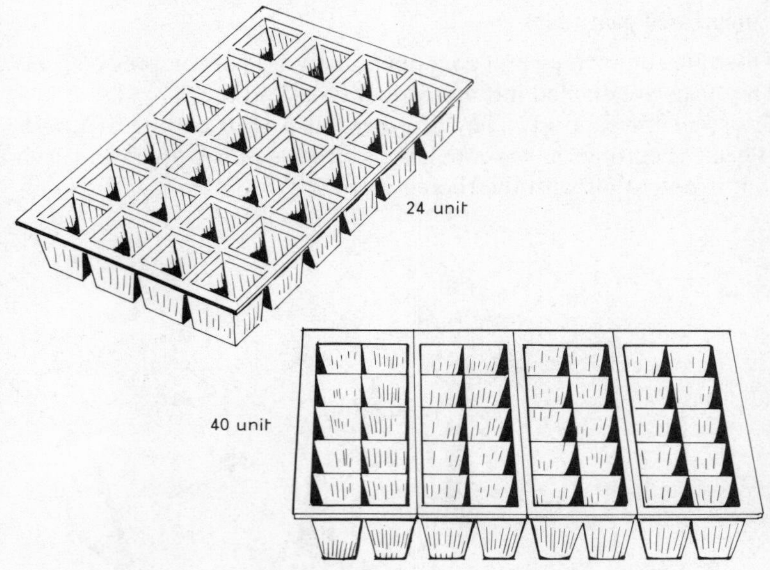

Fig. 48 Plastic unit containers

Japanese paper pot system

This container consists of many individual paper units, held together with water-soluble adhesive. It should be opened out and placed on an appropriate size of tray. It is then filled with compost. The system is used a lot for raising forestry seedlings, but can also be used for rooting cuttings. By the time the plants are ready for moving on the units will have become separated as the adhesive will have broken down. This system was discussed in Chapter 7.

Polythene-strip unit containers

There is a hand-operated machine on the market which will form a strip of clear polythene film, the depth of a seed tray, into a number of individual units to fit a standard-size seed tray. This is a very good system of making up your own unit containers on the nursery, and apart from the initial cost of the machine the production of unit containers is very cheap—you only need to buy rolls of polythene film and of course provide the cutting compost.

You will need a supply of seed trays, but these can be used many times if they are made of plastic. Various templates are provided with the machine to turn out different numbers of units: 6 × 4 (24 units), 8 × 5 (40 units), 8 × 6 (48 units) and 10 × 6 (60 units). Once the cuttings have rooted you simply take hold of one end of the polythene strip and carefully pull it out. Each cutting will be completely separate from the others, with no tangled roots, and it can be simply lifted out of the tray for potting off.

SEED BOXES OR TRAYS

The conventional way of rooting cuttings is in seed trays. One can use either wooden or plastic trays, but with the latter do remember that the compost does not dry out so quickly and therefore there is more risk of keeping the compost too wet. The number of cuttings per tray will vary according to the subject. Average-size cuttings can be inserted 6 × 10 (60 per tray) to 7 × 10 (70 per tray). Very small cuttings like heathers can be inserted 10 × 15 (150 per tray). As we have already stated, this system is more economical of space as compared to unit containers, but the rooted cuttings have to be lifted out and separated, causing root disturbance. Generally, a standard cutting compost (equal parts peat and coarse sand or crushed grit) is used.

POTS

Sometimes plastic pots are used as containers in propagation, particularly when long cuttings, such as hardwoods rooted in heat, are to be inserted. Seed trays or unit containers would not provide enough depth for this type of material. This also seems a suitable place to mention compressed peat pots: although they are not generally used for propagation, they are often used for potting off rooted cuttings. Then, when it comes to final containerization, the young plants suffer no root disturbance as the pots are containerized as well as the plant.

CONTAINERS FOR GROWING

Various types of containers and systems have been developed through the years for container growing and the 'ideal' container is constantly changing, with the result that the grower is now presented with a wide range of different products to do the same job.

The original pot was made of fire-hardened clay and was produced in various forms, from shallow pans to 'long toms' for tap-rooted plants. The clay pots are rapidly disappearing from the nursery as they are expensive, breakable and difficult to obtain, although the natural porosity produced rapid root growth.

The clay pot has been superseded by the plastic pot which is lighter, easier to clean and does not need watering so often. It is also virtually unbreakable, easier to store and the growing medium in the pot is kept warmer as the container is not porous. The disadvantages of the plastic container are that it is more difficult to judge when it needs watering, and that it has to be stored in a dark place as if exposed to light for long periods it becomes brittle, owing to the action of ultra-violet rays. Pots can now be purchased in tough polypropylene and these are more durable.

A cheap alternative to the polypropylene container is the 'poly bag', made from polyethylene film, which can be stored very easily in a small area as it will collapse into a flat layer. However, filling it with compost may take a little longer than with the plastic pot.

In recent years we have seen the introduction of biodegradable containers which will decompose naturally in the soil, yet have a long 'shelf-life' while being used as containers. These pots are normally made out of peat, which is often blended with pulp and fertilizer before being moulded into a container.

Containers are now available in various sizes, either round or square shaped. Size measurements for these containers can either be given as a diameter or by the volume of compost the container holds, and Table 7 gives a guideline to what is available in the market-place.

Another consideration for a grower is how many pots a cubic metre of compost will fill. This information is essential for planning the purchase of growing-media materials and mixing. A guide to this is given in Table 8.

Table 7 Container sizes

	Top	*Height*	*Bottom*
32 litres (7 gal)	350 mm ×	330 mm ×	290 mm
	14 in ×	13 in ×	11·5 in
22·5 litres (5 gal)	285 mm ×	280 mm ×	235 mm
	11·25 in ×	11 in ×	9·25 in
19 litres (4 gal)	265 mm ×	265 mm ×	230 mm
	10·5 in ×	10·5 in ×	9 in
9·5 litres (2 gal)	230 mm ×	210 mm ×	275 mm
	9 in ×	8·25 in ×	7·125 in
4·25 litres (1 gal)	170 mm ×	275 mm ×	135 mm
	6·75 in ×	7·125 in ×	5·25 in
1·08 litres (1 qt)	130 mm ×	130 mm ×	90 mm
	4·75 in ×	4·75 in ×	3·75 in

Table 8 Approximate number of pots filled with one cubic metre of compost

Diameter	*Number of pots*
6 cm (2·25 in) peat pot	7,300
8 cm (3 in) peat pot	3,400
10·5 cm (4 in) peat pot	1,700
10 cm (3·5 in) round rigid	2,550
11 cm (4·5 in) polyethylene bag	850
12·5 cm (5 in) polyethylene bag	400
15 cm (6 in) polyethylene bag	200

Often a grower will have to calculate how much compost is required and, as can be seen from Table 7, containers are often sold by the volume of compost they hold. The following is a quick guide to calculating compost requirements using a 3 parts peat to 1 part sand mix:

1 cubic foot of compost = 28 litres.
1 cubic metre of compost = 35 cubic feet.
Therefore *1 cubic metre = 980 litres*.

The amount of compost required will vary according to the type of container, that is, polyethylene bags have parallel sides while a plastic pot has tapered sides; therefore, while the diameter is the same, they will hold different amounts of compost.

PURCHASING CONTAINERS

A grower is confronted with so many types of container that it is difficult to decide on the ideal for a particular unit. Cost must be a prime consideration as no one can justify putting a cheap-selling product in an expensive container.

Secondly, a grower needs to consider the present position as far as equipment is concerned. If containers are changed the potting machine or handling system will have to be adapted at an added expense to the unit.

A major consideration with any type of container is the number of drainage holes at the base. The recommended hole space for container bases is a minimum of 20 per cent, although the bottomless pot is now being developed and this should remove any problems concerning porosity.

Obviously any container must be durable for at least the life of the crop and be of a non-toxic nature to the plant material.

Handling

One major task in any container nursery is the handling of potted plants. It is expensive to handle pots individually and any simple system should be adopted to ensure pots are handled in as big a unit as is feasible.

Many trades and industries have already found many advantages of using trays and crates for handling their produce and now the plant producer is finding value in using trays to handle container plants. A wide range of trays is available, but the major requirements are that the tray is light in weight, durable, inexpensive and has good load-bearing properties.

Two types of tray are commonly used in nurseries: the stacking skeleton trays constructed by injection-moulding of polypropylene and which are relatively cheap to purchase, and the more expensive type of propathene tray, which is more durable and can carry heavier containers.

Container systems

Commercial companies are now producing complete handling systems for containers and trays for use with containerized liner plants. This means that up to 30 containers can be carried with ease by one person. Types of materials used to make these handling systems vary from thermoformed acrylonitrile-butadiene-styrene sheets to moulded plastic using Alkathene and Propathene. As with any other system the method adopted must fit into the present production and improve work methods, not create further problems.

Systems currently available allow containers to be set up in the trays before potting, which means that a more efficient method of potting can be adopted by laying out the trays on a bench, filling the pots with growing medium and then finger potting. The ideal pot/tray system should be stackable when potted and not impede contact between the standing ground and the container (see Plate 7).

Before leaving the subject of container selection it is important to stress that a grower should keep to one type of container in a specific standing area. Different types of containers require different watering requirements and should therefore be kept separate.

THE EFFECT OF CONTAINERS ON PLANT GROWTH

Containers will restrict root growth, which can result in root girdling and kinking; because of this problem, plants should rarely be left in their final container for more than three years before planting out.

Once a plant is taken out of its normal situation and grown in a container, another factor becomes involved—the extremes in root temperature. In warm climates white containers are used in an attempt to reflect the heat and thereby keep the root run cool. In cold climates the reverse occurs and the problem is tolerance of roots to winter temperatures.

Table 9 gives the minimum safe root temperatures and killing temperatures for several species of one-year-old plants from rooted cuttings in 4·5 litre (1 gal) containers.

Table 9 Root-temperature limits

	Safe temperature, °C	*Killing temperature, °C*
Magnolia soulangeana	−3	−5
Magnolia stellata	−3	−5
Cornus florida	−4	−7
Daphne cneorum	−4	−7
Ilex crenata	−4	−7
Cotoneaster horizontalis	−5	−7
Pyracantha coccinea	−5	−9
Cryptomeria japonica	−7	−10
Viburnum carlesii	−7	−10
Cytisus praecox	−7	−10
Acer palmatum 'Atropurpureum'	−8	−10
Taxus × media	−9	−12
Exbury Azaleas	−9	−12
Kalmia latifolia	−9	Not established
Leucothoe catesbaei	−9	Not established
Mahonia aquifolium	−9	Not established
Pieris species	−9	Not established
Thuya occidentalis	−9	Not established
Euonymus fortunei 'Colorata'	−9	−14
Juniperus horizontalis	−12	−18

With increasing research and technology our methods of container growing are bound to improve and this sector of our industry is bound to increase.

POLYTHENE-ROLL SYSTEM

The last few years have seen an increase in the use of polythene in all aspects of horticulture, from propagation tunnels for protecting crops to mulching. One more recent adaptation has been to place rooted cuttings in polythene rolls instead of conventional plastic pots. This technique was first devised by the Finnish forest nursery producers who use the system for growing conifers for plantation programmes.

The polythene rolls contain 25–30 rooted cuttings, which permits easy handling of large numbers of plants—thus making this system very attractive for planting, especially where a work-study programme is in progress. Rolls can be rapidly unwound on site and each plant easily separated from its neighbour without root damage, unlike plants knocked out of boxes; and the long, narrow, fibrous root system enables the plants to be quickly planted in a spade nick. Post-planting time is not wasted in collecting pots; the polythene is simply collected up and deposited. This method is far less tiring than the conventional trowel planting which is necessary when planting from pots.

Another advantage of using polythene rolls is that the longer root system produced allows the plant to come into contact with available soil moisture further down the soil profile, which is notably useful on many landscape sites where regular irrigation is not normally possible.

The great advantage on the nursery is the higher densities of plants in the standing-out ground; also, when well spaced the rolls do not blow over.

Polythene rolls are hand-rolled unlike the original Finnish rolls which were produced on a machine. Hand-rolling requires no special equipment and can easily be carried out in a normal potting shed.

Method of rolling

The potting shed should be laid out to take a 5 m (16 ft 3 in) long bench; this needs to be about 1 m (3 ft 3 in) high to allow for easy working. Along one side of the bench a 4 m (13 ft) long wooden batten, 40 mm (1·5 in) wide × 20 mm (0·75 in) deep, is nailed to the bench. A further batten is nailed parallel to this 300 mm (1 ft) away. The gap between the two is the rolling area.

Black polythene, 38 μm (150 gauge), is used for rolling; experience has shown that unlike clear polythene it does not deteriorate in light. The polythene is sawn into 300 mm (1 ft) widths and, once cut, is unwound to lie between the two battens on the bench. Any normal container compost is then spread evenly over the polythene and flattened out with the hands; the amount of compost is equal to the amount that would be needed to fill 50 pots of 75 mm (3 in) size.

The next stage is to select and grade the rooted cuttings ready for

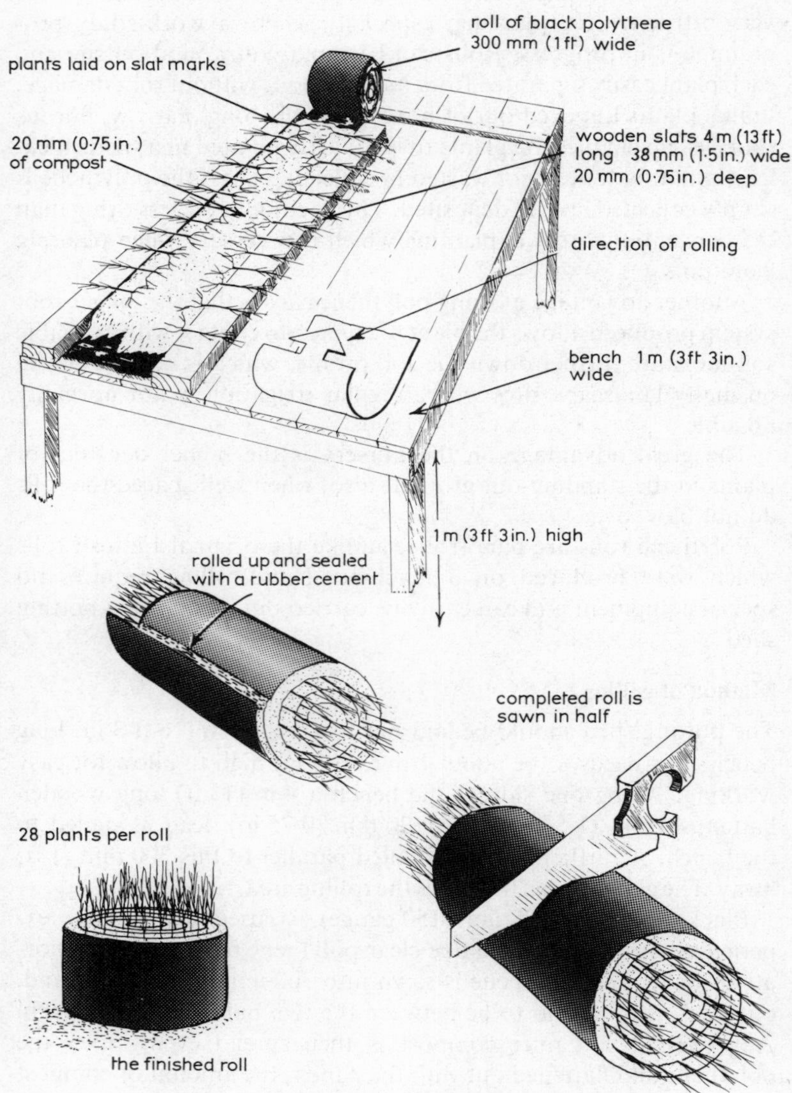

Fig. 49 Polythene-roll production

rolling; 50–60 cuttings will be required, as rolls are formed in pairs; therefore each roll will contain between 25 and 30 plants. Plants are placed along the top edge of the polythene and the same number also along the nearest edge. Normally 28 plants are placed on each edge as this allows for losses, and still permits a nurseryman to dispatch rolls containing 25 plants.

Plants, compost and polythene are now rolled, ensuring that, when rolling, equal pressure is given across the polythene and that it is firm, otherwise the resultant roll is loose and uneven. After rolling, the polythene is cut and pasted at the end with a brush stroke of bituminized lap cement. At this stage we have a swiss roll with rooted cuttings sticking out of each side; this roll is now sawn through to produce two equal halves.

The two rolls can now be placed on a flat truck for transporting to the standing area. If the roll has been rolled properly the compost will not fall out of the bottom and after watering and settlement the roll becomes very stable and can be easily handled. The rolls should be stood on polythene or loose gravel to prevent rooting through from the base of the roll.

Management considerations

It is estimated that in producing plants by this method the grower can make a saving of 50 per cent on labour and materials at the potting stage. Experience has shown that new workers instantly get into a rhythm of working as the system runs on a flow line.

One great saving, by using rolls, is space on the standing ground. By using this system it is possible to get 6·25–7·5 million plants per ha (2·5–3 million plants per acre), compared with 1 million–1·25 million per ha (400,000–500,000 plants per acre) by conventional methods.

The growing on of plants is also far easier; the roll has less surface area than a pot which means less evaporation of water, with the result that less irrigating is required to keep the roll at field capacity. This reduced surface area also means it is more difficult for weed seeds to germinate, with resultant saving in labour and herbicides.

Plants in rolls will grow satisfactorily for a period of two years, after which it is advisable to sell, plant or pot them off before deterioration in quality takes place.

When it comes to handling and transportation, a roll of 25 plants occupies far less space than 25 pots, and rolls can be easily stacked on their sides for transporting, thus reducing the cost of this operation. If plants are delayed either at the nursery or with the customer, they can be maintained with far less trouble than plants in pots.

This method of production is of great value for producing ground-cover plants in bulk, and cheaply, from rooted cuttings. Excellent results have been obtained from plants such as *Geranium macrorrhizum*; *Hedera colchica* and *H. helix*; *Lamium maculatum*; *Rubus tricolor*; *Symphytum grandiflorum*; *Tellima grandiflora*; *Trifolium purpureum* and *Waldsteinia ternata*. Rootstocks and young trees such as *Acer campestre* and *A. platanoides*; *Alnus glutinosa*; *Betula pendula* and *Robinia pseudoacacia* have also been grown successfully in rolls.

Plants such as *Hebe*, *Cotoneaster* or junipers are not recommended for this system, as the rolls will not provide adequate room for lateral development. These species have to be grown in conventional containers.

With an increase in ground-cover planting by landscapers, polythene rolls mean that a cheaper method of producing large numbers of plants is available, plus a more efficient handling and planting system.

It must be noted that the principle of rolling plants is not a new one and in the UK it is covered by an English patent (No. 1165543) which was taken out by the Finnish Nisula System.

21

Choosing the right growing media

During recent years great advances have been made in the understanding of growing media. Original composts contained loam, but now peat, sand, bark and rockwool can be used with great success.

The requirements of a growing medium are that it is cheap, non-phytotoxic to the plant, penetrable by roots, has the correct ratio of pore space to material, has little variability chemically or physically, and allows nutrients to be taken up by the plant.

INGREDIENTS

Most growers will use a peat/sand or loamless mix, the materials being easily available and relatively cheap. One of the major problems facing the grower is choosing the right ingredients or compost for the job. Growers require specialist growing media for particular crops and the management of these will vary greatly.

Peat

Variation in peat occurs owing to different botanical origins as well as to variation in suction force, available mineral contents, fibrous characteristics, air at field capacity, water capacity and whether its origin is from an upper or lower layer of the horizon.

Peat is basically the remains of aquatic, marsh, bog or swamp vegetation in a partially decomposed state. For growing media we use the light kinds, which are either moss or sedge peats.

Moss peat is produced in high-rainfall areas and high humidity. The peat has a low nutrient level resulting in a low pH (3·0–5·0). Young peats are less granular than older ones and may have a higher water-holding capacity and less air space. Moss peats are the main ones used in growing media, although their effect on a growing medium will depend on their source.

Sedge peats are normally produced in hollows or plains, and nutrient and pH levels can be higher (4·0–7·0) than moss peats. The structure also differs, particles being smaller than moss. This material is normally used in peat blocks for raising young plants.

Sand

Composed of small rock grains of between 0·05 mm and 2·0 mm (BSI sieve No. 7–No. 14), and being the heaviest of the rooting media, it is often used to give stability to the container. Sand contains no nutrients and should be lime free and weed free. It has no buffering capacity.

Growers often incorporate sand to improve drainage but the value of this depends on the other ingredients. Incorporating sand is of value, though, where drier conditions are required or in a pricking-out mix, as this can make the pricking-out operation easier.

The pH and lime content of sand varies with source, and damage to plants can occur if the free lime content is more than 1 per cent. Testing for free lime in sand can easily be carried out by adding 10 per cent hydrochloric acid and if the mix fizzes then free lime is present.

Loam

Growers still use loam as an ingredient although it is very variable and good-quality loam is increasingly difficult to obtain. It must be pathogen- and weed-free and therefore needs sterilizing, but in general loam-based composts are easier to manage, as the loam acts as a buffer.

Nutrients

Fertilizer is essential for healthy vigorous plant growth. It is important that it is in the correct amounts for the age of the plant and species. Fertilizer can be applied either to the compost or as a liquid feed from the first potting stage.

Nutrients in composts can be applied either as a quick-release fertilizer which may cause root scorch and soon needs replenishing, or as a slow-release fertilizer. Because of the type of crop the nursery trade grows, most growers will use a slow-release fertilizer. Various types are on the market and the mode of action varies with the type of product.

The advantages of slow-release fertilizers are that nutrients are applied in a single operation and some feed is always available, although the release pattern may not always be what is required. Many slow-release fertilizers come in capsules and, if crushed, root scorch may occur. Heat is also a governing factor in release and when growing under polythene structures or in glasshouses a half rate may reduce the possibility of damage.

Table 10 Mode of action of slow-release fertilizers

Fertilizer	*Decomposition*	*Nutrient supply*
Horn, hair	Microbial	Nitrogen
Urea formaldehyde	Solution – hydrolysis*	Nitrogen
Frits	Hydrolysis,* chemical reaction	Potassium and micro-nutrients
Resin-coated fertilizers	Diffusion,† osmosis‡	Many nutrients
Ion exchange fertilizers	Ion exchange	Many nutrients

* Hydrolysis: water vapour diffuses through the coating of the fertilizer causing rupturing.

† Diffusion: fertilizer dissolves and diffuses out through small pores in the coating.

‡ Osmosis: fertilizer percolates through coat and inter-mixes with other fluids.

A complete fertilizer programme supplies all the key elements for plant growth and their release pattern will be affected by the pH of the growing medium. The pH often rises in a medium for the first two weeks after mixing but then steadily drops.

The pH can vary for the following reasons:

1 The amount of free lime in the sand.
2 pH of the water applied to the media.
3 Liquid feeding with sulphur-based feeds.
4 Size of container – pH is often higher in a small container with the same compost.
5 Amount of fertilizer/lime added to the media.
6 Type of watering system adopted. Overhead watering results in a higher pH than sub-irrigation.

The pH can be controlled by the amount of calcium added to the mix. Ground limestone (calcium carbonate) can be used, or magnesium limestone, if magnesium is required, but both will increase the pH of a medium. But to lower the pH is more difficult and one may have to add something like choline phosphate.

Table 11 Compost-mixing information for one cubic metre

Materials	*First potting off rooted cuttings*		*Potting on from 70 mm and 90 mm pots*	
	General mix	*Ericaceous and conifer mix*	*General mix*	*Ericaceous and conifer mix*
USING RESIN-COATED SLOW RELEASE FERTILIZER				
3 bales moistened peat	✓	✓	✓	✓
2 level barrows of sand (0·12 m^3 capacity)	✓	✓	✓	✓
Magnesium limestone 11 % Mg	2,400 g	2,400 g	2,400 g	2,400 g
Ground limestone	1,200 g	Omit	1,200 g	Omit
Single superphosphate 18 %	1,500 g	1,500 g	1,500 g	1,500 g
Resin-coated slow-release fertilizer 18:11:10	1,500 g	1,500 g	3,000 g	3,000 g
Fitted trace WM255	300 g	300 g	300 g	300 g
QUICK-RELEASE FERTILIZER				
3 bales moistened peat	✓	✓	✓	✓
2 level barrows of sand (0·12 m^3 capacity)	✓	✓	✓	✓
Magnesium limestone 11 % Mg	1,000 g	1,000 g	1,000 g	1,000 g
Ground limestone	1,000 g	Omit	1,000 g	Omit
Quick-release fertilizer 10:6·8:10·2 plus trace elements	2,500 g	2,500 g	5,000 g	5,000 g

JOHN INNES SEED COMPOST		Seed compost		
2 parts loam	by volume	✓		
1 part peat	by volume	✓		
1 part sand	by volume	✓		
Superphosphate		1,000 g		
Ground chalk		500 g		
JOHN INNES POTTING COMPOST		**Number 1**	**Number 2**	**Number 3**
7 parts loam	by volume	✓	✓	✓
3 parts peat	by volume	✓	✓	✓
2 parts sand	by volume	✓	✓	✓
John Innes base		3,000 g	6,000 g	9,000 g
Ground chalk		500 g	1,000 g	1,500 g

1 Handibale of peat loosened and moistened = 0·34 m^3 (9·3 cu ft) 1 m^3 = 1·3 cu yd; 1 cu yd = 0·765 m^3; 36·4 litre = 1 bushel (1·3 cu ft); 21 bushels = 1 cu yd.

WM 255 = B 1 %; Cu 4·3 %; Fe 13·8 %; Mn 5·4 %; Mo 1 %; Zn 4·3 %.

The amount of lime required in a compost is far less for ericaceous plants, a pH of 4·5–5·0 is needed. The recommended level of pH for other plants has fallen over recent years and now a pH of 5·0–5·5, with a lower addition of calcium, is used.

Suggestions for composts containing slow-release fertilizers are constantly changing and will inevitably vary between growers, but Table 11 should act as a guide.

The first major advance in composts came during the period 1934 to 1939 at the John Innes Horticultural Institute when it was shown that a wide range of plant material could be grown in a standard mix. Many growers still use this mix, although, as mentioned earlier, good-quality loam is getting difficult to obtain.

Table 12 Fungicides that can be incorporated in composts

Fungicide	*Application*	*Disease*
ETRIDIAZOLE	Incorporate in the compost or drench	*Pythium*, *Phytophthora*
PROTHIOCARB	Drench	*Pythium*, *Phytophthora*
FURALAXYL	Incorporate in the compost or drench	*Pythium*, *Phytophthora*
IPRODIONE	Drench	*Rhizoctonia*
ETRIDIAZOLE AND CHLOROTHALONIL	Incorporate in the compost	*Pythium*, *Rhizoctonia*, some *Phytophthora* species
QUINTOZENE	Incorporate in the compost	*Rhizoctonia*

Liquid feeding

Some growers prefer not to add fertilizer to the growing media but to apply it at regular intervals by liquid feeding. This method will also be needed with long-term container crops where the feed is a supplement once the slow-release fertilizer has been used up.

Liquid feeding normally commences three weeks after potting and can then be carried out at every watering, or one stronger feed on a weekly basis. Feed can be applied overhead, which can result in foliage scorch, especially during hot summers, or by low-level irrigation, when standing grounds may need to be leached to avoid a build-up of soluble salts.

Normally potassium nitrate and ammonium nitrate are recommended for liquid feeding of nursery stock, but proprietary brands can be used instead.

CALCULATIONS FOR LIQUID FEEDS

The majority of recommendations for the composition of nutrient solutions used in plant liquid feeding are quoted in parts per million (ppm) of nitrogen (N), phosphate (P_2O_5) and potash (K_2O). The grower needs to be able to convert these figures into terms of grammes per litre (ounces per gallon) of concentrate or to compare various recommendations given in grammes per litre by converting them to the standard ppm.

Most liquid-feed materials are purchased by the grower in the form of a wettable powder, and are made up by him into a concentrated stock solution. This is put into an automatic dilutor which regulates the quantity of stock solution passing into the irrigation water. The rate of dilution of the liquid feed depends on the amount of water the grower wishes to apply to the crop, and the frequency at which he wants to feed. The diluted liquid feed must not be at too high a concentration or root damage may occur.

1 Dilutors operate on a volume basis, that is, one volume of concentrated stock solution (or concentrate) is automatically added to, say, 200 volumes of water giving a dilution rate of one in 200, written 1:200.
2 The concentration of the stock solution is calculated as a weight of fertilizer per volume of stock solution, that is, kilogrammes per litre (pounds per gallon).

Example

1 kg (2·2 lb) of fertilizer is dissolved in 10 litres of water (2 gal). 10 litres (2 gal) of water weigh 10 kg (22 lb). Therefore we are dissolving 1 kg (2·2 lb) of fertilizer in 10 kg (22 lb) of water.

To calculate this as a percentage you divide the quantity dissolved by the quantity of water, then multiply by 100 to give percentage composition. That is

$$\frac{1}{10} \times 100 = \frac{1}{1\not{0}} \times 10\not{0} = 10\%$$

3 The concentration of a particular nutrient can also be expressed as a percentage concentration of that nutrient. This is found by multiplying the percentage concentration of fertilizer by the proportion of nutrient in that fertilizer.

Example

Potassium nitrate contains 46% K_2O (or potash). Using the example above you know that the percentage concentration of potassium nitrate is 10%. To find the percentage concentration of K_2O in this stock solution multiply 10 by 46%, or

$$10 \times \frac{46}{100} = 1\not{0} \times \frac{46}{10\not{0}} = 4{\cdot}6\%\ K_2O \text{ in this stock solution}$$

4 Once you have found the concentration of the nutrient in the stock solution you can calculate the percentage of nutrient in the liquid feed after dilution. This is found by dividing the percentage concentration of the nutrient by the dilution rate.

Example

Assume we require a dilution of 1:200. Divide 4·6 % by 200, or

$$\frac{4{\cdot}6}{200} = 0{\cdot}023\%\ K_2O$$

5 A decimal figure of 0·023 % is difficult to deal with so it is normally converted to a number in terms of parts per million, that is, 230 ppm.

Thus you can now calculate the nutrient contained in a dilute liquid feed in terms of ppm in four stages.

FORMULA A: formula for calculating concentration of nutrient in dilute liquid feed

$$\text{ppm nutrient} = \frac{\text{Weight of fertilizer (in kg)} \times \%\ \text{Nutrient (in fertilizer)} \times 10{,}000}{\text{Volume of stock solution (in litres)} \times \text{Dilution rate}}$$

Using the example above:

$$\frac{1 \times 46 \times 10{,}000}{10 \times 200} = 230\ \text{ppm}$$

The above formula can be used to find out what the quantity of nutrient in the dilute feed is, when a quantity of fertilizer is added to a quantity of water which is then diluted. However, growers normally require a definite level of the nutrient in the dilute feed. They therefore need to know what quantity of fertilizer to add to a given volume of water to provide a stock solution which when diluted supplies the correct quantity of nutrient.

This is calculated by another formula as below:

FORMULA B: formula to calculate the weight of fertilizer required per litre of stock solution to obtain a given level of nutrient in the dilute feed

$$\text{kg of fertilizer per litre} = \frac{\text{ppm (of diluted feed)} \times \text{Dilution rate}}{\%\ \text{Nutrient (in fertilizer)} \times 10{,}000}$$

Example

A dilute feed of 200 ppm K_2O is required. The dilution rate is to be 1:200. Thus

$$\frac{200 \times 200}{46 \times 10{,}000} = \frac{4}{46} = 0{\cdot}087\ \text{kg/l} = 87\ \text{g/l}$$

kg of potassium nitrate needed = 87 g/l.

By using both formulae you can now calculate quantities of fertilizer required for any combination of nutrient levels.

Saline damage

Plant losses can occur because of excessive salts in the growing media. In high concentrations the plant absorbs considerable amounts, which accumulate in the leaves, resulting in leaf-margin burning. High saline conditions in the growing media will cause root death.

The main sources of salinity are: the fertilizer, especially if the formulation has been miscalculated, resulting in a toxic effect; the compost itself, especially if loam is used; and the water used in irrigation.

Salt concentration occurs because of water evaporation leaving toxic deposits; therefore composts must be kept moist, although still free-draining. If salt toxicity does occur then the growing media need to be leached by means of heavy waterings.

Water

For vigorous plant growth irrigation will be required to obtain optimum returns from the crop. Water, as mentioned earlier, can alter the pH of the media as well as carrying harmful fluorides, *Phytophthora* species, weed seed and other impurities. Also, as mentioned previously, the salinity of the media is governed by the amount of water. Halve the water in the media and you double the salt concentration, except for chemicals with low solubility such as calcium and sulphate. Water can also act as a leaching agent, removing nutrients from the compost.

The amount of water which needs to be applied will depend on the amount lost through transpiration, evaporation and drainage; this often varies depending on the type of container used. Clay pots lose water through the base, sides, evaporation from the surface and the plant itself, while plastic pots have no loss of water through their sides, meaning they are warmer and wetter.

Oxygen

Apart from water, another important ingredient of a growing medium is oxygen, which is required to produce rapidly grown, healthy plants. To supply adequate oxygen a media should have a minimum large-pore-space proportion of 10 per cent. Peat-based composts can have a pore space between 4 and 40 per cent depending on the grade. If fine sand is added it will fall between the peat, reducing the air spaces, which may or may not be beneficial, depending on the type of peat used. On the other hand coarse sand may force the peat apart, increasing the air spaces.

BUYING OR MIXING YOUR OWN

A grower has the choice of mixing his own compost or buying in. The advantages of buying in a compost are that it is mixed to a known standard; there is a saving of labour for mixing and of capital in equipment outlay, and the grower has the back-up service of a supplier. Obviously there are disadvantages. Firstly, is it cost effective for your particular enterprise; are there storage facilities and, although it may be of a set standard, is it the standard you require?

Many growers still prefer to mix their own compost and if this is the preferred option it is important that the mixing procedure is known to all personnel so that a set standard can be maintained. The following method is recommended for small mixes:

1 Peat spread evenly over mixing area.
2 Magnesium and ground limestone added to the peat in right amounts. Do not add lime and nitrogenous fertilizers together as ammonia gas is released.
3 Peat is now moistened thoroughly.
4 Add sand to the layer of peat.
5 All other fertilizers are spread evenly over the heap, any lumps of fertilizer being broken down.
6 Mix thoroughly by shovelling or using a shredder, care being taken not to overmix as this will result in fertilizer separation.
7 Place mixed compost in the correct storage bay and label the mix, giving date mixed as well as type of mix.

ALTERNATIVE GROWING MEDIA

All that is required of a substrate for growing plants is that it will support the plant, be stable and supply the plant with water, air and nutrients. With the advanced knowledge of nutrient uptake and liquid feeding in recent years we now have a wider range of materials in which to grow plants.

Rockwool

A recent advance introduced from Denmark has been the use of rockwool as a growing medium. Rockwool was first used in 1958 and there has been much interest in this product ever since. It is composed of 60% Diabas (granite), 20% limestone and 20% coke, which are melted at 1,600 °C (7,000 °F) to produce fibres which are joined by the use of a binder and wetting agent.

It quickly became apparent that rockwool in blocks was well suited for use as a cutting compost. When roots are sufficiently well developed the units can be transplanted into larger blocks with a hole corresponding to the size of the original block.

Research has shown that excellent results can be achieved by inserting cuttings and plants in rockwool, with some trials showing 100 per cent rooting of cuttings. Easy transplanting of rooted cuttings into growing-on blocks without root damage also removes the shock caused by transplanting.

Granulated rockwool is now being produced which can be used on its own or with peat as a growing medium, one of its major advantages being that, unlike peat, it does not decompose with age.

Bark

Pulverized bark has been used since the 1960s as a growing medium in the USA, Canada, Russia and Scandinavia. When using bark it is critical that the processing operation is done with care and the bark is left for a few weeks before use. The main reasons for this are, first, to remove the risk of infection by any rhizomorphs of *Armillaria mellea* which may be present as fragmented rhizomorphs. These are capable of causing damage for a few weeks. Conifer barks also contain monoterpene which is toxic to plants. This toxin is removed by natural thermophyllic bacterial activity in the heap.

Bark has a slow rate of decay, retains moisture and resists wind-blown weed-seed germination, as well as having good drainage and being a sterile medium.

Bark contains a small amount of nutrients and these need taking into account when calculating fertilizer requirements.

Polyurethane foam

A sterile medium which readily holds water and plant nutrients. Polyurethane foam is available in pre-cut sheets for use with cuttings.

Diatomaceous earths

These are fossilized remnants of aquatic plants called diatoms, which are honeycombed, being 93 per cent air space. When mixed with clay they make an ideal growing medium.

Vermiculite, which consists of magnesium, aluminium and iron silicates, is one of these products. It has similar properties to peat in water uptake and retention, although it tends to break down into a slimy aggregate. Another product is Perlite, based on aluminium silicate, which expands into an open cellular structure when heated.

It is impossible to cover all the aspects of growing media in one chapter. This material is designed as a guideline, but expert advice should always be sought when in doubt, as a mistake in preparing growing media cannot usually be corrected – and this will result in reduced quality of plant material.

22

Potting systems

The majority of potting on a nursery will take place between January and April, using a variety of containers and growing media.

During the past few years potting machines have become more familiar on nurseries, enabling growers to either increase production with the labour available or decrease the time allocated to potting. The grower can use less-skilled labour on a machine, although some training is required before a worker is completely familiar with it.

Before obtaining a machine, management needs to consider the negative side. For instance, the quality of the product may deteriorate, especially when polythene bags are used, although potting may be more uniform than that obtained by hand potting.

The structure of the compost is also important. Sand in the mix can wear down machine parts, such as the auger, resulting in expensive repair and replacement bills, and therefore a sandless mixture may be worth considering. The moisture content is also important; if the compost is too wet, it will stick to the auger and if too dry the auger hole will collapse.

A potting machine should act as a pacemaker and fit into a system, not take over and create bottlenecks, or delays if insufficient materials are ready to hand. With this in mind the handling of materials at either end of the potting operation can be a problem if the flow of potting is to continue without interruption. Forward planning is essential to ensure that sufficient growing media, pots and standing area are available, especially if machines are to be hired.

Most machines available rely on team work. When selecting operators the nursery manager should pick people carefully to avoid friction within a group.

Machines available

A variety of machines are available. They vary a great deal in sophistication and the number of operators required to ensure efficient running. Potting rates will vary from one machine to another, as well as from one situation to another with the same machine. Results depend on the type of holding, type of container used, type of compost and skill of the operators (see Plates 4 to 6).

A guideline on potting rates, using 4·5 litre polythene bags for potting, excluding the preparation or standing-down time, is as follows:

Hand potting: 1,000 containers in 16 man hours

Machine potting: 1,000 containers in $2\frac{1}{2}$ man hours (i.e. a team of four take 40 minutes)

It is advisable to allow a 15 per cent error margin when using a machine, to allow for missed opportunities, to plant the maximum number of containers that the machine offers the worker per hour.

Potting machines can be either bought or hired. The advantages of hiring are that it avoids tying up capital that may be needed elsewhere, it avoids obsolescence (a better machine may be available next year); it reduces running costs (that is, no repairs or spares); and finally the hiring company provides specialist back-up facilities for service and adaptations to the customer's needs. When hiring, one should check the power supply. Some machines run on single-phase electricity while others require three-phase electricity.

The alternative to hiring is buying which means that the machine is always available and can be fitted into the growing programme whatever the season. It is also a valuable asset to the nursery which should be depreciated over a five-year period.

Using a potting machine

Potting machines have many moving parts and therefore it is important that the operators do not wear loose clothing, which can become caught in the machine and result in a serious accident. Before using the equipment the operators must also be well acquainted with the ON/OFF switches and know how to quickly neutralize the machine.

The first operation when using a potting machine is the placing of containers in the pot holders. The work flow will depend on the operator having sufficient pots close at hand so that there is no interruption of work. One should aim at putting a container in each pot holder and the machine speed can be controlled to ensure this is achieved. Pots must be placed squarely in the holders to ensure the

1 A selection of nurseryman's knives

2 *Mahonia* leaf-bud cuttings

3 *Mahonia* leaf-bud cuttings inserted in tray

4 A Dutch potting machine

5 A Dutch potting machine: a close-up of the pot holders

6 German potting machine

7 Empot handling system in use at Bloom's Nurseries Ltd

8 Machine planting rootstocks

9 Machine lifting of *Salix*

10 Rootballing machine for use in the field or in a shed

11 and 12 Conifer being rootballed using elastic netting

13 Rootballed conifers:
a plant balled by hand,
and a machine-balled plant

14 Alpine beds at Bressingham Gardens

15 Aquatic tanks

drill or auger does not catch the pot and throw it across the machine.

The next operation is at the planting station. Ideally plants for potting should have been selected and graded out before potting commenced. This will ensure a good work flow, as planting is a full-time job.

After potting, a third person can remove potted plants from the holder and place them in the transport container.

Potting-machine maintenance

Maintenance can be divided into pre-season and post-season checks of the potting machine. Before carrying out any repairs or adjustments to the machine ensure it is not connected to the power supply. Before a machine is used, all moving parts need to be checked and lubricated where necessary. At the same time protection guards need to be inspected to ensure they are in good order and fitted correctly. Once the machine has been thoroughly overhauled the speed controls can be set at the right work rate and the pot holders adjusted for the size of container to be used. The auger and pot firmer also need to be checked to ensure the correct size is fitted.

After the potting season the machine needs to be stored until required again. Pot holders need to be removed, cleaned and stored, rust spots treated with a rust inhibitor and gloss paint, and compost removed from the chains and elevator. Ideally, the pot track should be removed, the chain links checked and placed in a bath of diesel oil. Finally the machine should be stored in a weather-proof building until required again.

If the machine is treated properly problems should not occur in the first few seasons. However, the first parts to wear will include the conveyor which moves the soil along, and the track with the pot holders and the springs. With this in mind it is essential that spares are kept in store to avoid long periods of idle time in the middle of the potting season.

Potting system

As mentioned earlier, whichever potting machine is obtained it is only one part of a system and a continuous work flow can only be obtained by a smooth supply of materials to and from the potting station. The supply of these materials will vary with individual nursery holdings, but may include the supply of growing media by conveyor or gravity and the transport of containerized plants away from the potting station by conveyors. In all cases double handling must be avoided otherwise the advantages of increased potting output will be lost to excessive handling.

Hand potting

Not all nurseries can justify the expense of hiring or buying a potting machine and will therefore pot by hand. The important consideration in hand potting is bench layout, and throughput of containerized plants will be governed by minimum movement by the operator.

The layout for 'potting on' plants is shown in Fig. 50, but it can be modified to suit individual holdings and personnel.

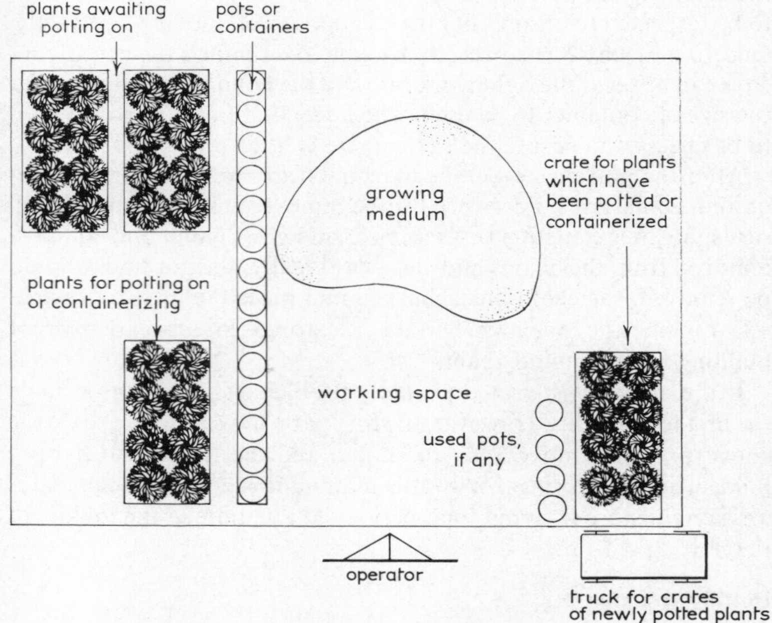

Fig. 50 Bench layout for potting on/containerizing

Before potting ensure that the right growing media and containers are being used. Filling the container can be done either by using one's hands or a small trowel. With polythene bags ensure that the compost reaches the bottom of the bag to give a firm base to the container. Plants must be placed centrally in the container and firmed. The final level of compost in the container is important; with a loamless compost the media can come to the top of the container to allow for subsidence. If loam-based compost is used a space for watering must be left at the top of the pot.

After potting, some plants will need pruning back to induce bud break from the base of the plant. This is important with plants such as *Forsythia*, *Cornus* and *Weigela* if high-quality bushy plants are required.

If climbers are being potted, for example *Clematis* species, they will need staking to give them support.

Potting on

'Potting on' is the term used when a containerized plant is placed in a larger pot. The advantage of potting on at the optimum time is that a check to growth is avoided. If potting on is delayed the result may be pot-bound plants, which have curled roots resulting in poor growth.

Plants should be removed from their existing pot (if necessary invert and tap the pot on the work area) and the surface area cleaned of weeds and moss to avoid introducing weed seeds to the new container. This operation should be carried out some distance away from the fresh potting media to ensure that no contamination occurs! The potting operation is carried out either by hand or machine as mentioned previously.

Potting aids

In recent years various aids have been introduced to increase the rate of potting per man hour without involving the grower in a large amount of capital expense.

One such aid is the potting bench, which avoids plants, pots and soil being taken to the potting shed only to be transported back to a standing area. By taking a mobile potting bench to the area where plants have to be stood down versatility is brought into the potting operation and this can increase output by 400 per cent over traditional hand potting, because the bench is mobile and can be handled easily.

Another potting aid is the bag gripper which is used with polythene bags. Many growers prefer bags, as they are cheaper than rigid containers and take up less storage space. A bag gripper is very useful for large polythene bags as they can be placed on protruding prongs which open the bag and keep it open while the plant is being potted. This attachment is ideal when containerizing prickly plants such as gooseberries or roses.

Whatever potting system is adopted a few important guidelines should be noted. All containers should be filled to the same level with growing media which not only makes for a better appearance but also ensures more uniform growth. Plants should not be planted too deeply and, in general, should be at the depth at which they were previously grown. When potting on, the plant should be deep enough to ensure the original rootball is just below the surface of the new soil and not left as an 'open ring' at the top of the container.

Whichever potting system a grower prefers, it is essential that labour is used efficiently as this is a major expense in a potting operation.

23

Standing grounds

A standing ground is the term used to describe land where container plants are stood for growing on, either for sale or moving on into a larger container.

This land should be an ideal growing area, being sheltered and easily accessible both from the potting area and for despatch. Various types of grounds have been constructed but whichever method is used the area should aid the management of the container plants and remain functional for at least the life of the crop. The area must be weed free, not harbour pests and diseases and aid irrigation and drainage of the crop. It should also require minimum maintenance to keep it functional as the ground will not add value to the crop, and maintenance can only be reflected in high-priced containers.

The type of material selected for the base of the standing ground will have an effect on the container plant as the standing media affects the oxygen/water relationship in the pot. The ideal standing area should retain water, for use in the summer, but at the same time drain sufficiently to avoid waterlogging of the container compost, especially during the autumn and winter.

A reduction of air spaces in the container compost means roots do not penetrate to the full depth of the pot, resulting in poor-quality plants. It was once thought that good drainage could be obtained by placing containers on wire beds, polythene or gravel; however, the result of this is that water is held in the container and plants often suffer due to reduced air spaces in the media. It is therefore recommended that a medium is selected that allows water to move out of the container to overcome waterlogging and also to act as a reservoir in dry seasons. The best compromise is to use either matting or sand which has an aggregate size similar to the compost.

As mentioned previously many methods of constructing a standing ground are available but few meet with the correct criteria for efficiency and we therefore recommend the following materials.

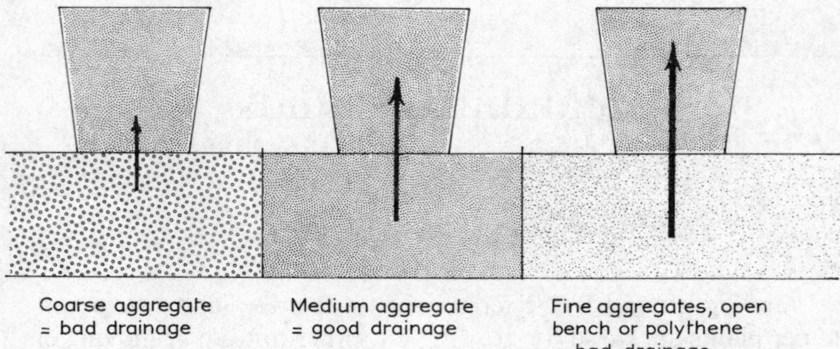

Fig. 51 The effect of standing-out-ground aggregate on capillarity

Drained sand beds

Sand is an ideal medium for capillarity and when watering from below it acts as a water reservoir.

If you are starting a new standing area then select a sheltered, level site which is easily accessible. Once the land is level and compacted a sheet of polythene is laid on the site to separate the beds from the soil which may be harbouring diseases. Without this separation diseases could easily spread into the beds. Many nurserymen will use side boards around their beds to prevent any loss of sand. If boards are used then the polythene can be turned up at the sides to a height of 20 mm (0·75 in) and stapled to the boards. This means a shallow trough is formed which will help conserve water during the summer.

Once the polythene and boards have been laid out, clean, sharp, lime-free sand can be spread over the bed to a depth of 50 mm (2 in). Any surplus water will drain from the top 30 mm (1·25 in) of the bed which is above the polythene.

Beds wider than 2 m (6 ft 6 in) often get waterlogged during the winter. This can be easily overcome by laying the polythene so that it protrudes beyond the end board. In summer the polythene is stapled to the end board to give a reservoir; in the winter it is unstapled to allow drainage, as long as a grid or similar material is placed along the end to prevent sand being washed out of the bed.

Some nurseries have developed more sophisticated sand beds by installing drainage pipes in the bed to remove surplus water. The water-holding capacity of these beds is 200,000 l/ha (16,000 gal/

acre) and therefore, once established, the frequency of watering is less than where shallower sand beds or other materials are used.

We have already mentioned the advantages of using sand but, as with all materials, there are problems in using this medium. In construction it is important to get a level site to obtain maximum stability and capillarity for the container. It is recommended that sand beds work most efficiently if they are level and with a slope of 1 in 45. This also means an even compactness and nursery workers should be discouraged from walking on the made-up beds as feet will soon compact the bed.

Also, sand is a heavy medium to handle and, for example, 50 mm (2 in) of sand will weigh 300 kg/m^2 (674 lb/sq yd), and therefore handling needs to be minimized, and mechanized, if possible.

The source of sand is important as it needs to be weed free, lime free and not carry *Phytophthora*.

Finally, if not treated, sand beds tend to increase rooting out of the container, because they are an excellent capillary media; this can be a problem when containers are subjected to temporary water shortage and also when lifting containers for dispatch as it slows down the operation and means the plant is subjected to root pruning.

Capillary sand beds

Capillary sand beds are far more sophisticated than drained sand beds. The bed must have a slope of 1 in 45 to give adequate watering and drainage. The initial construction is the same as in the previous system, except that water-distribution pipes are laid in the sand, two pipes for a 2 m (6 ft 6 in) bed. The pipes run down two-thirds of the bed, the lowest third being watered by drainage from the higher portion. The tube when purchased is unperforated and holes need to be punched in it to allow water distribution. The distribution of these holes, to allow even watering, will vary down the pipe and the following is recommended:

At highest point punch holes 100 mm (4 in) apart
At middle point punch holes 200 mm (8 in) apart
At lowest point punch holes 300 mm (1 ft) apart

The water level in the bed is maintained by using a polystyrene float contained in a seed tray or separate compartment; this acts as a sensor, and an overflow pipe, at the same level, prevents water-logging.

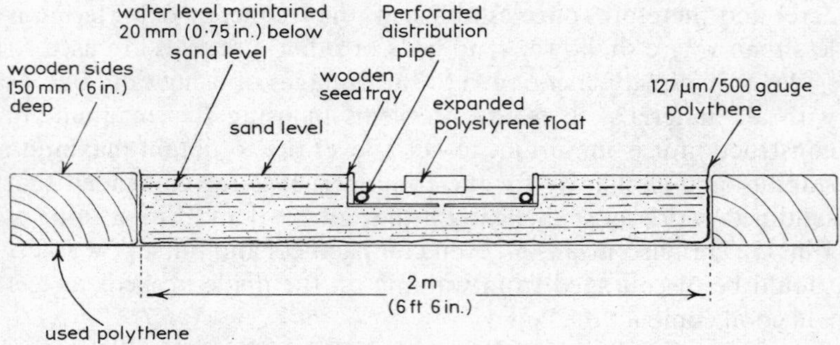

Fig. 52 Low-level capillary sand bed

As one can see this is an expensive system and although used under glass it is a method which many growers feel is too elaborate for outdoor use.

Capillary matting

Matting has been used for many years by pot-plant producers as an alternative to sand as a water-retentive material. It has many advantages over sand, being light, easily laid and sterilized, and more hygienic. Many mats are now available, ranging from white polyester-based materials to woollen felt and nylon. Most come in 1 m (3 ft 3 in) widths and varying grades. The laying of matting is fairly simple; again a level site is required and a polythene sheet is laid over the area before the matting is rolled out.

Compared with the use of matting indoors there are a number of disadvantages; firstly the life of the material outside is questionable and it is best to purchase the heavier-grade mats for outdoor use. In addition, mats hold far less water than 50 mm (2 in) of sand; an average mat will hold 60,000 l/ha (6,000 gal/acre) of water and therefore irrigation must be more frequent; also the capillary lift is not as good as sand.

Winter drainage of matting is more difficult and it is recommended that to assist drainage the mat is laid on a slight camber, which should not be too great otherwise the higher spots will not hold water during the summer.

During dry summers the mats need washing on a monthly basis to prevent a build-up of salts. It must also be stressed that the mat should not be allowed to become bone dry as rewetting is often difficult.

Other materials

Apart from sand and matting many growers will use gravel, concrete or polythene, on its own, as standing media. These materials often result in containers being poorly drained although rooting through is not such a serious problem.

Pallets have also been tried as standing areas as they reduce handling, but the initial capital outlay is high and therefore few growers would be able to adopt this system.

Sheltering standing grounds

One time-consuming operation is standing containers upright that have been blown over by the wind. To reduce this handling, as much shelter as possible should be given and this can also provide winter protection. Not only will shelter reduce handling, but it will also lead to a better-quality plant in a shorter period because of the reduced movement of young plants. Shelter can be provided on a permanent or temporary basis, using natural or artificial materials. It is important that the shelter material is effective without taking up a large area of land.

Growers are now using two types of material for shelter: hedges, for example of × *Cupressocyparis leylandii*, which can be clipped to keep them within certain limits, and which can also be used as stock hedges; alternatively, plastic netting or webbed materials can be erected like a fence to provide temporary or long-term shelter.

Management of standing grounds

The first operation on a finished standing area should be the spacing of containerized plants on the area. This requires the maximum number of plants per area with the minimum deterioration in quality. However, the spacing of plants will be governed by the type of crop, size of container and type of container. Small containers can often be stood pot thick on the area, while larger containers will need spacing.

The following example shows how pot shape can affect numbers per area.

Example

Alpine plants pot thick in a frame 30 m (98 ft) × 1·5 m (4 ft 11 in).

1 Using 70 mm (2·5 in) square pots
70)1,500 = 21 pots along width of bed
70)30,000 = 428 pots along length of bed
= 8,988 pots per frame.

2 Using 90 mm (3.5 in) round pots (hold same volume of compost)
90)1,500 = 16 pots along width of bed
90)30,000 = 333 pots along length of bed
= 5,328 pots to frame.

With larger containers the pattern of spacing can either be on the square or triangle. Normally, to make maximum use of the area, a triangular spacing is the most suitable.

Clearing beds

Very little management of the bed should be needed until plants are cleared for sale. After removal of saleable plants, dead or unsaleable plants should be dumped; this now gives you the opportunity to prepare the bed for the next crop.

On sand beds there may be fungal spores in the sand and to control these the bed should be sprayed with captafol. At the same time there will have been a build-up of weeds, both germinated and dormant seed. Growing weeds can be controlled by using a contact herbicide, such as paraquat, while one can prevent new weed seeds germinating by spraying with chloroxuron.

If liquid feeding is the normal method of feeding nursery stock, then it is not uncommon for algae and, later, moss, lichen and liverwort to appear on matting. If these are allowed to establish they reduce capillarity and use valuable plant foods, as well as being unsightly. Some mats contain a fungicide and therefore the problem is avoided. With other mats one has to use an algaecide such as Empigen.

One problem with container growing is rooting through from the pot into the standing ground. With many species this can be overcome by using a quarternary ammonium chloride in sufficient water sprayed on to the standing ground prior to standing down. Depending on the product, the application rates will vary between 400 ml/

4·5 l water/10 m^2 (14 fl oz/1 gal water/100 sq ft), and 150 ml/4·5 l water/10 m^2 (5·5 fl oz/1 gal water/100 sq ft).

The beds will now be ready for the next crop and again should remain functional for the life of that crop with the minimum of management.

Overhead irrigation for standing grounds

Successful overhead irrigation of containerized plants depends on many factors, including the judgement and experience of the nurseryman. As there are so many elements to be considered, more and more nurserymen are changing over to subirrigation of container plants, which is far less wasteful of water. Many nurserymen realize that the cost of applying water to containerized plants is greater than the cost of fertilizers or electricity used throughout the production programme and therefore the most economical system of irrigation has to be chosen. During the summer up to 11 million litres (244,000 gal) of water can be used on 1 ha (2·5 acres) of container beds.

ADVANTAGES

There are some advantages of overhead irrigation, so we will consider these first. For instance, it is much easier to liquid feed container plants than with a subirrigation system. Also it is possible to quickly wash herbicides and liquid fertilizer off the foliage after application to prevent possible damage to the plants.

DISADVANTAGES

Unfortunately, there are also many disadvantages and problems with overhead irrigation systems on container-plant beds.

The biggest problem is wastage of water, for a large amount of water may never reach the crop. Water often falls between the plants and on to the pathways. It has been found that up to 80 per cent or more of water applied can go down the drain. Even with a reasonably good layout of rotary sprinklers, for every 454 litres (100 gal) put on 34 per cent could be lost instead of reaching the plants.

Overhead sprinklers can be troublesome, and they are subject to variable performance and distribution patterns, particularly in windy conditions. In a windy situation much of the water can be blown away, or lost through excessive evaporation. Sprinklers are poor at distributing water evenly owing to problems such as uneven water pressure in the mains supply and also within the irrigation system itself. Very often, if insufficient water is applied, the top layer of compost in the containers is saturated but the lower layers remain dry: water will not move downwards in the containers if insufficient has been applied. Very small doses of water may not even penetrate the surface of the compost. In addition, foliage can deflect a great deal of water so that it ends up between the plants instead of soaking into the compost.

Weeds are more of a problem with overhead irrigation owing to the surface of the compost being constantly moist (that is, if watering is carried out correctly). With subirrigation the surface of the compost tends to be dry and therefore fewer weeds germinate.

Unless the nurseryman keeps a constant eye on the containers, water may not always be available to the plants when needed. There is therefore often variable moisture status in the compost with overhead irrigation; there is also variable nutrient status and this is due to leaching of the nutrients. All this leads to loss of plant quality and a percentage of plant deaths. It also leads to a variable growth rate within batches of plants.

It has been found that constant wetting of foliage during high temperatures can encourage plant diseases such as *Pestalotiopsis* species (leaf spots) and *Botrytis*.

MANAGEMENT AND TYPES OF SYSTEM

Firstly, container beds which are to be irrigated overhead should be protected from wind by means of substantial windbreaks. These will help to reduce evaporation, and loss of water during application: considerably less will be blown away. The path to bed ratio should be carefully considered to minimize wastage, and a circular distribution pattern (rotary sprinklers) over a rectangular bed is very wasteful. Also, if the rotary sprinklers are not positioned correctly, one ends up with 'dry areas' in the corners and on other parts of the bed – so ensure that the sprinklers, placed in a line down the centre of the beds, are so positioned that the distribution pattern of each sprinkler overlaps those of the adjacent ones. Leave an adequate pathway down each sprinkler line for easy access. Ensure the distribution pattern of each sprinkler reaches the edges and ends of the beds.

An oscillating sprayline producing a rectangular distribution pattern is less wasteful of water. Such a line can often water several beds at once but beware of wide pathways between the beds, as these will result in wastage. If the site is windy we would suggest that if using rotary or oscillating sprinklers then coarser nozzles are fitted to produce large droplets which are less prone to drift.

Individual nozzle application is the least wasteful system but this is generally only used for watering larger trees in containers: for example, a tree in a 450 mm (18 in) square container could be given two nozzles. It is not a practical proposition to use this system of watering on large numbers of small containers. The system is popularly known as the 'spaghetti system' because of the thin lateral distributors or tubes spaced along the main supply pipe.

The number of drips per container will depend on the size of container, type of plant and location. For a drip system to work efficiently one will need a header and pressure gauge to control the flow of water to the containers. Because of the variability in setting driplines, it is recommended that you contact an irrigation specialist who will submit a quotation and system for your own requirements. Often irrigation companies will install the unit in the nursery to your requirements.

We have indicated that water is expensive, so use a system which is most economical and reduces wastage. Remember that on a large standing area 45,450 litres (10,000 gal) per day may well be needed.

Plant spacing on the bed has an effect on economical use of water. If 150 mm (6 in) diameter containers are spaced so that there is 38 mm (1·5 in) between the edges of each, then only 45 per cent of the bed area is occupied by the containers—therefore at least 55 per cent of the water applied is wasted between the containers.

The denser the crop cover, within reason, the less will be the water loss due to evaporation and wastage between the containers. It seems that 80 per cent crop cover on the beds should be the aim.

On a hot breezy day in summer 0·40 ha (1 acre) of plants could lose 27,724 litres (6,100 gal) of water through their leaves. If 29,542 litres (6,500 gal) of water were applied per 0·40 ha (1 acre), 25,907 litres (5,700 gal) of this could be wasted or lost. One would need to apply 68,175 litres (15,000 gal) per 0·40 ha to compensate for losses in the above weather conditions.

With overhead irrigation there must be a water-retentive base to further prevent water wastage (this will result in some capillary action). For example, one could use a 50 mm (2 in) deep layer of sand, which can hold 200,000 litres (16,000 gal) of water per 1 ha (2·5 acres); or capillary matting which can hold up to 60,000 litres (6,000 gal) per 1 ha (2·5 acres) depending on the type.

A few other points need to be considered to ensure efficient overhead irrigation. Keep the beds full of plants for maximum use of water, and do not let the compost become too dry (especially peat-based types) otherwise it will be difficult to wet right through again, and much water will simply run straight through the container due to a shrunken soil ball.

Overhead irrigation with hard water can substantially increase the compost pH level. Test water for alkalinity and permanent hardness before use. The level of hardness will give an indication of the effect of the water on the compost pH. This will determine whether or not a fertilizer with an acidifying effect should be used in a liquid-feed programme to counteract the rise in pH. For overhead irrigation it is suggested that less lime should be used when mixing compost if the total hardness of the water is greater than 250 ppm $Ca\ CO_3$.

Leaching of nutrients means that the full quota of base fertilizer must be used in the composts during mixing. (One can reduce the amount of base fertilizer when using a subirrigation system.) Also, a liquid-feeding programme will be necessary to compensate for loss of nutrients due to leaching.

24

Protected growing

Today the trend is to make increasing use of polythene or plastic-netting walk-in tunnels for the growing on of containerized plants. In recent years research has been carried out into the suitability of plastic and netting structures for various groups of plants. So we will discuss the advantages and disadvantages of each type of structure and finish with a list of plants and the best type of protection for them.

There are of course various reasons for protecting potted and containerized plants, the most important being to keep very young plants and rooted cuttings, etc., safe from inclement weather over the winter. Young shrubs and similar material are often very vulnerable to cold wet weather in the winter and many losses could occur unless protected. Wind protection is just as important, as a cold searing wind can desiccate such plant material. The usual practice is to move young plants from the propagating area into tunnels, once they have been acclimatized to the normal glasshouse atmosphere.

Another use for tunnels is to increase the growth rate of plants with a view to reducing production time. This works well for some plants but with others poor-quality specimens may result, especially under polythene tunnels.

POLYTHENE TUNNELS

Most growers now cover their tunnel structures with white polythene in 500 gauge, or 127 μm, and also choose a type with ultraviolet inhibitors for longer life. White polythene results in higher light-intensity within the structure—2–10 per cent—which is important in the winter. White also reduces plant scorch.

One should choose a sheltered site for plastic tunnels, as high winds and gales can result in severe damage to the polythene and possible distortion to the frame.

One of the disadvantages of polythene tunnels is the excessive amount of condensation. Growers in areas of high humidity, especially, should bear this in mind. Large droplets of condensate are formed on the inside and this can result in disease problems and reduced light intensity. It is now possible to obtain a material, which, if sprayed on the inside of the polythene, will disperse the large droplets so that they run down the side of the structure leaving a film of moisture on the inside of the polythene. It is said that this increases insulation and also light transmission, and the material certainly stops condensate dripping on to the plants and creating damp conditions.

Tunnels are not generally heated and therefore with some subjects there may be damping-off in cold wet weather – this applies especially to such plants as *Lavandula* and *Skimmia*. Tunnels are also a breeding ground for insects such as vine weevils and fungus gnats and therefore suitable control measures should be taken to avoid crop damage.

As there is minimal leaching of nutrients under polythene one generally experiences a rapid build-up of nitrates in the compost. This is also due to the higher temperature in the tunnels. Phosphate and potash depletion is also slower under polythene due to minimal leaching. It is generally recommended that slow-release fertilizers are reduced by half when growing under polythene, particularly during autumn or winter containerization. This is also very important if the plants are irrigated via sand beds, as opposed to overhead irrigation.

So what are the advantages of growing plants under plastic tunnels? We have already said that they provide winter protection (from rain, snow and wind) for rooted cuttings and other tender young plants, and there is no doubt that tunnels prevent many losses among young stock. Tunnels provide a controlled environment for containerized plants and result in faster growth. Quality is very often improved compared with growing on outdoor container beds, but we should say that most subjects should not spend their entire nursery life under tunnels as they can make excessive growth which is very soft and their natural habit can be ruined. It is therefore generally better to move container plants to outside beds (or remove the polythene) once they have had a suitable period under tunnels, before quality starts to deteriorate. Many months of production time can be saved by using this system.

Let us now consider the management of plants under polythene tunnels. For a start, watering is reduced by this form of protection. Capillary irrigation, using sand beds for instance, is a particularly suitable method of watering container plants under tunnels, or, alternatively overhead spray lines could be installed. At all costs do avoid overwatering plants in the winter otherwise excessively wet conditions will result in plant losses. Sand beds are generally drained off during the winter period. Adequate ventilation is important all the year round in order to avoid a very damp atmosphere which only leads to *Botrytis* and other fungal diseases building up.

It is essential to be very conscious of good hygiene, again to prevent *Botrytis* from infecting plants, so remove dead and dying plant material regularly and spray with benomyl if there is any sign of disease.

PLASTIC-NETTING TUNNELS

The trend today is to grow container plants under plastic-netting tunnels rather than under polythene. They have many advantages over polythene—for instance, there is better air flow but at the same time excellent wind protection. Shading is also provided, a factor particularly appreciated by many evergreens. Generally one achieves better-quality growth than under polythene as plants are not forced to the same extent and therefore there is not the problem of very soft growth.

The plants, especially conifers and variegated evergreens, have much better colour and habit, through affording extra protection without boosting or maintaining unnatural temperatures. Plants can therefore be grown to saleable stage under netting tunnels without fear of undesirable growth. It seems that netting tunnels have no disadvantages—there is one, however, as they are more expensive than polythene.

The netting for tunnels comes in various colours: white, green and black. It has been found that white netting is best for both summer and winter protection and that green and black result in darker conditions in the winter, which present difficulties in growing.

Management is less critical than under polythene although one should, of course, still pay careful attention to irrigation and hygiene. Plants under netting do not need the same amount of irrigation as plants in the open. A certain amount of rain will get through to them but the netting does deflect fairly light rain. Again capillary or overhead irrigation may be used.

PLANTS' RESPONSE TO POLYTHENE AND NETTING

Plants respond differently to protected cover and below we give a list of common subjects and their response to polythene and netting structures:

1 *Berberis:* best growth and colour comes from plants under netting; under polythene weaker growth is produced.
2 *Camellia:* more flower buds are produced under protection. Under polythene long straggly shoots can result over a prolonged period. Also *Oedema* can occur. Very good growth is produced under netting.
3 *Clematis:* both polythene and netting give excellent growth and considerably reduce the production time.
4 Conifers: best growth and colour under netting. Polythene results in a weaker habit and loss of colour.
5 *Cotoneaster:* types like *C. horizontalis* have been tested under both types of protection and it has been found that the growth form changes under polythene. Under the latter the habit is fan-shaped or flattish, excellent for wall-training, while under netting vigorous, more upright plants are produced.
6 *Elaeagnus:* netting is decidedly better, as the plants retain their natural colour and habit.
7 Heathers: continuous protection is undesirable as soft straggling growth results, plus pale colours. This applies especially to polythene.
8 *Hydrangea:* best shape and growth under netting. Softer and weaker growth results under polythene.
9 *Magnolia:* polythene gives very much increased growth but often the plants are too tall and of poor shape, therefore stopping may be needed. *Botrytis* damage can also be a problem under polythene. Limited growing under polythene, however, can be recommended. Netting ensures good steady growth.
10 *Potentilla:* protection of either type results in increased growth

and larger flowers, although the shoots will be soft under polythene.

11 *Pyracantha:* these shrubs are best under netting. Growth is, however, good under polythene but there is less branching.

25

Container management

In Chapter 21 we discussed the methods of feeding plants. In this chapter we will look at the other aspects of management required to produce high-quality nursery stock in containers.

Before standing down plants, the standing area and irrigation system should be prepared so that both will last for the life of the crop with minimum maintenance.

Modern growing media are light, often resulting in plants becoming top heavy and blowing over. Plants that have blown over need to be placed upright as soon as possible, an operation involving labour which could be used more productively, therefore wind blow should be minimized as much as possible.

A number of things can be done to reduce wind damage: firstly, when laying out the standing area, shelter belts, either natural or artificial, should be considered to reduce wind turbulence. Containers should never be allowed to dry out; besides putting the plant under tension, dryness also means the container is lighter and more prone to being blown over.

Some nurseries use plastic netting over the growing area, the plants being allowed to grow through the netting. When plants are moved the netting is simply cut away from around the plants.

Plants that need supporting in the pot are often caned, with the cane going through the base of the pot and into the standing ground.

Watering

Plants should be given the right amount of water immediately they require it. The frequency of watering will vary with the type of plant, growing media, type and size of container and location. Irrigation is basically supplementing rainfall and so there can be no basic guidelines, as each year's irrigation requirements can be different.

Plants that have the same water requirements should be placed together; as a rough guide, zerophytic plants, those adapted to growing in dry conditions, have narrow leaves, e.g. *Pinus*; hairy leaves, e.g. *Senecio* 'Sunshine' (syn. *greyi*); or firm leaves, e.g. *Hebe* species. All of these should be grouped together.

Weed control in containers

One of the most labour-intensive operations can be weed control in container plants. The most common weeds are hairy bitter cress, *Cardamine hirsuta*; willow, *Salix* species; groundsel, *Senecio vulgaris*; sowthistle, *Sonchus* species; willow herb, *Epilobium* species; and liverwort, *Marchantia polymorpha*.

Weeds can invade a container from numerous sources:

1 Wind-borne from outside the nursery.
2 Via the irrigation water.
3 From the headland.
4 From pathways.
5 From neighbouring plants.
6 From dirty plants at the potting stage.
7 From contaminated sand or growing media.
8 From the standing ground.
9 On workers' feet and clothing.

Weeds in containers compete for nutrients, causing a deterioration in plant quality, as well as making the plant look untidy and reducing its sales appeal. Prevention is better than control and whenever possible the nurseryman should aim at preventing weeds growing in the compost. The following points will help reduce the weed problem in containers, resulting in a saving in labour and money:

1 Keep peat and sand covered in the stack so that wind-borne weed seed cannot enter the heap. Also sterilize pots and loam.
2 Irrigation tanks should be kept covered and weeds controlled near abstraction points of ponds and streams.
3 Stock plants should be kept in a weed-free environment and no weeds allowed to come via propagation material.
4 A contact and residual herbicide must be used on the standing area before plants are stood out.
5 Remove weeds from containers before potting on.
6 Remove weeds from containers before they flower to keep seed dispersal to a minimum.

As it is not possible to prevent weeds entering the container from all outside sources some control is inevitable. The traditional method of control is hand weeding which is expensive, time consuming and laborious; the ease of weeding varies with genera and species of container plants.

It is often easier to weed under evergreen plants, as less weeds appear owing to the constant shading effect; the most difficult subjects to weed are prickly plants. When weeding, also remove dead plants; if left they become a source of future weed dispersal.

Residual chemicals have now been developed for use in container production. Chemicals must be applied at the correct rate when compost is moist and plants are turgid, otherwise damage can easily occur to plants grown in such a confined environment. The most widely used chemical is chloroxuron which has been used successfully for a number of years. The following is a guide to the use of this chemical.

1 Put the chemical on before weeds germinate. Wash off the foliage immediately afterwards. Repeat every six weeks. There should be no need for hand weeding and the cleaning up required before dispatch.
2 The following directions are recommended for the application of chloroxuron used at 4 kg/ha (2 lb a.i./acre):
 (a) By knapsack sprayer—14/15 litre (3·5 gal)
 28 g (2·25 oz) chloroxuron per 13·5 litres (3 gal) water over 60 m^2 of containers.
 (b) By watering can—6·5 litre (1·5 gal)
 9 g (0·75 oz) chloroxuron per 6·5 litres (1·5 gal) water over 20 m^2 of containers.

Chloroxuron can easily damage plants if not washed off the foliage immediately after spraying. Not all plants are resistant to the chemical and it is recommended that you should not use chloroxuron on the following plants:

Azalea 'Addy Werry'
Berberis gagnepainii
B. × *ottawensis* 'Superba'
B. thunbergii atropurpurea
B. thunbergii 'Erecta'
B. thunbergii 'Rose Glow'
Buddleia 'Border Beauty'
Cotoneaster adpressus praecox
C. conspicuus 'Decorus'
C. 'Coral Beauty'
C. franchetii
C. horizontalis
C. salicifolius 'Autumn Fire'
Deutzia 'Mont Rose'

D. × *rosea*
D. 'Rose Carmine'
Erica carnea 'Aurea'
E. cinerea 'Golden Drop'
Escallonia 'C.F. Ball'
E. 'Donard Seedling'
Forsythia × *intermedia* 'Spectabilis'
F. 'Lynwood'
Hydrangea
Lonicera fragrantissima
L. nitida 'Baggessen's Gold'
Osmarea 'Burkwoodii'
Pernettya mucronata
Philadelphus × *lemoinei*
P. microphyllus
Pieris 'Forest Flame'
Rhododendron 'Mother of Pearl', 'Mrs. R. S. Holford', 'Pink Pearl', 'Rosamundii', 'White Swan', 'Windlesham Scarlet'
Salix gillotii
Senecio 'Sunshine' (syn. *Senecio greyi*)
Spiraea 'Gold Flame'
S. thunbergii
Stranvaesia davidiana
Syringa cvs.
Thuja orientalis 'Aurea Nana'
Viburnum × *bodnantense* 'Dawn'
Weigela florida 'Variegata'

This list is not complete but covers the main genera which have proved susceptible to chloroxuron.

Simazine, another residual herbicide, can also be used on container-grown plants, although a wide range of plants are sensitive to the chemical resulting in severe damage or even death. It is recommended that one applies simazine at 28 g (1 oz) of commercial product in 27 litres (6 gal) of water over 300 m^2 (1,000 sq ft) of containers. Spraying should be repeated every 6–15 weeks, although the effective period of control will depend on the local weed population, season and the type of watering system.

The trees and shrubs that are sensitive to simazine are as follows:

Acer japonicum
A. negundo
A. palmatum
Aesculus
Aucuba japonica 'Variegata'
Berberis media
B. × *ottawensis*
B. × *stenophylla*
Betula pendula
Buddleia davidii 'Royal Red'
Buxus
Calluna vulgaris 'Gold Haze'
Caragana
Cercis
Chaenomeles japonica
Chimonanthus
Choisya
Cistus × *obtusifolius*
Clerodendrum
Cornus alba 'Spaethii'

C. mas 'Aurea'
Corylopsis
Corylus
Cotoneaster 'Cornubia'
C. franchetii
C. salicifolius 'Autumn Fire'
Daboecia
Deutzia
Elaeagnus × ebbingei
Erica carnea 'Springwood White'
Euonymus
Exochorda giraldii
E. korolkowii
Forsythia
Fothergilla
Fraxinus
Fuchsia
Halesia
Hebe 'Autumn Glory'
H. 'Midsummer Beauty'
H. rotundifolia
Hibiscus
Hoheria
Hydrangea
Hypericum elatum
H. henryi
H. patulum
Ilex aquifolium
Indigofera
Kerria
Kolwitzia
Laburnum
Lavandula
Leycesteria
Ligustrum
Lithosperum
Lonicera
Morus
Olearia
Philadelphus
Physocarpus
Picea pungens 'Glauca'
Pieris
Pinus mugo
Poncirus
Prunus
Pterostyrax
Robinia
Sambucus
Santolina chamaecyparissus
Senecio 'Sunshine' (syn. *Senecio greyi*)
Spiraea 'Anthony Waterer'
S. arguta
S. trilobata
Syringa
Tilia
Viburnum
Weigela

Mulching

Mulching can be used on weed-free composts to control weeds. More labour is required for this type of weed control than using herbicides, although one avoids the problem of sensitive plants being damaged. Various types of material have been tried for mulching but the ones most commonly used are as follows:

1 Sand/grit as a top dressing will inhibit moss growth on top of the container.

2 Peat and simazine to a depth of 25 mm (1 in). Normally sphagnum peat is used with 2 per cent simazine granules at a rate of 42 g (1·5 oz) of simazine per 36 litres (bushel) of peat.
3 Plastic dishes are now being produced which will fit around the plant and prevent weed-seed entry, although these may also prevent overhead irrigation water getting into the container.

Trimming and pruning

The nurseryman should have control over the type of product he wishes to produce. Some plants will grow naturally into the type of product required for sale, while others will need pruning to produce a good-quality plant. Pruning should encourage plants to become bushy and more compact and can be carried out by one of two methods:

1 Shearing: this is where the whole plant is cut back, using a pair of garden shears. New growth should then appear uniformly all over the plant. This type of pruning can be carried out on subjects such as *Buxus sempervirens*, *Lonicera nitida* and dense-growing conifers.
2 Pruning: normal pruning is where selective cutting of branches takes place to keep the plant in shape. This is generally done with secateurs or a pruning knife. Pruning must be to a node to encourage a healthy bushy plant. Plants which can be thus treated include broad-leaved evergreens and most deciduous plants.

Pruning and trimming should be started at the liner stage and followed through until sale.

Winter protection

As mentioned earlier, once a plant is taken out of its normal situation and planted in a container another factor becomes involved: extremes in root temperature. In warm climates plants are often placed in white containers in an attempt to reflect the heat and thereby keep the roots cooler. In colder areas the reverse occurs and root protection in the winter becomes of prime importance.

Winter injury to plants will vary according to the cold hardiness of the species, each species having different requirements. Normally, when mentioning cold hardiness we think of the coldest days in winter, but we must emphasize that a lot of plant damage occurs in the spring when the plants have started growing before a late cold spell.

Plants develop hardiness in the autumn due to the environmental changes of shorter days and lower temperatures. The effect of this is to stop terminal growth and to influence hormones in the plant to induce hardiness. The grower can help in this by reducing the irrigation and fertilizer programme during late summer and autumn. Soft growth will soon be damaged in the first autumn frosts.

Plants therefore need acclimatizing before winter or entering cold storage and the following guide is suggested:

1 Reduce the amount of nitrogen received by as much as half during the autumn.
2 Double the amount of potash given to the plants from mid-August (both these factors will slow down growth and induce hardiness).
3 Reduce the amount of irrigation to the plants from late August.

METHODS OF PROTECTION

In recent years a number of methods of winter protection have been tried, both in Europe and the USA. The following have been used successfully by nurserymen.

1 Protection under polythene structures: various types of structure are in use for the purpose of protecting plants during the winter. During daytime light hits the polythene; some of it is reflected and some is absorbed and transformed into heat energy, which is trapped as the polythene impedes radiation of this heat to the outside. During the night the heat 'stored' within objects in the tunnel acts as a buffer to the outside low temperatures and therefore gives the plant some protection.

   Plants should be allowed to acclimatize before being covered with polythene to ensure they are hardy. Ventilation of the house during the winter should be minimal and only practised if warm sunny days occur.
2 Polythene blankets: this is the simple operation of draping polythene over the container plants when cold weather is imminent. The blanket should be secured around the edges to create an air-tight seal. Plants must be watered before the blanket is used and removal of the blanket should not occur until warmer weather arrives. One disadvantage of this method is that while a warm environment is created, and this protects

the plants, it also attracts rodents, and traps may have to be placed under the blanket.

3 Microfoam: microfoam or white styrofoam has been used by a few growers. It will transmit 50 per cent of available light, although it deteriorates in direct sunlight. The material can be supplied in rolls which can be rolled out like a polythene blanket.

Winter protection of container-grown nursery stock in the British Isles is limited. One of the main reasons for this is that the expansion in container production has been fairly recent and has taken place in a period of mild winters. When a severe winter does occur we need to be prepared to give the more tender plants some means of protection as is the case in Scandinavia and parts of the USA.

Selling container plants

The important requirement at sale is quality, the standard varying according to the outlet. The landscaper may accept a good-quality plant that has an uneven shape, while a garden-centre operator requires the same quality in an evenly shaped plant. Plants should not be sold with roots breaking through the base of the container; this is often an indication that the plants need moving to a larger container. At sale, plants should be labelled, preferably with the full botanical name, making sure the details are correct and legible.

26

Container tree production

The transplanting of large standard trees can present a number of difficulties and this has resulted in the development of container-grown trees. The advantages of container-grown trees are:

1 More successful establishment, especially on difficult sites, due to the root system being retained intact and therefore undisturbed at planting.
2 Planting operations can be carried out all the year round, an important consideration with, for example, landscape contractors.
3 Prestige projects can have impact with 'instant' trees in summer.
4 The handling of trees is easier in the sense that they can be stored for longer periods without deterioration.

One initial disadvantage with container trees is that the capital outlay to start such a project is high, compared with field-grown trees where the major expense occurs at the end of the crop in the lifting.

The market for container trees can be divided into two categories. The professional market requires advanced nursery stock, and producing trees for such outlets in containers is highly specialized. The normal practice is to plant field-grown standard trees in containers and for these plants to be grown on for a further two years in the containers. Obviously this involves extra costs and trees often sell for at least 100 per cent above the price asked for similar field-grown trees.

The alternative is the retail market, normally through garden centres. The customer here requires a smaller convenience tree, normally an ornamental species and of a size which will fit in the average car.

Growing area

Standing grounds for large trees need to be well protected from wind, as this will result in less money being spent on picking up trees which have been blown over and also on tree supporting. Various supporting systems have been developed for trees, but the conventional post and wire system is the one most commonly used. This is erected by inserting stakes, at intervals, along the proposed run of plants, then either one or two strands of wire are nailed along the line. If two are used then one runs along the top of the stake and one half way down. Trees are then tied in to this wire, care being taken to ensure the wire does not cut into the expanding trunk.

Containers and composts

Containers vary in type from Weldmesh crates with liners to bonded, polythene-lined, bituminized-fibre containers. It is important that the container lasts the life of the crop and is large enough to give ample root development. Sizes readily available are:

400 mm (15·5 in) (dia.) × 275 mm (10·75 in), 18 litres (0·6 cu ft)
600 mm (23·5 in) (dia.) × 400 mm (15.50 in), 45 litres (1·58 cu ft)

Depth of pot is just as important as diameter, as trees are deep-rooted subjects and a deep root run will reduce root problems once the tree leaves the nursery. Containers are also available as rounds or squares. Trees of this size are often mechanically planted using a post-hole borer which produces a round hole, therefore, a round root ball is preferable. Further developments now include degradable peat-based containers which can be planted along with the tree and which disintegrate in the planting situation.

Composts for tree production have been developed by various nurseries, each having their own blends. Basically the growing media is the same as for conventional container production, except that a long-lasting fertilizer is recommended. It must be stressed that large volumes of compost are required to fill containers; in fact one cubic metre (one cubic yard) of growing media will fill only about 20 containers of 45 litre (1·58 cu ft) size.

Potting

Owing to the large amount and weight of compost used the normal procedure for potting is difficult, and therefore a more efficient system has to be developed. Below is one such example; with this system the operators work around the heap of growing media. The first operator shovels compost into the containers; he is then followed by a second who places the trees in the containers and then a third person tops up the containers. Even with this system a three-man team cannot be expected to pot any more than 60 of the 45 litre (1·58 cu ft) pots during one hour's work.

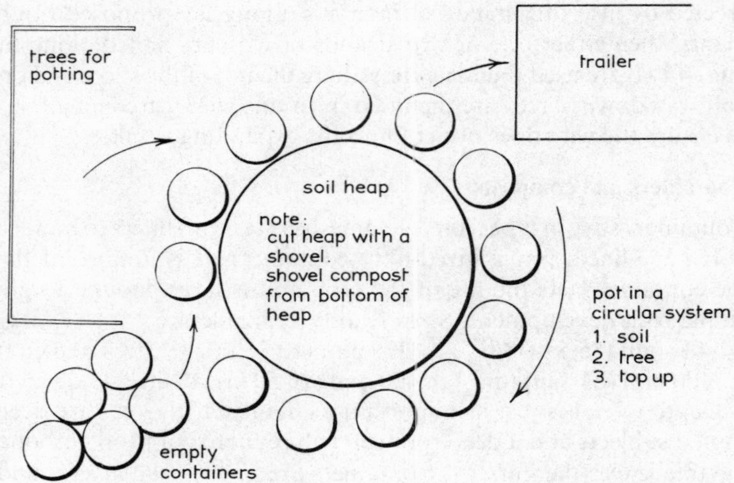

Fig. 53 Potting trees in large containers

Spacing of containers

A grower requires the maximum number of plants per given area with the minimum sacrifice in quality. Closely spaced containers often result in leggy plants with sparse foliage, whereas what is really required is a tapered trunk, a well-branched head and plenty of foliage to promote maximum growth. The following minimum spacing is recommended for container trees that are actively growing, where the pot diameter is 600 mm (23·5 in).

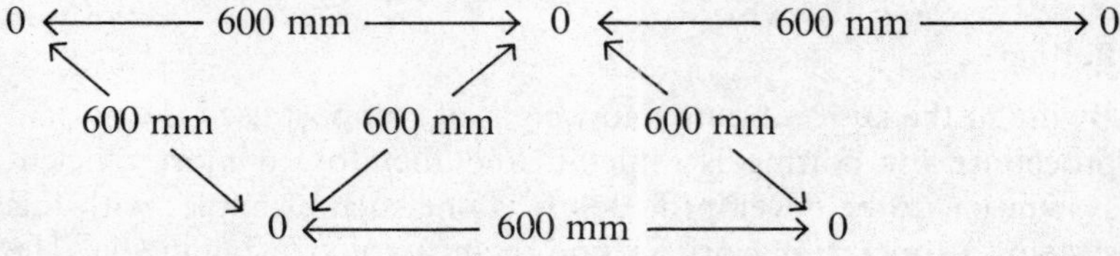

During the winter when growth has ceased, the containers can be moved closer together to reduce damage by wind and, if stood pot thick, root damage due to pot freezing will be reduced.

Growing on

The major variation, compared with conventional container production, is the application of water. Water costs are constantly rising and therefore an efficient method of irrigation must be adopted. Overhead irrigation lacks efficiency as water is wasted on paths and standing areas, and the waste is increased by the umbrella effect of trees in foliage shedding water into the standing area. Wind can also distort the spray pattern, and extra cost is involved if pipes have to be regularly moved.

The alternative method is to use a drip system, a method where water is applied direct to the container by individual nozzles placed in the pot. Careful positioning of the nozzle is important. It should be placed in the centre of the pot as spraylines are constructed of plastic, which means that expansion and contraction due to weather changes can be as much as 2 per cent; this could result in nozzles moving out of the container.

In large containers the recommended flow rate is 2–5 litres (0·5–1 gal) of water per hour to each container, although this varies with season and weather conditions.

Weed control and feeding of container trees follow the same principles as for normal container production (see Chapter 25). For information on tree training see Chapter 30.

Handling

At the beginning of this chapter we mentioned that one of the advantages of container growing was that handling was easier in the sense that plants can be stored for longer periods. It must be stressed that an efficient handling system must be devised to make this method of tree production viable. A 600 mm (23·5 in) × 400 mm (15·5 in) container plus a tree will weigh at least 44 kg (97 lb) when dry and up to 63 kg (139 lb) when the compost is moist. Various methods have been devised to handle this large weight and they include the use of pallets, on which the containers are stood, specially devised fork lifts or simply designing the standing area so that trees can be rolled to collecting points.

Trees produced for the professional market are normally sold with a 600 mm (23·5 in) diameter, fibrous root system and with a stem girth at 1 m (3 ft 3 in) above ground level of between 100 mm

(3·9 in) and 160 mm (6 in). The time factor governing production will alter with plant species; for example an *Alnus cordata* will grow a lot faster than *Quercus ilex* and careful forward planning is therefore needed to obtain what is necessary at the desired time.

Trees that prefer container growing

We have mentioned container growing as an alternative to field production; this is not always the case as some species will grow far better in a container than in the field. The reasons for this vary between species, but normally it is owing to the fact that they need more protection, especially in winter, and more control generally because of their more tender natures.

Plants that fall into this group include: *Catalpa* species; *Juglans* species; *Liquidambar styraciflua*; *Liriodendron tulipifera*; *Quercus ilex*.

Alternative growing methods

The main advantage of container trees to landscape contractors is the safe extension of the planting season. This is especially important to firms which are landscaping around large buildings and have a contract to complete as soon as possible. A number of growers, using slightly different methods, have moved away from the conventional container to achieve the same aims.

A method seen in Europe and in the UK has been to plant the tree, in the container, in the ground. Containers are formed of 4·5 μm (19 gauge) wire lined with 127 μm (500 gauge) black polythene on the sides to encourage root growth within the container; it is important to leave the bottom of the container unlined to allow for drainage. Thick polypropylene string can be threaded through the wire to form handles to assist with lifting. Holes for the container can be dug out by the use of a post-hole borer. Growing is then similar to the normal system for container-grown trees. Lifting of such trees can be mechanized by attaching the strings to the hydraulic lift on the back of a tractor. Contractors can then purchase trees as field grown with an undisturbed root system.

Container tree production is a specialized, small market which is not likely to increase in size, owing to the high production costs incurred. Trees in containers do have a use in landscaping, but only on prime sites or where finance is not a limiting factor.

Part 5

CROP PRODUCTION IN THE FIELD

27

From soil management to planting

In Part 5 we deal with the production of hardy nursery stock in the field. To produce quality crops, a soil that is in good heart and that is well drained should be chosen. We have given some guidance on this matter in Chapter 1 and readers should therefore refer to that information which will be found in the section on soils.

Perennial weed control

Before growing a crop of trees, shrubs, or other plants the land should be as free from perennial weeds as possible. Most nurserymen would agree that it is virtually impossible to completely eradicate all perennial weeds from a field, but great improvements can be achieved by the use of suitable herbicides before any cultivations take place. These can be applied in the late summer or autumn prior to planting in the spring.

There are many herbicides which are suitable for perennial weed control in fallow land, such as aminotriazole, which will kill most perennials including couch grass. A more recent chemical is glyphosate, which is very good and gives better control of couch and other perennial grasses. It is also particularly effective on bindweed and thistle, and should be applied in the autumn.

Sterilizing

Sterilizing land with a soil sterilant is often practised by growers of hardy nursery stock, particularly in areas where the soil-borne disease *Phytophthora* is a problem. As well as controlling many soil pests and diseases, both weed seeds in the soil and existing weeds are also killed so that there is far less trouble from weed seedlings in the crop or on seed beds.

Dazomet is the most commonly used soil sterilant, applied as prilled granules which break down in moist soil to form methyl isothyocyanate, an effective sterilant gas. The granules should be applied evenly to moist soil at a suitable rate for the soil type. Application rates are given on the container. The best time of year for application is between April and December. The granules are incorporated in the soil to a depth of 150–200 mm (6–8 in) by use of a rotary cultivator. The soil surface should then be sealed by laying polythene sheeting over it, by flooding to 'cap' the surface, or by rolling.

Complete sterilization will take 5–6 weeks if the soil temperature is in excess of 7 °C (45 °F), at a depth of 150 mm (6 in), but 8–12 weeks if the soil temperature is from 2 to 7 °C (36 to 45 °F), as the gas is less volatile at lower temperatures.

After treatment the soil should be cultivated to ensure all remaining gas is released. Do not cultivate deeper than the initial depth of incorporation and check soil samples by means of a cress test prior to planting or sowing, to ensure that it is safe to introduce plant material.

Drainage

One should endeavour to choose a well-drained site for field-grown crops as it is cost-prohibitive to install a drainage system on a large scale. Perforated-plastic drainage pipes are certainly cheaper than conventional tile drains but even with these the drainage system will be far from cheap. One can also have problems with perforated-plastic pipes as they are inclined to silt up, especially on light sandy or silty soils. In some areas ochre is the problem, causing the perforations to become blocked, especially in sandy localities.

Various cultural operations can improve drainage if the site is inclined to be wet. For instance, using a subsoiler, either tractor mounted or winched through the soil, will break up hard iron or cultivation pans in the lower layers of soil, which would otherwise result in waterlogged conditions. Do not carry out subsoiling when the soil is wet as the subsoiler will simply slide through the soil with no effect whatsoever.

If used when the soil is dry, the subsoiler will shatter the hard pan and thereby improve the drainage of excess water.

Organic matter incorporated in the soil will also help to improve drainage, especially on heavy soil types. Organic matter will 'open' them up so that surplus water drains away to the lower layers. Suitable forms of organic matter are discussed in the section on manuring later in this chapter.

Ploughing

Ploughing or turning over the soil is generally carried out after subsoiling, the best time being in the autumn prior to spring planting or sowing. This allows time for frost and snow to have their effect on the soil, so that spring cultivations can be easily carried out. Creating a good planting or sowing tilth in the spring is much easier if the soil has been well weathered over the winter.

If you intend incorporating organic matter, this should be spread over the field before ploughing so that it can be turned in by the plough. On no account use the plough if the ground is very wet, as the soil structure will be damaged. Soil which is moderately moist, not bone-dry and hard, is in the ideal state for ploughing.

Ploughing depths vary from 300 to 450 mm (12 to 18 in) and we would suggest for hardy nursery stock that one ploughs to the maximum depth to ensure deep root penetration, which is particularly important if good-quality trees are to be grown. Ideally the ploughing depth should be varied from year to year to avoid a cultivation pan forming in the lower soil.

This seems an ideal place to mention rotary cultivators which are often used as an alternative to ploughing. There are pedestrian-operated, self-propelled machines available for small-scale work, or tractor-mounted machines driven by the tractor p.t.o. for large areas. The latter can turn over the soil to a good depth but the pedestrian-operated machines will only penetrate to a depth of 150–200 mm (6–8 in). In our opinion, rotary cultivators are often used indiscriminately. These machines can result in a 'fluffy' texture, which if left can turn into a quagmire after rain. The soil structure can be damaged by over-cultivation with a rotary cultivator and also a hard cultivation pan can develop by cultivating to the same depth year after year. It is far better to initially turn over the soil by ploughing, and then perhaps use a rotary cultivator to obtain a fine tilth just prior to sowing or planting. Again, never use these machines when the ground is very wet as the soil structure will be ruined. It is also very difficult to rotovate very dry hard soil – the blades will just bounce off the surface. And remember not to leave the soil in a light 'fluffy' condition for too long after rotovating as it could be impossible to get on the land after a heavy shower of rain. On some soils rolling can be carried out to overcome 'fluffiness'.

Manuring

It is necessary to maintain a high level of organic matter in the soil and therefore the land should be manured before a crop is grown. It should be applied in the autumn and ploughed in. Organic matter supplies the soil with humus, which is vital for maintaining a high population of beneficial bacteria. It is these bacteria that convert fertilizers into nutrients which can be absorbed by plant roots. Organic matter is especially useful on light well-drained soils as it can act as a sponge and help to retain soil moisture during dry weather. Organic matter can help to 'open up' heavy soils and therefore improve the drainage of surplus water. Nutrients can also be supplied by organic matter, but the amounts and types depend very much on the type of material used.

Light sandy soils generally need far heavier applications of organic matter than the heavier soil types as they are unable to hold on to the material. If 75 tonnes of farmyard manure is applied per hectare (30 tons per acre) the organic-matter content is increased by 0·5–1·5 per cent but most is lost due to natural breakdown. In the first year 75 tonnes will provide approximately 90 units of nitrogen, 120 units of phosphorous and 225 units of potash. Very often one applies heavier applications than this—in the region of 125 tonnes per hectare (50 tons per acre), especially on very light poor soils.

There is no doubt that farmyard manure is the best type of organic matter to apply, but other materials are also suitable. For instance, spent hops are often used and these have a higher nitrogen content than farmyard manure but a lower potash content. The moisture content is around 75 per cent. Poultry manure, if available, is a very good form of organic matter. It is variable in nutrients as shown below:

Deep litter manure:	31 % moisture 1·7 % nitrogen 1·8 % phosphorous 1·3 % potash	average %
Battery hens manure:	71 % moisture 1·7 % nitrogen 1·4 % phosphorous 0·7 % potash	average %

Peat is a good source of organic matter but is very low in nutrients, e.g., 0·7 % nitrogen, 0·1 % phosphorous and 0·2 % potash. It would be cheaper to buy coarse sedge peat in bulk for field work.

Green manuring, by means of a short summer catch-crop ley, is a useful way to increase the content of organic matter in the soil if the land is laying fallow for the summer. Sow mustard at the rate of 23 kg/ha (20·4 lb/acre) and plough in the crop during the autumn.

Cultivating

In soil preparation a cultivator 'follows the plough', and is used to break up the furrows and create a surface tilth. Cultivating is part of final soil preparation and is carried out in the spring prior to planting or sowing. Tines are drawn through the soil to break it up: they have a 'shattering' and stirring effect on the soil. Cultivators are available in various types and are tractor mounted.

1 Rigid-tine cultivators: these can cultivate up to a depth of 600 mm (2 ft) and are very widely used. As the name suggests, the tines are rigidly fixed and do not move in any way. They are just pulled through the soil.
2 Spring-loaded tine cultivators: the tines, although rigid in themselves, are held by strong springs and are therefore able to pass over objects like stones without any fear of damage. This type of cultivator is therefore very useful on stony or flinty soils. The depth of penetration is limited to 250–300 mm (9–12 in).
3 Spring-tine cultivators. In these, the tines are made of spring steel and they vibrate as they are drawn through the soil, shattering the clods and lumps—a pulverizing action.

Harrowing

The harrow normally follows the cultivator and it is used where a very fine soil surface is needed, for example in seed-bed preparation or for machine planting. The harrow can also be used to incorporate a fertilizer dressing. Harrows have small tines which break down the soil and the working depth is approximately 150 mm (6 in). Rigid or spring tines are available and of course the harrow is tractor mounted.

Disc harrows are an alternative to cultivators where there is a lot of surface rubbish. This does not often apply to the nursery producing crops like trees and shrubs. The disc harrow has a set of rotating discs which cut into the soil.

Levelling

To achieve uniform machine planting the surface of the soil needs to be level—free from hollows and bumps. To ensure this, a land-leveller can be drawn over the soil. It consists of a series of steel bars on a framework and is pulled over the soil by tractor.

Fertilizers

During final cultivations prior to planting, it is generally necessary to apply fertilizer to encourage optimum growth. The usual approach is to apply a compound, slow-release fertilizer according to the maker's instructions, to provide all the major and trace elements. This is generally satisfactory but it could be that some nutrients are not in fact required, or maybe the compound fertilizer is not supplying enough of some particular nutrient. In fact, this approach is very hit and miss and could result in unsatisfactory plant growth.

It is far better to carry out a soil test to ascertain which nutrients are required and in what amounts. Table 13 indicates fertilizer requirements for field-grown nursery stock and it is based on the nutrient index obtained by means of a soil test. The nutrient index applies to phosphorous, potash and magnesium. With nitrogen, it simply recommends an application of 50–150 kg/ha. Note that an application of fertilizer will be needed before planting, plus annual applications by means of a top dressing, again after carrying out a soil test. Advice can also be sought through advisory services or commercial laboratories.

It is recommended that fertilizers, whether applied before or after planting, are incorporated into the soil surface as then they are made more quickly available to the plants.

Lime may be needed to provide calcium, which is a major nutrient, not just used to adjust pH. The ideal pH for the general run of hardy nursery stock is 6·0–6·6. Ericaceous plants and other lime haters need a pH of 5·0–5·5. Again lime requirements can only be ascertained by means of a soil test. Indiscriminate use of lime can raise the pH to an unacceptable level. In a very alkaline soil many plants, such as roses, soft fruits and other shrubs, will suffer from lime-induced chlorosis—yellowing leaves and poor stunted growth. If you have a naturally acid soil, say in the region of pH 5·0–5·5, we would suggest it is left that way rather than raise the pH by liming, as then you will be able to grow a much wider range of plant material. The general run of hardy nursery stock will be quite all right

Table 13 Recommendation for fertilizer requirements in field-grown nursery stock (recommended rates for nutrients per annum in kg/ha)

Nutrient Index	N	P						K					Mg			
		0	1	2	3	4	Over 4	0	1	2	3	Over 3	0	1	2	Over 2
	kg N	kg P_2O_5						kg K_2O					kg Mg			
Before planting	50–150	100	75	50	25	0	0	200	150	100	50	0	75	50	25	0
After planting	50–150	50	25	0	0	0	0	100	50	25	0	0	25	0	0	0

in acid conditions, and will make quite acceptable growth, provided the pH is not excessively low, say in the region of 3 or 4.

Rotations and leys

Ideally land should be rested after a crop of trees, shrubs, roses, or other nursery stock, and this means having sufficient land to lay fields fallow – or ideally putting them down to grass leys. By rotating crops you will prevent a build-up of pests and diseases in the soil and will overcome the problem of replant diseases, which are particularly troublesome with roses and many fruits. Land should be rested for a minimum of one year and preferably much more than this. Never plant the same crop on the same piece of land more than once in every six or seven years if this can be avoided. We realize of course this is out of the question with many small nurserymen. The alternative is to sterilize soil if rotations are not possible, using dazomet as discussed earlier in this chapter.

There is no doubt that grass leys help to improve the soil structure and increase the content of organic matter in the soil. A suitable seed mixture for a grass ley is as follows:

9 kg (20 lb) Italian ryegrass
9 kg (20 lb) perennial ryegrass
4·5 kg (10 lb) late-flowering clover
2·25 kg (5 lb) white clover
} per hectare (2·5 acres)

The grass should be cut regularly during the mowing season with a flail mower. Before planting, the ley can be burned off with paraquat and then the field should be subsoiled. An application of farmyard manure should be given, at the rate of 125 tonnes/ha (50 tons/acre) and this can be ploughed in to a depth of approximately 300 mm (1 ft).

Inter-row cultivations

Finally a few words on inter-row cultivations for weed control as an alternative to the use of herbicides. Row crop cultivators, which are tractor mounted, are available and hoe blades cultivate the soil between growing crops. They can work very close to plants, provided the tractor is in the hands of a skilled driver! Such cultivation is best done when the soil is dry on the surface, as then there is no risk of damaging the soil structure, and of course the weeds very quickly dry up and die. So choose a warm day, preferably with a breeze blowing, for this type of work. It is of course advisable to cultivate before any weeds set seed.

PLANT ARRANGEMENT AND SPACING

The spacing of plants in the field is governed by two factors, the physiology of the plant and the management of the crop.

The physiology of the plant affects the scale of planting. Research has shown that in some tree-species, trunk caliper and taper increases, as does weight of root and branches, as scale of planting decreases, although increase in height and weight of trunk occurs. At close planting the lower foliage of trees becomes sparse, the tree takes on a leggy appearance and, apart from the trunk, weight decreases, although this effect will vary with species.

The reason for these differences was originally thought to be due to the variation in light-intensity which occurs between close and wide spacing. It is now believed that reduced movement in the region of shoot development, due to closer spacing, produces elongation in closely spaced trees.

As indicated, the scale of planting can change the habit of the plant and in some species also changes the maturity process (juvenile to adult). At close spacing uniformity increases, but a decrease in relative uniformity occurs by a self-thinning process. Whatever scale of planting is selected a ceiling will be reached where the species concerned will not grow any more due to the limitation of radiation.

The second factor in spacing is a managerial decision which decides the pattern of planting. The aim of any planting pattern should be to standardize and so reduce costs, as time can be saved by reducing time taken for changing implements or tractors.

One should aim at making maximum use of space, water, light and nutrients with minimum deterioration in quality. The ideal spacing should give the maximum number of plants to a given area with the correct quality, maximum uniformity, reduced outside competition and best use of machinery and labour.

Seedling rootstock production

To illustrate the thinking behind organizing the plant layout we can use seedling rootstock production as an example. The optimum

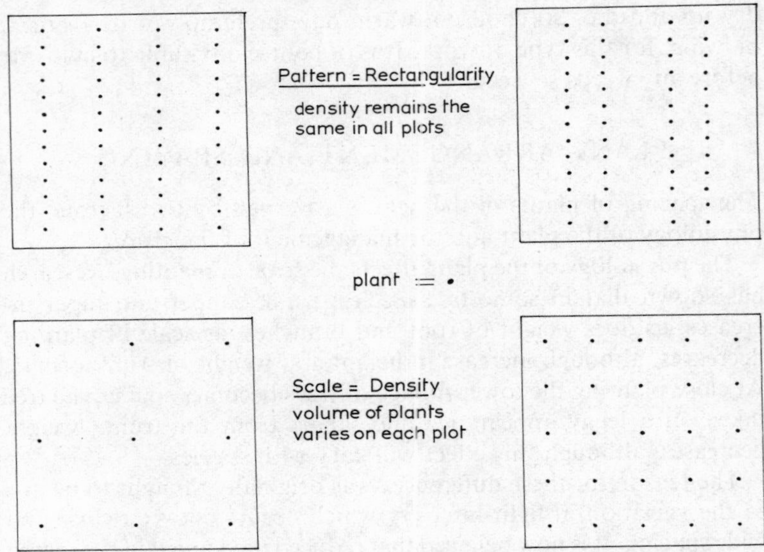

Fig. 54 Plant arrangement and spacing

plant density will give the correct quality and, therefore, the maximum economic returns. We already know that the fewer seedlings to a given area then the larger the increase in collar girth. This being the important measurement of quality in seedling rootstocks, if we crowd the seedlings together then collar girth will be between 2–6 mm (0·07–0·2 in) while wider spacing will encourage girths between 6–10 mm (0·2–0·3 in). A larger diameter can mean twice the financial returns for a given number of rootstocks.

The problem occurs in finding the optimum spacing and on how to implement it once found.

Growing trees and shrubs on the bed system

Once the scale of planting has been decided, a grower can then decide on the most efficient method of managing the crop. Standardization of planting arrangements and machinery will result in reduced costs and a more efficient holding. One method of reducing costs is to grow plants on the bed system.

This method of growing was developed in the 1930s on the 'muck' lands of Long Island, USA, for vegetable production.

Eventually the idea was taken up by the British vegetable producers and the system is now used on a wide range of vegetable crops and nursery stock.

A bed is a strip of land for growing a crop, over which a tractor can straddle to facilitate mechanization of crop management.

LAND PREPARATION

Ploughing should be done with a one-way plough and the land worked along a straight base line. It is important that all cultivation equipment, such as discs, harrows and rollers, should be matched to fit the width of the bed and be mounted on the tractor so that they work within the width of the tractor wheels. Final bed preparation should include fertilizer incorporation by a cultivator, tine harrow or a combined piece of equipment.

PLANTING

Row spacing within the beds can either be on a four, three or two row system; for shrubs and conifers a four or three row system can be easily maintained; for tree production a two row system is preferred, the reason for this being the difficulty of straddling standard trees with an overhead tractor; with two rows the vineyard tractor can be used and pass down between trees.

Some nurseries have planted trees and shrubs in alternate beds and this means that when the trees become too tall to drive over it is still possible to work on them from the side by passing over the shrub bed.

CROP MANAGEMENT

All crop operations should be carried out on the tractor. Top dressing and crop spraying can be done on a multiple of beds using boom sprayers, if this type of equipment is available. It is advisable that plant rows are kept straight, otherwise damage is likely to occur when using tractor-mounted equipment.

When using a bed system it is important that equipment used can be hitched to a tractor, and unhitched, quickly and efficiently. To achieve this, a coupling consisting of a triangle on the tractor and a similar triangle on the implements must be used. When coupling up, the two triangles slide into each other to form a perfect, simple and safe connection. By simply adjusting the top link, the equipment can be hitched very quickly.

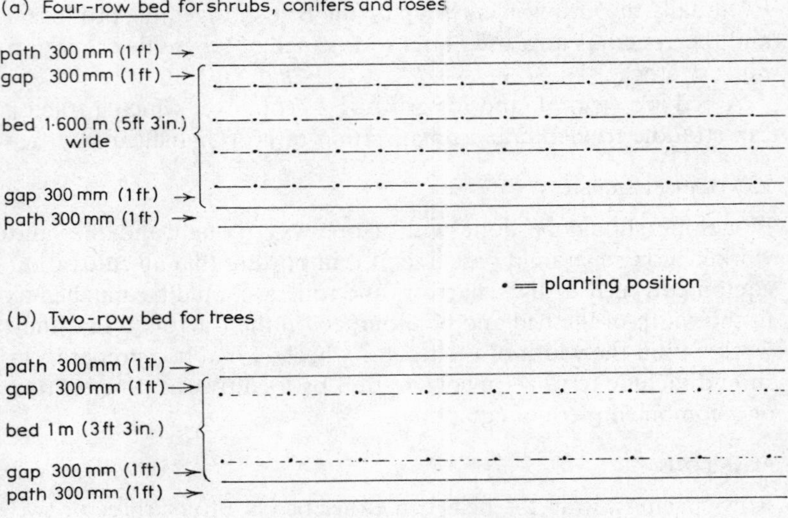

Fig. 55 Examples of suggested bed systems

PLANTING

Historically, labour has usually been cheap to employ in large numbers and this resulted in hand planting of nursery stock. However, labour is now relatively expensive and many nurseries are going over to mechanical planting methods. Whichever method is adopted it is important that soil conditions are optimal for plant survival. If too wet, damage, such as compacting, can occur at planting; if too dry, wilting of the plants will occur if irrigation is unavailable. Planting should take place either in the autumn or as soon as it is possible to get on the land in the spring. Autumn planting has the advantage that the plant is ready to grow away as soon as possible in the New Year, but damage may occur due to frost lifting.

The importance of planting into clean soil must be stressed. Perennial weeds should be controlled in the fallow period prior to planting and the organic status of the soil should also be replenished before planting occurs.

Hand planting

Many nurseries still use hand planting as the main method of planting their nursery stock. Land is prepared using tractor-mounted tines or other suitable equipment. Many growers find the quality of hand planting is of a higher standard than machine planting and the labour force find it less monotonous although the job takes far longer.

Plants are collected from a 'heeling-in' area where they have been stored since delivery from the plant raiser or since lifting from the propagation area. Plants should have been trimmed and graded either before 'heeling-in' or before planting. This will ensure more even plant growth after establishment.

The simplest method of planting is to use a line and spade, and nick-plant the nursery stock by taking out a narrow trench along the line. Rows must be straight to make management easier; if the site is on sloping land care should be taken to arrange rows across the slope rather than down it in order to keep erosion to a minimum.

With large plants such as trees dig a hole that is large enough to accommodate the full spread of the roots and then replace the soil around the roots. Whichever method of planting is used it is important that the soil around the roots is firmed to ensure proper soil contact and prevent drying, as well as to enable the plant to remain upright.

Where residual herbicides are likely to be used after planting it is advisable to plant deeper to allow 50 mm (2 in) of soil above the rooting zone. This means that no roots will be damaged by herbicides and growth will not be checked.

Once planting has been completed, water should be provided, either naturally or by an irrigation system.

Machine planting

The cheapest method of planting is by machine; efficient working depends on a constant supply of plants to maintain an even flow of work and also on long planting rows, as time is wasted when manoeuvring around at headlands. Plant preparation is just as important with mechanized planting methods and satisfactory work from the machine only occurs when plants are of a uniform size (see Plate 8).

Planters for nursery stock can be divided into four groups:

1 Gripper planters: Most planters fit the three-point linkage of a conventional tractor so that they can be locked clear of the ground when being taken to the field. The first operation in

planting is for a V-shaped share to open the soil ready for the planting mechanism which follows closely behind. The planter consists of a distributor disc with plant grippers placed equally around its circumference. The number of grippers varies with the different types of discs, and these discs are interchangeable. Each gripper has a rubber cushion which holds the plant without causing damage. Plants are placed into the grip with the roots facing the right direction when it reaches the planting position. Once the plant reaches this position an automatic cam opens the gripper and the plant falls into the already opened soil trench. The final operation is for two presser wheels, which follow the disc, to close the soil firmly around the roots of the plant.

A nursery worker with very little experience can plant quickly with this machine and planting depth, row spacing and plant spacing can easily be adjusted on it.

2 Disc planters: Some nurserymen prefer a straightforward disc rather than grippers for planting. The machine is basically the same as for gripper planters, except the grips are replaced by two simple discs. The discs, made of flexible steel, are inclined together so that they almost touch for about half their circumference. Plants are placed between the discs which firmly hold each plant until it reaches the planting position. At this position the discs start moving apart, leaving the plant in the ready-made planting trench. The advantage of this method is that plants can always be placed in the disc; with grips, if you miss a planting station, there is no way of correcting it and the operator has to wait for the next grip to be in position. Again, after planting, the plants are firmed in by the use of pressure wheels that follow the discs.

Machines have been developed for tree planting using this principle. With these much larger plants, the initial opening share needs to be far stronger as more soil needs to be moved to obtain an adequate planting zone without cramming the roots. The other alteration is for a larger storage area on the machine for trees pre-planting. Each operator needs a large carrier in front of him from which he can take the plants, and adequate feeding of trees to this carrier is important to ensure smooth running of the machine.

3 Plant-furrow shares: The aim of a plant-furrow share is simply to produce a trench along the line of planting. The depth and

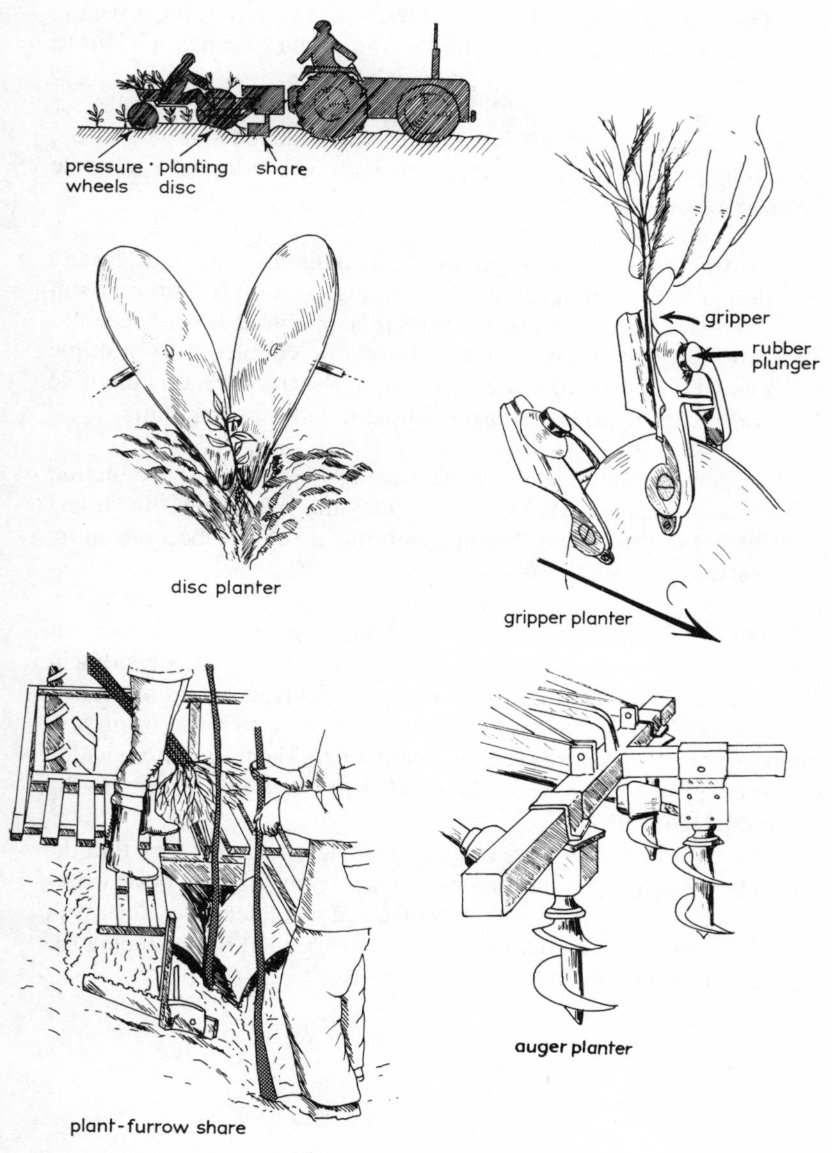

Fig. 56 Mechanized planting methods

width of the furrow will vary according to the size of the share. The planting operation is still carried out by hand, but a heavy, time-consuming part of the operation has been made more efficient.

The above machines are intended for bed systems or multiple-row plantings whereas the final type of planting is adopted for single planting methods.

4 Post-hole borers or auger planters: This machine is normally used for tree or large-shrub planting. It simply removes soil from the planting position leaving a prepared hole. Machines can either be single post-hole borers or coupled into multiple plant-hole borers. They are driven off the tractor p.t.o. and hole width can be varied by using different width boring units.

Mechanization has encouraged great progress in field production methods in recent years. Markers, spades and large gangs of planters are now becoming obsolete as planting machines become more sophisticated and efficient.

One topic we have not covered is planting-hole preparation and this is a controversial subject. Some growers add peat as an amendment to the hole when planting trees. Research evidence could result in a change of thinking, as experiments show no difference in growth between trees that have received a soil amendment and those which have not. If this is so, growers could save costs by simply planting into the local soil.

It is important with long-term crops such as nursery stock that the density, spacing and planting is correct. A mistake, or poor workmanship, at this point cannot be corrected at a later date. The result will be a reduction in quality, a higher work load in producing the crop and, inevitably, a lower selling price.

28

Bush rose production

Many nurserymen may feel that the production of bush roses—hybrid teas and floribundas—is best left to the large specialist growers, but nevertheless many nursery-stock producers do go in for roses and, therefore, some guidelines on the subject may not come amiss in this book. As roses are propagated by budding on to a rootstock, let us first consider the types of rootstocks used and, briefly, their production. It should be said at the outset that most nurserymen probably buy in rootstocks from the Continent, but there is a trend now towards increased rootstock production in the UK.

Rootstocks used

Traditionally *Rosa canina* 'Wild' was used as a stock but it was found that the seedlings varied tremendously in respect of suckering, vigour and general quality. However, it is still used to some extent, but is rapidly being superseded by more uniform stocks. The most commonly used stock today is *R. dumetorum* 'Laxa'. This buds early and is ideal on a calcareous soil. There are few suckers.

Some of the *Rosa canina* selections are also popular, like *R.c.* 'Inermis' which is almost thornless. There is a slight tendency to suckering. The excellent budding neck 'runs' well late in the season.

R.c. 'Pfander' is used a great deal, although rather sensitive to mildew. However, it has a long straight neck and is useful for late budding. Very little suckering is one of its advantages, plus the fact that it reacts well to light sandy soils.

Other less widely used stocks include *R.c.* 'Pollmers', which is drought resistant, useful for early budding and prone to Black Spot; *R.c.* 'Schmids Ideal', a good all-round stock, which performs well on the lighter soils; and *R.c.* 'Heinsohns Record', which has a slight tendency to suckering, is prone to mildew, and is suitable for late budding.

R. multiflora is sometimes used but is rather prone to mildew.

There is little suckering and a good deal of vigour in the stocks so budding may not be too easy. There are various selections one can use, like 'Inermis' and 'Japonica', both of which are virtually thornless.

Producing rootstocks from seed

Rose rootstocks are seed-raised and in recent years much research has been carried out, especially with *R. dumetorum* 'Laxa', on pre-sowing treatments to speed germination, as natural stratification takes 12–18 months.

Hips are collected from the stock plants in early October while still firm. Then the hips are crushed to expose the seeds. The mixture of seeds and pulp is placed in water for several days for separation by flotation. The seed may need several washings after separation, to ensure it is completly free from debris. The seed is then dried in a warm place for several days.

There are three possible storage treatments for the seeds. The traditional method is natural stratification. The seed can be stored in sand or Vermiculite—alternate layers of seed and sand/Vermiculite—in a cold aspect out of doors; it must be protected from vermin. It is desirable to turn the seed/storage medium occasionally during the stratification period, which lasts from 12–18 months. The seeds are then sown. Germination is poor when this method of storage is used, from 7 to 15 per cent is all one can expect.

The second method of storage is commonly called the 'entire treatment', or temperature-control storage. This is as follows: 30 days' storage in a temperature of 20–24 °C (68–75 °F), then 12 weeks or more at a temperature of 5 °C (41 °F). Place the seed in trays between layers of Vermiculite, and turn the whole lot about once a week to ensure the seed is well aerated. This treatment can commence in early December and is completed by the end of March at the latest. Then the seed can be sown and one can expect a germination percentage of between 25 and 50 per cent.

The third method is acid treatment. This is a highly skilled operation as concentrated sulphuric acid is used to reduce the thickness of the seed coat or testa. The length of time the seeds are subjected to the acid depends on the size and condition of the seeds. The seeds are placed in a glass container and sufficient acid added to cover the testa of all the seeds. Stir the seeds constantly and do not allow the temperature to rise above 24 °C (75 °F). The seed coat will turn black and when it has been sufficiently reduced (test by cutting through samples of seed with a sharp knife) the seeds must be immediately washed several times in large volumes of water to remove all traces of acid. Then dry off the seed, and remove the blackened part of the testa (this is in fact charcoal) by vigorous rubbing. The seed is then given temperature-control storage as described earlier. This treatment gives 65–75 per cent germination.

Seed is sown in March or early April in well-prepared seed beds on fertile, stone-free, well-drained land (see seed-bed preparation in Chapter 6). Sow in double rows to give a stand of 150–180 seeds per metre length of double row. Not all seeds will germinate and, of course, there will be some seedling losses, so the final seedling stand will fall short of 150–180.

Sowing in sterilized beds will help weed control, but one can apply chloroxuron pre-emergence to ensure a longer period of control. Irrigation should be used to ensure good germination in dry weather and also good growth during the growing season. A further application of chloroxuron may be given if necessary. Spray regularly with benomyl to control rose powdery mildew. Apply at 10-day intervals throughout the growing season.

Lift the young rootstocks in the autumn, after irrigating if the land is dry. Then grade them according to size. The usual grades are 3–5 mm, 5–8 mm and 8–12 mm neck diameter. Reject any spindly rootstocks or those with deformed or crooked necks.

Planting rootstocks

The rootstocks should be planted or lined out as soon as possible after lifting from the seed beds. Before planting the top growth should be reduced to about 100 mm (4 in) and the roots to about the same, using a guillotine.

The site should be prepared well in advance of lining out. Remember that roses should not be grown on the same piece of land more than once in every four years otherwise there will be trouble from replant disease and the bushes will make poor growth.

The land is prepared by deep ploughing, and we find, on our light soil, that a heavy application of farmyard manure is beneficial – up to 100 tonnes/ha (40 tons/acre). A pH of 5·5–6·0 is ideal. Roses need adequate nitrogen and potash and therefore a base dressing of fertilizer containing NPK should be applied prior to lining out, according to results of a soil test.

Just before lining out it is best to harrow the land, especially if using a planting machine, to ensure a fine tilth; and if necessary also use a levelling harrow, as a level surface results in better machine planting.

The rootstocks can be lined out in rows up to 1 m (3 ft 3 in) apart, but the distance depends on the machinery used. The stocks should be spaced 300 mm (1 ft) apart in the rows. The necks of the rootstocks must not be too deep as this can lead to inconvenience when budding. It is better to ridge up the necks of the stocks after planting to encourage fresh succulent necks for budding. The ridged-up soil is easily drawn away from the stocks to expose the necks immediately prior to budding.

After lining out spray with simazine at 4·5 kg cp/ha (4 lb cp/acre) to control germinating weed seeds.

Budding

Shield budding can take place the following summer, from about mid-June through to early September. Be sure to irrigate the rootstocks a day or two before budding if the soil is dry, as this encourages the stocks to 'run' well.

Draw the soil away from the neck of the rootstocks just prior to budding, and bud as low as possible. Full details of budding are given in Chapter 18. It is now the usual practice to use the rubber budding patches to hold in the buds and of course these reduce labour costs as one tier can keep three budders going, as opposed to one if the traditional raffia was used. Bud the largest rootstocks first.

After budding make another application of simazine to control germinating weed seeds. The stocks are then left until the following early spring.

Heading back

In the following February or early March head back the stocks. This involves cutting off the head of the rootstock immediately above the dormant bud and this action will quickly stimulate the bud into growth. If you find any 'shot' buds (buds which have grown away in the summer following budding) then these shoots should be cut back hard at the time of heading back. After heading back apply another simazine spray.

Management

During the growing season one will need to carry out pest and disease control. Powdery mildew is the most troublesome disease of roses and this can be controlled with regular sprayings of benomyl. Also, dodemorph gives good control of this disease. Mildew is less prevalent during a rainy summer as the mildew conidia do not germinate well in water, so increased irrigation may help to control mildew. Young leaves are more prone to infection than older leaves. Carry out spraying once a fortnight for optimum control.

Blackspot is another serious rose disease and this can be controlled with regular sprayings of dodine or maneb. Rose rust should be controlled by spraying with a mancozeb/zineb mixture or with zineb alone.

For aphid control spray with dimethoate or formothion; use trichlorphon for caterpillars; and spray with HCH (BHC) to control sawfly larvae.

A top dressing of nitrogenous fertilizer may be necessary during the season according to the growth being made by the plants. There is, of course, need for adequate irrigation during dry weather to ensure optimum growth.

Lifting

The bushes can be lifted from October onwards. On a large scale a tractor-mounted flail defoliating machine is used to remove the leaves. Also, large-scale producers trim the stems to facilitate lifting by using a tractor-mounted 'topping' machine. Generally the topping machine is mounted on the front of the tractor with the defoliator on the back, and the two operations are done in one pass.

The bushes are then undercut to a depth of at least 300–350 mm (12–14 in) to make lifting easy. There is a mechanized lifter with a shaking device which loosens the soil from the root systems.

Grading

The bushes are then graded for quality and size. There should be a minimum of two strong shoots, hard, ripe, and at least 450 mm (18 in) in length. There should be at least three major roots of a minimum length of 200 mm (8 in), plus a good quantity of fibrous roots. The sum of the diameters of two stems should equal 25 mm

(1 in) at least, measured at their base. These are minimum specifications and growers generally well exceed these.

The bushes must of course be true to name and they should be maidens at sale date. They should also, of course, be free from pests and diseases. There should be no damaged roots or shoots–damaged parts should be trimmed back cleanly after lifting. Also remove any suckers, dead growth and immature growth. Protect the roots from exposure after lifting.

The bushes will then be bundled and labelled and can, if necessary, be held in a cold store, until dispatch, with the temperature maintained at 1 °C (34 °F).

Marketing methods

Bare-root bushes are still marketed in fairly large numbers in the UK but there is a great increase in the volume of pre-packed bushes. These bushes are packed individually in polythene, often with the roots in moist peat and frequently with a cardboard backing to the pack with an illustration, in colour, of the cultivar.

Rootwrapping is a good method of marketing and is quite widely used. The roots are packed in peat and polythene.

The pre-packed roses are probably most suitable for chain-stores where the atmosphere would probably desiccate rootwrapped bushes. The latter are better for garden-centre sales, as they can be displayed in a sheltered position in the open.

29

Shrub production

Today, field production of shrubs has been largely superseded by container production but nevertheless one can still find many local nurseries growing shrubs in the open ground.

Before the container revolution most shrubs produced were field grown, so it is necessary to look first of all at the advantages and disadvantages of this system.

Advantages and disadvantages of field production

There is no doubt that one can achieve larger plants and much bushier growth in the field, as opposed to container growing, because of the fact that there is no root restriction. The plants, when lifted, generally have a really substantial root system.

Field production is probably more suited to large-scale producers, where many thousands of subjects are required as, for instance, hedging material or shrubs for reclamation work. This system is less labour-intensive than container production except perhaps when it comes to lifting. Some subjects, particularly evergreen shrubs, will need rootballing, but there is now a rootballing machine from Holland which greatly speeds up the operation and probably makes a better job than hand-rootballing.

In fact it is possible to almost completely mechanize field production by means of a planting machine for lining out, a tractor-mounted sprayer for weed, pest and disease control and an under-cutter to make lifting easier; but of course such mechanization means very high capital outlay and many small nurseries will have to rely on hand work for most, or all, of these operations.

Another major disadvantage of field-grown shrubs, apart from lifting, is the fact that the growing environment cannot be as accurately controlled as with container production. For instance, in container growing the growth can be controlled by keeping the plants under netting or polythene walk-in tunnels. Many months' growing time can, therefore, be saved as well as plants being protected from inclement weather and cold, searing winds. Field-grown shrubs are exposed to all that the weather can offer and there is no doubt that damage can occur and growth is slower; but, on the other hand, the standard of growing and the control of the crop need to be far better with container-grown plants. We are probably thinking in terms of two- to three-year crops of shrubs in the field.

Still on the subject of the growing environment, one cannot control as accurately – compared with container production – the feeding, irrigation and weed-control programmes. Many nurseries do not, in fact, have a field irrigation system and so plants may suffer a moisture deficit in dry weather. Also, without irrigation, one cannot always apply residual herbicides exactly when needed, for instance immediately after planting, as the soil may be too dry for them to work properly.

With field production it is not always possible to line out at the optimum time owing to unsuitable soil conditions – in other words, too cold and wet, or even too dry. Soil conditions can also influence time of lifting. If we have a wet autumn, lifting is often delayed for many months and this means holding up orders. Of course, field-grown shrubs cannot be dispatched all the year round as with container plants, the main sale period being in the autumn and winter, and through to early spring, that is, while the plants are dormant.

Plants suited to field production

There is a wide range of subjects suited to field production, but beware of those shrubs which resent root disturbance and grow these in containers. Typical examples are magnolias, which have very fleshy brittle roots, and are easily damaged during lifting. It is mainly the coarse-rooted shrubs which come in this category, such as *Cytisus*, *Genista*, *Spartium*, *Elaeagnus*, *Cistus*, and so on.

Shrubs which make a good fibrous root system are much better adapted to lifting and transplanting. Rhododendrons are a typical example and these plants make really good growth in a sheltered aspect. *Berberis* and the related *Mahonia* are very much suited to field production, making really large plants; and things like *Hebe*, shrubby *Cornus*, *Sambucus*, *Salix* grown as shrubs, *Hypericum*, and ground-cover subjects like *Ruscus*, *Lonicera pileata* and cotoneasters, also make good growth in field conditions. Hedging subjects which are often required in large quantities and of a good size are probably best grown in the field rather than in containers. Examples include *Prunus laurocerasus*, *P. lusitanica*, *Ligustrum* species, *Lonicera nitida*, *Fagus sylvatica*, *Carpinus betulus*, *Euonymus japonicus*, *Ilex aquifolium*, *Buxus sempervirens* and *B.s.* 'Suffruticosa', and of course all the coniferous hedging material apart from *Cupressus macrocarpa* which has a coarse root system and therefore does not transplant well. Conifers, however, are discussed in detail in Chapter 31.

For lining out one can use bare-rooted liners produced under low polythene tunnels, rooted hardwood cuttings from cold frames, one-year-old seedlings off the seed beds, or even pot-grown liners. The latter can be machine planted just as well as bare-root liners.

Soil preparation prior to planting

The soil should be thoroughly prepared and cleared of as many perennial weeds as possible prior to lining out shrubs. As this initial preparation was discussed in Chapter 27 it warrants only a brief mention here. Suffice it to say that all necessary cultivations should be carried out, such as perennial weed control, subsoiling if necessary, application of organic matter and deep ploughing, fertilizer application and final cultivation by harrowing, etc., to obtain a reasonably fine tilth for lining out.

Lining out shrubs

Lining out or planting shrub liners can be carried out in the spring as soon as the soil is in an ideal state, that is, moist but not wet and warming up to ensure quick establishment of the plants. If there is a jacketed cold store on the nursery then one can delay lining out until the soil is in optimum condition—for instance, lining out could take place as late as May or June, when the soil is warm, to give much quicker and better establishment. The plants will still be dormant of course. If you intend using residual herbicides for weed control among shrubs then do ensure the roots are well down in the soil when planting so that there is no risk of root damage from the herbicides.

There are various systems of lining out shrubs and one can machine plant, or hand plant by using a spade to take out a continuous slit for the roots. The roots should go straight down in the spade nick and be thoroughly firmed in with the heel.

One planting system is to line out the shrubs 300 mm (1 ft) apart in rows 1 m (3 ft 3 in) apart, to give about 36,000 shrubs per ha (14,500 per acre).

Probably a more popular approach, nowadays, is to use the bed system. For example, a three row system could be used. One could have shrubs between beds of trees so that a tractor can still be used for cultivations on the trees even when they have grown tall, as the tractor will be able to pass over the shrubs without damaging them. A bed system is less labour intensive owing to the fact that tractor work is still possible. For the three row system, shrubs should be planted in rows 600 mm (2 ft) apart, with 300 mm (1 ft) between the shrubs in the rows. The total width of each bed should be 1·5 m (5 ft).

Weed control

For pre-planting weed control refer to Chapter 27. Here we will concern ourselves with the control of mainly annual weeds in the growing crop. Generally nurserymen apply a residual or soil-acting herbicide to control germinating weed seeds. The programme should commence immediately after planting, before any seedling weeds appear. An annual programme generally consists of an application of residual herbicide in the early spring followed by another later in the year, say late summer or early autumn. The soil must be moist at the time of application otherwise the material will be ineffective. If there are any weeds present, these can be burnt off with paraquat prior to the application of residual material.

Simazine is the most popular material for controlling germinating weed seeds among crops of shrubs. It can be used at the rate of 2·2–4·5 kg cp/h (2–4 lb cp/acre). Simazine will not control such weeds as knotgrass, black bindweed, common orache, cleavers, wild oats and perennial weeds. Either avoid using simazine on plants which are sensitive to this herbicide, such as *Deutzia*, *Kerria*, *Choisya*, *Forsythia*, *Cornus*, *Hebe* and *Lonicera*, or use it at a reduced rate on these crops. However, it would be far safer to use another residual such as lenacil.

Lenacil can be used at the rate of 2·2 kg cp/ha (2 lb cp/acre). It controls a wide range of annual weeds but it will not control annual nettle, groundsel, speedwell, cleavers and perennials. It will control black bindweed, fat hen, common orache, knotgrass and redshank. Some plants are sensitive to lenacil and these include *Forsythia*, *Lavandula*, *Santolina* and *Weigela*.

A useful herbicide for the control of couch grass and other perennial weeds, such as dock, in the established crop is propyzamide. This can be applied either as a spray or as granules. It is applied when the soil is cold or cool, in the autumn or winter. It must be sprayed or applied to the foliage of established weeds.

Irrigation

There is no doubt that an irrigation system helps field production in various ways. Firstly it ensures continued growth of shrubs during drought conditions, and secondly it allows one to ensure moist soil conditions prior to herbicide applications. A portable system of lightweight alloy, which can be easily moved over the field, is generally favoured. Such systems normally have 'snap-on' couplings to speed setting up and dismantling. Pulsating rotary sprinklers are generally used to apply the water.

Trimming

Trimming young shrubs to ensure bushier growth is probably not carried out as much in the UK as in the USA. Many shrubs make far better growth, branching from the base, if they are trimmed over several times during their nursery life. All too often, tall shrubs are produced which are bare or thin at the base, simply because they have not been trimmed. Hedging material, especially, needs to be well branched at the base. Shrub liners can be trimmed either before or after lining out in the field and the plants can be reduced by about half their height. A further trimming of the resultant laterals in the second growing season is also desirable for the majority of subjects. In this instance just tip them – do not cut back hard.

The trimming can be carried out either with a pair of secateurs or, to speed up the task, with a pair of hand shears.

30

Tree production

The early stages of tree production have been covered in other sections. In this chapter we will take the production from the maiden (one-year stem) through to lifting.

It must be stressed at the outset that trees are long-term crops and soil conditions, drainage and weed control must be correct before planting commences. The cropping time in the nursery varies with species as follows: minimum of three years for *Betula*, *Alnus* and *Populus*; four years for *Malus* and *Prunus*; five years for *Quercus*.

TREE TRAINING

Before studying training methods in detail it is important to understand how a tree grows. Growth is governed by a number of factors:

1 Inherent factors: the variation in growth between species is governed by the genetic differences between plants.

2 Apical control: excurrent leaders dominate, forming an upright-growing tree, while decurrent leaders result in the laterals growing as fast as the leader which eventually disappears and a round-headed tree is produced.

3 Modification of form with age: a shift may occur, with age, from decurrent to excurrent growth and vice versa; this varies with species, competition, plant density and moisture content. An example is *Pinus sylvestris* which loses vigour with maturity and becomes flat topped.

4 Branch angle and crown form: branch positions change with octogency, e.g. *Aesculus*. An upright-pointing branch in the nursery may be pendulous on the mature tree.

5 Epinastic effect: branches growing upwards at acute angles often exert a mutual epinastic effect, that is, grow at the same rate. This is common in opposite-budded trees, e.g. *Aceraceae* and *Oleaceae*; if left this can result in twin leaders. Nurserymen need to

remove one of these branches, preferably at the bud stage, to ensure the remaining leader assumes a vertical position.

6 Environmental influences on form: apart from the epinastic effect, the nurseryman can do very little to alter or control any of the above influences, but he can manipulate the environment in the regions of movement, light and water stress.

7 Intermittent growth: growth rates vary between species; this is normally associated with the nutritional status of the plant and the pattern of bud release. Trees can generally be divided into four groups:
   (a) Single flush followed by a resting stage before the next flush, e.g., *Quercus robur*. Elongation periods are of two to three weeks before shoots become dormant and another terminal bud forms:
   (i) first flush – April/May;
   (ii) second flush – around July;
   (iii) third flush – early August;
   (iv) fourth flush – occasionally in October.
   (b) Recurrent flushes with terminal buds forming and flushing straight after the previous one, e.g. *Liriodendron tulipifera*.
   (c) One flush of growth a year, e.g. *Pinus sylvestris*.
   (d) Sustained flush of growth, which produces late-formed leaves prior to terminal-bud formation, e.g. *Betula pendula*.

   Some plants often abort their terminal bud at the end of each season which results in zig-zag growth as with *Tilia × europaea* and *Robinia pseudoacacia*.

At first this may seem of only academic interest to the grower, but a detailed knowledge of tree growth can assist in pruning, training and general plant management.

Methods of training

When looking at the training of a tree it is best to view the tree as a three-unit component composed of roots, stem and head. The pruning of these three units is completely different and should be carried out in the order suggested if a high-quality tree is desired.

ROOTS

The aim of any root pruning should be to produce a well-established fibrous root system. The normal method of achieving this is to undercut the plant to remove any tap roots or strong laterals and encourage fibrous roots near to the stem. What in fact happens is that the root/shoot ratio is upset and the plant gets a shock, resulting in a reduction in stem growth. If root pruning is required it should be carried out in the autumn so that new spring growth can adjust to the restricted water intake capacity.

Alternative methods have been used by a few nurserymen to achieve well established root systems. In the summer a one-year whip is allowed to grow in the normal manner. During the following winter the whip is cut down to 150 mm (6 in), which will result in two or three shoots emerging in the spring. The strongest of these shoots is selected as the new whip. During the second summer the grower has achieved a one-year whip with a two-year root. This plant has taken an extra year to produce, but is far more vigorous and has a well-formed root system.

This system of production will work with budded/grafted trees as well as unworked trees. It is used commercially by some growers on *Acer platanoides*, *Tilia*, *Quercus*, and *Carpinus*, although little success has been found with large-leaved subjects such as *Aesculus*. The more vigorous whip often does not need supporting and can be spaced closer together.

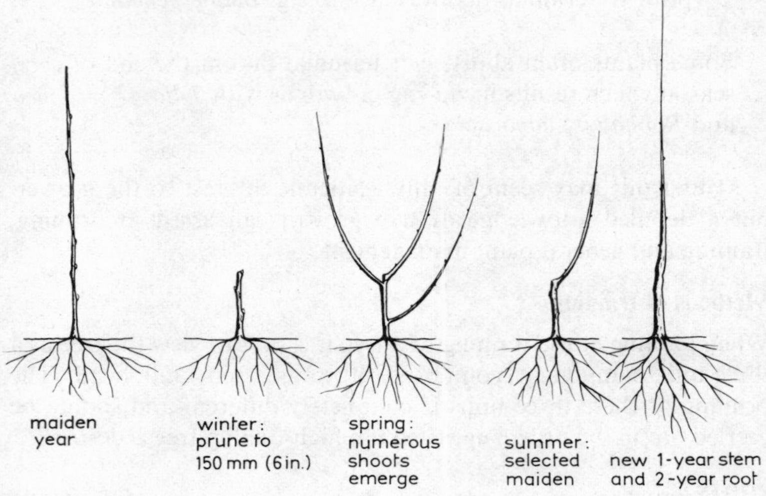

Fig. 57 A method of establishing a good root system

STEMS

The side branches in stem budding are called feathers and the purpose of these is to increase the photosynthetic area, resulting in an increased stem diameter, strengthened trunk, larger roots and reduced height. Stem diameter increases due to new cells being formed from the meristematic areas which are stimulated by the growth hormones produced in the leaves of the feathers. Stem-diameter growth takes place over a longer time than stem elongation, provided there is sufficient moisture.

Stem elongation is governed by the growth pattern; length of growing season varies with species and is often associated with géographical origin:

Betula pendula grows for 98 days in the UK and is from a northern origin

Acer saccharinum grows for 80 days and is from a mid-northern origin

Gymnocladus grows for 36 days and is from a south-northern origin

Feather production is controlled by the apical dominance of the plant. Trees with weak apical dominance produce feathers readily, while strong apical dominance means few feathers are produced. Feathers can be induced by removing the apical dominance. This can be done physically or chemically by using materials such as maleic hydrazide or alpha-naphthalene acetic acid.

One method we have seen for increasing stem caliper is given below (Fig. 58).

Feather management: once the required number of feathers has been achieved pruning is needed to obtain maximum effect. Complete removal of feathers in the spring will, as expected, reduce stem thickening as also does hand tipping of feathers, in the summer, close to the stem. For best effect, feathers should be left untouched during the summer until August, except for removal of thick feathers which are competing with the leader and very thin feathers which are spur pruned to 75 mm (3 in).

After August no regrowth will occur from pruned feathers. The lower third of feathers are now removed as they have served their purpose. The remaining feathers are pruned back to three pairs of leaves. Pruning should be carried out with a sharp pruning knife, secateurs or pneumatic secateurs. Many growers prefer secateurs

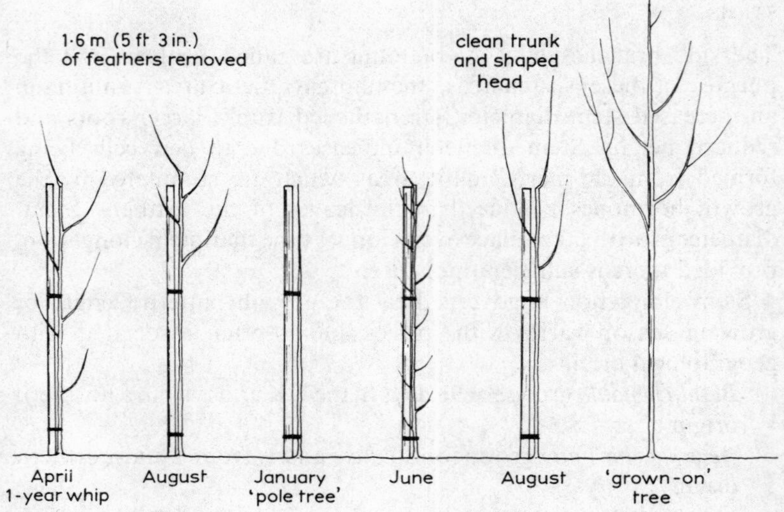

Fig. 58 A method of increasing stem diameter

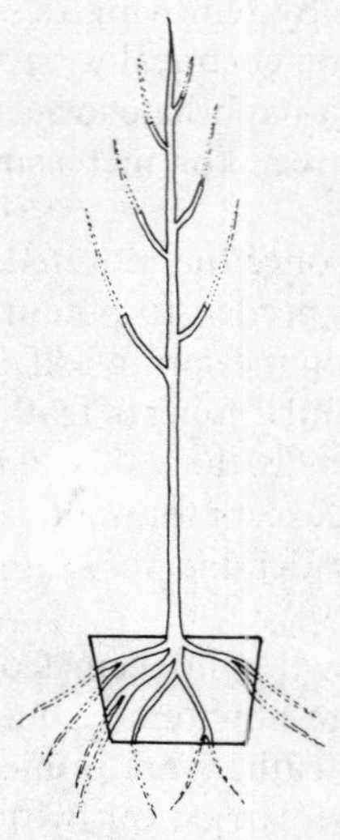

Fig. 59 A method of head pruning at lifting

now and these must be sharp and not the type which crush plant cells as this will induce rotting, especially in *Fraxinus* species.

HEAD PRUNING

The aim of head pruning is to maintain a leader, if required, a well-balanced head and no overcrowding of branches. Specifications for the shape of head will vary with species and customer requirements. Some species require hardly any head pruning, e.g. *Prunus* 'Rancho' and *Prunus* 'Amanogawa' which, if pruned, produce open or umbrella-shaped heads, when a leader will grow naturally if left.

Some nurserymen will prune branches back heavily, except for the leader at lifting. The objective here is to produce a well-balanced head with a dominant leader that will guarantee survival. The reason for the heavy branch pruning is to counteract the root pruning which occurred at lifting (Fig. 59).

In this part of the chapter we have tried to review the alternatives in pruning. Table 14 gives the technique normally adopted for pruning ornamental trees.

TREE SUPPORTING

A common operation in tree production is to tie in the tree to a cane to obtain a straight leader. In recent years a great deal of research has been carried out to find the validity of this operation. Once a tree has been caned a number of characteristics of the tree are influenced:

1 Less caliper occurs at the base of the trunk.
2 More growth in height may occur due to the etiolation effect of the cane.
3 The trunk may produce less of a taper and often a parallel-sided tree is produced.
4 The tree is subject to more stress. In a naturally-grown tree the stress point is at the base of the trunk. Once a cane has been placed next to the trunk the stress point is moved to the top of the cane, an unnatural position often resulting in tree heads being damaged.
5 Due to a dark side being created on one side of the tree by the cane, the xylem tissue is not uniform and this makes it more difficult for the tree to support itself and cope with the elements once the cane is removed.

Table 14 Ornamental-tree-training programme (not including feathered, weeping or fastigiate trees). Varying specifications may be required to achieve customer requirements

Time	*Stem*	*Normal head with dominant leader*	*Small flowering tree with branching head*
ROOTSTOCK YEAR	Remove rootstock suckers Encourage one leading shoot on grafted plants		
Autumn/winter	Head back budded stock		
MAIDEN YEAR	Remove suckers Cane and tie to stock and scion those subjects which require support		
Summer	Leave feathers Tie in stem on caned trees		
Autumn/winter	Remove lower feathers up to 300 mm (1 ft) Shorten one-year feathers to 100 mm (4 in) Remove epinastic effect where this applies Top maiden stem growth at 2·4 m (8 ft 9 in)		
SECOND YEAR	Continue to tie in stem to cane where used, if height not reached in maiden year*	For subsequent treatment see operations starred (*)	

	Maintain one leader Remove dead/dying terminal buds to one lower healthy bud	Leave branches to develop into head of tree	Leave branches to develop into head of tree
Summer	Leave all feathers to grow on stem		
Autumn/winter	Remove two-year-old feathers Shorten one-year growth to 100 mm (4 in) and premature 'branches'		
THIRD YEAR	Top stem growth at 2·4 m (8 ft 9 in)*	Shorten branches by one-third leaving one dominant leader untouched except where an epinastic effect occurs	Shorten branches by one-third to a half to produce an open-centre head
Summer	Leave feathers, except those competing with stem branches	Remove competing leaders	Remove crossing branches Tie in base of head for support where caning used
Autumn/winter	Remove remaining feathers to produce a clean stem (this depends on customer requirements)		
FOURTH YEAR	Remove two-year-old feathers, shorten one-year-old to 100 mm (4 in)*	Shorten branches by one-third leaving one dominant, untouched leader*	
Summer	Leave feathers*	Check for development of single leader*	
Autumn/winter	Remove remaining feathers to produce a clean stem*		

* Indicates trees which will not produce a maiden of the required height in one year.

On top of these factors the grower has the expense of providing support, both in materials and labour. It is important that a grower asks himself if this is a justifiable cost. If he does not cane will the percentage loss in trees be greater than the cost of supporting? Another important consideration is the availability of canes, often a difficult commodity to purchase in bulk.

Some trees can be grown successfully without support and these include: *Fraxinus* species; *Malus tschonoskii*; *Prunus* 'Amanogawa' and *P.* 'Kanzan'; *Prunus avium* 'Plena'; *Prunus dulcis*; *Prunus* × *amygdalo-persica*; *Prunus* × *pollardii*; *Quercus* species and strong-growing *Sorbus* species.

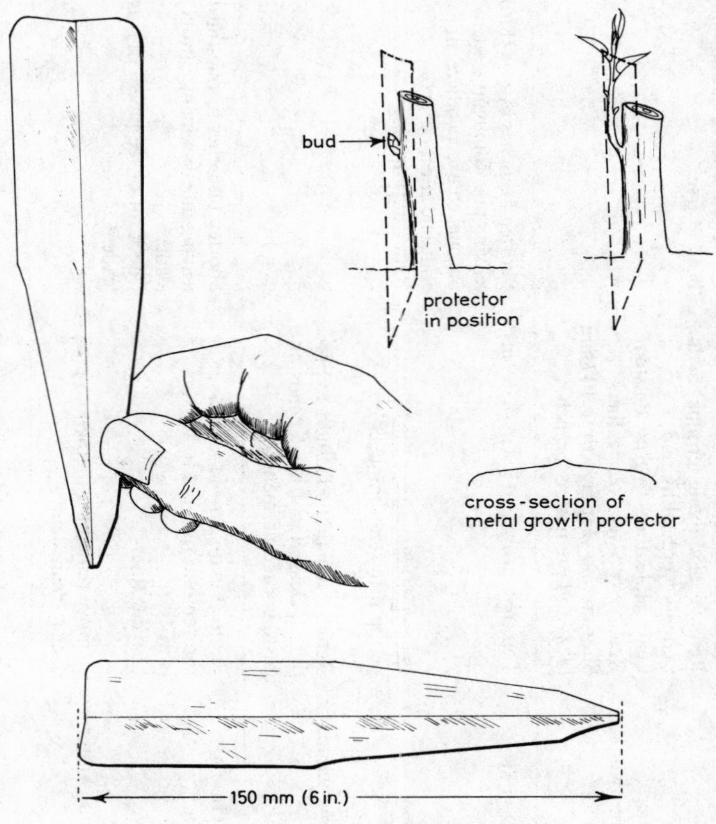

Fig. 60 Metal growth protector

Others will need supporting, for example: *Crataegus oxycantha*; *Nothofagus* species; *Platanus* species; *Prunus cerasifera*; *Prunus hillieri* 'Spire'; *Prunus-sargentii*; *Pyrus salicifolia* 'Pendula'; *Tilia* species; *Ulmus glabra* and many grafted trees.

If a grower decides on caning then a 2·6 m (9 ft) bamboo cane, which is relatively cheap and flexible, should be used. The length of cane is important, especially if a 2 m (6 ft 6 in) standard stem is required. The cane is inserted close to the tree using an iron spike to make the preliminary hole. If caning a budded/grafted tree then the cane should be at the back of the union.

Tying in can be done with raffia, or plastic tying material using a tying gun. The number of ties will vary depending on the length, strength and straightness of stem—normally three ties will be adequate.

With developments in new techniques of production, e.g. chip budding, producing a stronger union, there are now alternatives to caning to achieve the same aim. The most common method is the use of a 150 mm (6 in) metal device to direct and protect the new leader shoot as it emerges from the bud. The shield is placed 7 mm (0·25 in) in front of the dormant bud and eliminates the dog leg which is often produced when this shoot emerges. The shield also protects the bud from wind and reduces the labour input on the crop.

MANAGEMENT PROCEDURES

Apart from training and supporting, a detailed management programme needs to be devised to obtain quality and maximum yield.

Fertilizer programme

It is important that such a programme is planned thoroughly and recorded to make maximum use of fertilizer. Below is an example of how a programme could be laid out on a record sheet.

The fertilizer requirement for trees will vary with species. Very little is known about the optimum for each species and even if it were possible to apply optimum rates it would often be impractical unless monoculture is practised.

One of the ways we can record fertilizer effectiveness is to note the stem diameters of fertilized and unfertilized trees. Researchers have shown, by doing this, that once the optimum has been reached on growth output further fertilizer application is being wasted.

Crop	*Nutrient requirement, in units*	*Fertilizer*	*Rate*	*Time of feeding*

Record sheet for a fertilizer programme

The first consideration is to find out if the tree needs fertilizing. A number of nurseries are now using leaf analysis to detect nutrient deficiency before visual symptoms in growth reduction occur. The time of year when samples are taken is important, as nutrient levels vary throughout the year; e.g., calcium increases and nitrogen decreases in the plant as the year progresses.

Samples are taken from the most recently mature leaves on a branch, 40–50 healthy leaves being removed and analysed in the laboratory, along with information on soil type, pH and species. It is important to stress that leaf analysis will not replace soil analysis, but acts as another link to get a more complete picture for accurate feeding. Leaf-analysis ranges for woody plants are: 2–4·5 % nitrogen, 0·2–0·6 % phosphorous and 1·2–3·5 % potassium.

The amount of nutrient deciduous nursery trees will remove from the soil depends on the soil, age of plants, density and species. Research indicates that trees will absorb nutrients in winter when temperatures rise above 2 °C (35·6 °F) with absorption time varying with species. For example, February to November is the maximum absorption period for black poplar, and May to June is the maximum absorption period for cherry. Therefore the time of applying the nutrient is important to get maximum effect.

Feeding methods

A number of methods have been devised for applying fertilizer although the conventional means is to use a slow-release granular feed which will release nutrients slowly to provide a constant supply of nitrogen, phosphates, potassium and magnesium. The recommended method is to apply a band of fertilizer, either manually or mechanically, along the row of trees.

Some nurseries are looking at the possibilities of foliar-applied fertilizers. All above-ground plant area can absorb a limited amount of nutrient, the rate varying with the element and crop.

Example

Nutrient element	*Time required for 50 per cent absorption*
Nitrogen as urea	1–36 hours
Phosphorous	7–15 days
Potassium	1–4 days
Calcium	4 days
Magnesium	20 per cent in 1 hour
Iron	8 per cent in 24 hours

(Ref: Penn. State University)

Under nursery conditions only a small portion of the foliar-applied nutrients is absorbed. Most ends up in the soil and is then taken up by the roots. Reasons for this are that up to 50 per cent of the nutrient will not reach the leaf, and what gets on to the leaf may evaporate or be washed off by rain. Foliar feeding therefore only has a limited use and could, possibly, be used when the soil locks up certain essential nutrients.

The final method is to use fertilizer tablets or sticks which are inserted in the soil in the rooting zone where they slowly release nutrients. An auger is required to make a hole for the fertilizer and the number of tablets or sticks per tree will vary according to age and size of the plant to be fed.

Irrigation programme

There is a lot of controversy on the value of irrigating trees. To have an efficient watering system means a high capital investment and the results are not always visible. Irrigation is obviously important in dry growing seasons, but these will vary in their frequency. Watering can assist normal management procedures, such as before budding, to give the bud maximum possibility of take; before inserting canes, to make the job easier; and before lifting, for the same reason. However, many growers produce excellent trees without watering facilities, and irrigation should only be considered once other growing procedures have been established.

Herbicide programme

The recording of the herbicide programme is as critical as the fertilizer programme. The layout of the records should be along these lines:

Crop and area	*Herbicide*	*Rate*	*Time of application*

Record sheet for a herbicide programme

The field at planting time should be free of perennial weeds and therefore the only herbicides that need to be applied are residual herbicides early in the spring and a contact herbicide for selective control of growing weeds in mid-summer.

In the year before lifting, some growers will leave the weeds around the crop. Competition at this stage from weeds is negligible and a weed cover can also help at lifting, especially in wet seasons as the weeds act as a ground stabilizer.

Pest and disease control

A grower must aim at maximum growth in any crop he produces and this means an adequate pest and disease control programme is desirable. One of the major problems are aphids which will quickly reduce growth. An aphicide must be applied early in the summer and applied at regular intervals.

Diseases vary between species and Table 15 acts as a guide.

TREE HARVESTING

If 25,000 rootstocks or whips were planted to the hectare, one can assume 80–85 per cent will be saleable at lifting time.

Trees are sold on the basis of stem height, diameter or circumference at 1 m (3 ft 3 in), and overall height. Tree diameter can easily be measured with a tree caliper which can be fitted around the tree at the required height. An example of tree specifications is given in Table 16, but one must remember standards are constantly being revised and will differ among countries.

Two methods of lifting are used, either balled or bare-root. The decision on which to use is governed by the size of the plant, species, market and time of year that lifting takes place.

Table 15 Tree diseases

Disease	*Occurrence*	*Pruning guidelines*	*Control chemicals used when spraying is necessary*
Bacterial Canker (*Pseudomonas morsprunorum*)	*Prunus*, especially imported Limburgh stocks.	Infection via wounds including leaf scars. Prevention by winter pruning.	3 copper sprays at 3-week intervals from end of August, e.g. Bordeaux mixture.
Bacterial Canker of Poplar (*Pseudomonas syringa*)	*Forsythia*, *Populus*, *Prunus*, *Syringa*. Resistant cultivars: *Populus eugenei*—drier site; *P. serotina*—frost pockets.	Control by pruning out dead wood. Use resistant cultivars.	3 copper sprays at 3-week intervals from end of August, e.g. Bordeaux mixture.
Fire Blight (*Erwinia amylovora*)	*Rosaceae*, especially *Cotoneaster*, *Crataegus*, *Malus*, *Prunus*, *Pyracantha*, *Sorbus Stranvaesia*.	Close observation of growth during and immediately after flowering. Remove diseased material by pruning well into healthy wood.	Sterilize implements with Lysol.
Canker of Apple and Pear (*Nectria galligena*)	*Fagus*, *Fraxinus*, *Juglans*, *Malus*, *Populus*, *Pyrus*, *Salix*.	Prevention by winter pruning. Summer pruning means spores enter and cause die-back by autumn.	Spray with copper or mercuric oxide or thiophanate-methyl.

Table 15—*continued*

Disease	*Occurrence*	*Pruning guidelines*	*Control chemicals used when spraying is necessary*
Canker of Apple and Pear (Spur Blight) (*Gleosporium perennans*)	*Fagus*, *Fraxinus*, *Juglans*, *Malus*, *Populus*, *Pyrus*, *Salix*.	Prevention by winter pruning. Summer pruning means spores enter and cause die-back by autumn. Occurs where feather growth is trimmed in early summer.	In early stages of disease spray with benomyl or captan.
Coral Spot (*Nectria cinnabarina*)	Most trees on dead branches. On live wood on plum and *Acer*, especially if in poor health or in a wet season. *Ulmus*, especially 'Christine Buisman', very susceptible.	Remove dead and diseased branches and burn.	Sealants to be used.
Silver Leaf (*Stereum purpureum*)	*Cotoneaster*, *Fagus*, *Laburnum*, *Malus*, *Populus*, *Prunus*.	Remove diseased branches by cutting well into healthy wood during summer. Open cuts painted with a sealant.	Sealants to contain mercury or be of a bituminous type.
Die-back (*Botrytis* species)	Most trees on snags and open wounds. Serious on ash if using blunt secateurs.	Good pruning should avoid this problem. Prune back any snags or dying shoots to live buds.	Spray with benomyl.

Apple Mildew (*Podosphaera* species)	*Rosaceae*.	Cut off diseased branches and burn. Special awareness needed in spring.	Spray with benomyl or carbendazim.
Die-back of Poplar (*Dothechiza populeae*)	*Populus*, *Salix* especially prone in damp weather. Avoid overcrowding in nursery.	Prune during summer when healing is more rapid (before August).	Sealants to be used.
Verticillium Wilt (*Verticillium albo-atrum*)	Many trees, especially *Acer* and *Ulmus*, *Tilia*, *Syringa*.	Causes die-back and wilting. If only odd plant then remove completely.	Plant into sterilized soil. Some suggest manuring with ammonium sulphate.
Willow Anthracnose (*Marssonina salicicola*)	*Salix*.	Remove badly affected shoots.	Spray with Bordeaux mixture or quinomethionate.

Table 16 Deciduous tree planting material specifications

Form of tree	*Overall heights*	*Suitable sites and uses*
SEEDLING Remaining undisturbed since sowing	Up to 1·00 m (39 in)	1. Forestry 2. Amenity woodlands 3. Shelterbelts 4. Land reclamation and soil stabilization 5. Hedging 6. Rootstocks
TRANSPLANT Transplanted one or more times in the nursery	Up to 1·00 m (39 in)	

Form of tree	*Overall heights*	*Suitable sites and uses*
WHIPS Including transplants, young worked trees and young trees from cuttings, e.g. *Salix* Trees transplanted in the nursery but not necessarily staked and without significant feathered growth	*Height range* 1·00–2.50 m (3·3–8·08 ft) *Grades* 2·10–2·50 m (6·8–8·08 ft) 1·80–2·10 m (5·8–6·8 ft) 1·50–1·80 m (4·9–5·8 ft) 1·20–1·50 m (4–4·9 ft) 1·00–1·20 m (3·3–4 ft)	1. Rural countryside planting 2. Motorways 3. Shelterbelts 4. Hedgerow trees 5. Mass planting and in mixtures, conservation 6. Growing on in nurseries 7. Larger grades containerized for garden centre sales

Table 16—*continued*

Form of tree	*Overall heights*	*Suitable sites and uses*
FEATHERED TREE Transplanted tree with a defined reasonably straight upright central leader, stem shall be furnished with evenly spaced and balanced *lateral shoots* to near ground level	*Height range* 1·80–3·50 m (5·8–11·3 ft) *Grades* 3·00–3·50 m (9·75–11·3 ft) 2·50–3·00 m (8·8–9·75 ft) 2·10–2·50 m (6·8–8·08 ft) 1·80–2·10 m (5·8–6·8 ft)	1. Rural planting 2. Shelterbelts 3. Specimen planting in protected areas 4. Garden use

STANDARD TREES	Circumference of stem at 1 m from ground	Overall heights	Clear stem heights from ground level to lowest branch	Sites and uses
SELECTED St. Tree	10–12 cm (4–4·7 in)	3·00–3·50 m (9·75–11·3 ft)	1·80 m (5·8 ft)	1. Suitable for streets, highways and suburban housing areas
STANDARD St. Tree	8–10 cm (3–4 in)	2·50–3·00 m (8·08–9·75 ft)	1·80 m (5·8 ft)	
LIGHT St. Tree	6–8 cm (2·5–3 in)	2·50–3·00 m (8·08–9·75 ft)	1·50–1·80 m (4·9–5·8 ft)	2. Specimen trees in parks and arboreta
GARDEN St. Tree	4–6 cm (1·5–2·5 in)	2·10–2·50 m (6·8–8·08 ft)	1·50–1·80 m (4·9–5·8 ft)	
HALF St. Tree	—	1·80–2·10 m (5·8–6·8 ft)	1·20–1·50 m (4–4·9 ft)	3. Light standards and smaller grades convenient for garden planting
SHORT St. Tree i.e. shrubs grown on a single stem	—	—	1·00–1·20 m (3·3–4 ft)	

Table 16—*continued*

Form of tree	*Circumference of stem at 1 m from ground*	*Overall heights*	*Clear stem height from ground level to lowest branch*	*Sites and uses*
ADVANCED NURSERY STOCK 				
Extra heavy nursery trees	16–20 cm (6–7·8 in)	3·60–6·00 m (11·7–19·7 ft)	1·8 m	1. Vandalproof trees for urban planting 2. Factory screening 3. Immediate effect in new towns 4. Recommended in place of semi-mature trees
Heavy standard	14–16 cm (5·5–6 in)	as above	as above	
Whips and ordinary standards transplanted and grown on for a further period at wide row spacings	12–14 cm (4·7–5·5 in)	as above	as above	

Form of tree	*Circumference of stem at 1 m from ground*	*Overall heights*	*Clear stem height from ground level to lowest branch*	*Sites and uses*
SEMI-MATURE TREES Rootball prepared and protected	 20–75 cm (7·8–29 in)	6·00–9·00 m (19–30 ft)	—	1. Impact planting, prestige areas in towns and business centres 2. Immediate screening 3. Vandalproof planting

In Chapter 32 we will discuss the normal method of lifting nursery stock, but in this chapter we will concentrate on the equipment that has been developed for lifting extra-large nursery stock trees. An ELNS tree has a rootball, to protect the root and increase survival, of between 1·6 m (5 ft 3 in) and 2·4 m (7 ft 9 in) depending on species and size of plant.

Equipment can be divided into three main types:

1 Tree lever: the tree to be lifted is trenched around by hand or by using a trenching machine to define the rootball. The tree lever is then attached to the stem of the plant by a padded clamp. The tree is then pulled out by a levering action and the lever then acts as a trolley to carry the tree to the planting site.
2 Tree spade: the most expensive lifting equipment is the tree spade, which has hydraulically operated blades. These dig the tree up and carry it to the planting site or place it into a handling basket. Spades can either take out a V-shaped rootball or a U-shaped ball depending on the type of equipment used.
3 Tree digger: a tree digger has two hemispherical shells which have powered digging teeth. The teeth work under the tree and join to allow lifting and carrying of the tree.

A number of firms are now using mobile cranes and other lifting equipment and the success of these methods can only be judged on the survival rate of the planted trees. The trend now is towards small mobile lifters.

The important factor is rootball diameter as the bulk of the rooting zone is in the surface layers of the soil. Certain soil conditions will mean plants will have roots of proportionately less depth and greater diameter and therefore rootball widths and depths will vary.

For the most part ball specifications should be of the following ratios:

1 Balls with diameters of less than 500 mm (20 in) – depth not less than 75 per cent of diameter.
2 Balls with diameters of 500–750 mm (20–30 in) – depth not less than 65 per cent of diameter.
3 Balls with diameters of 750–1,500 mm (30–60 in) – depth not less than 60 per cent of diameter.
4 Balls with diameters of over 1,500 mm (60 in) will have the depth scaled down proportionately.

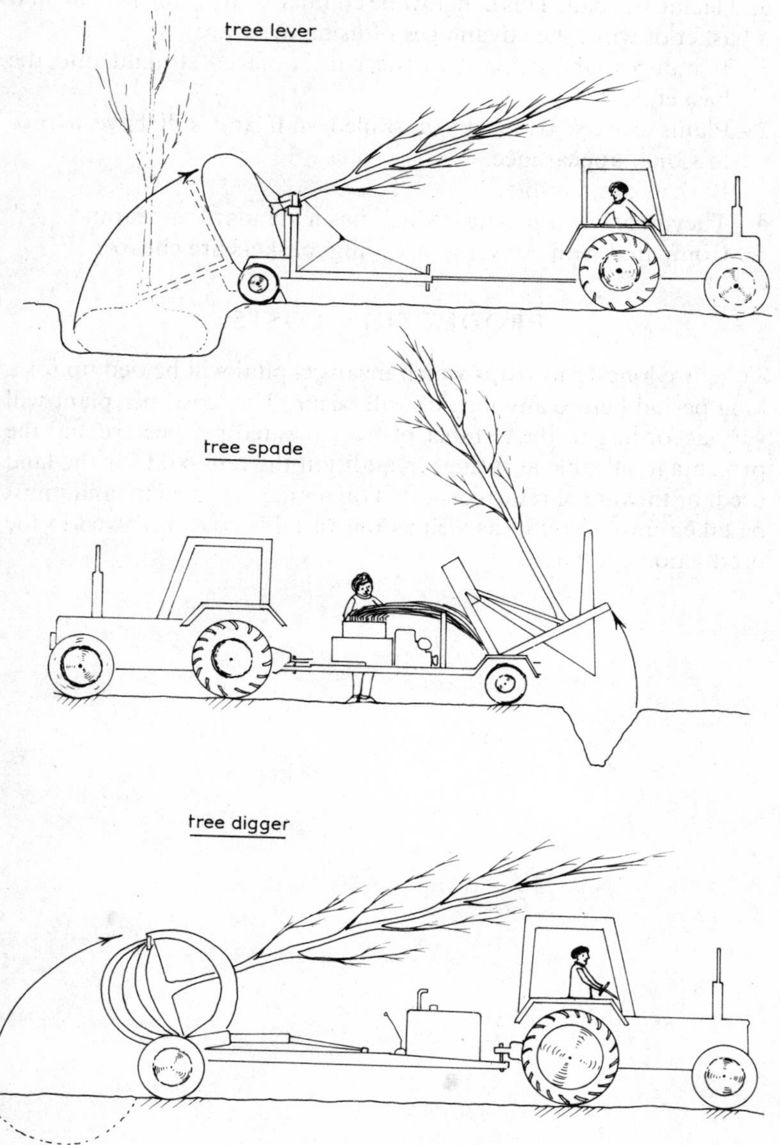

Fig. 61 Methods of lifting large trees

The old system of balling trees has been to use hessian, and tying and lacing the ball. This can now be eliminated by using hessian and a basket of wire; the advantages of using these are:

1 It reduces labour input as the ball is placed straight into the basket.
2 Plants can be balled by unskilled staff and still have a professional appearance.
3 Baskets are durable.
4 They produce a product which has a standard appearance.
5 Compared with conventional tying, baskets are cheaper.

PRODUCTION COSTS

Trees are long-term crops which means capital will be tied up for a long period before any income will occur. The 'cost' per plant will vary according to the number of trees planted per hectare and the percentage saleable at lifting. In addition the rent paid for the land used, or the rate of return expected on money invested in land, must be taken into account, as well as the variable costs involved in the production cycle.

31

Conifer production

Conifers are normally planted in the field as one- or two-year seedlings, cuttings or grafts, to be grown on for up to five years or more at a spacing of 1 m (3 ft 3 in) between plants at lifting time.

A well-drained soil and one that contains sufficient clay to hold a rootball should be selected for conifer production. Weed control and irrigation are essential, especially until the plants are established, otherwise high losses will be incurred. Generally, growing management is the same as for field-grown shrubs; we will therefore concentrate on the main points concerned with this crop.

Trimming

The customer, when selecting forms of *Chamaecyparis*, *Thuya*, *Cupressus* and some *Cryptomeria* and *Juniperus* species, requires a natural-looking plant that is well foliaged and has a natural leader. To obtain a dense symmetrical plant the nurseryman needs to trim the lateral branches to maintain one leader and vigorous dense growth. Trimming should be carried out in the summer of the year prior to sale using a pruning knife or shears and occasionally, depending on species, in the growing year prior to lifting.

Pinus species produce 'candles' of new growth and the pruning method will vary according to the product being produced. Some *Pinus*, e.g. *P. sylvestris*, should have the leader retained in the nursery, while *P. mugo* is required as a dense bush and the growing point can be pruned to encourage this habit. If candle pruning is needed it should be carried out in mid-summer by removing half of the new growth. This operation will encourage dormant adventitious buds in the lower candle to produce new shoots which will produce a bush plant.

Rootballing

Rootballing is the term used for wrapping conifers and evergreens to keep the rootball intact for handling and marketing.

Most conifers are still hand lifted using a spade with a reinforced shaft. Plants with an open habit are tied up before lifting to avoid damage during lifting and in transit. The first operation is chamfering, the removal of the top 20 mm (0·75 in) of soil, including weeds, for 150 mm (6 in) around the stem; care must be taken not to damage the stem or expose the surface roots.

At this stage, with large conifers, one may need to calculate the weight of the rootball for ease of handling. The calculation used is:

$$\text{Weight of ball} = \frac{(\text{Width})^2 \times \text{Depth}}{26}$$

This assumes that 1 m^3 (1 cu yd) of soil weighs 1,300 kg (26 cwt).

Assess the size of the rootball required and dig around the plant by pushing the spade in and rocking from side to side. Each spit should overlap slightly. When the plant is trenched completely insert the spade under the roots and gently rock the conifer to sever all roots; it can then be lifted out of the hole and on to the rootwrap.

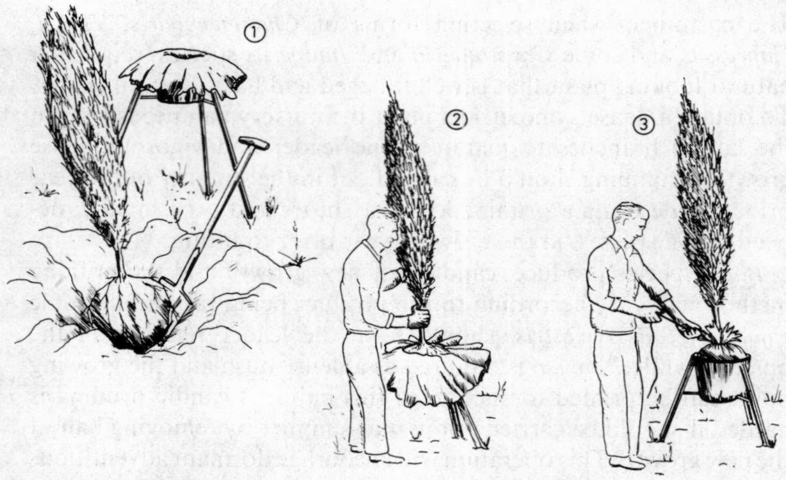

Fig. 62 A rootballing stand for conifer balling

Rootwraps normally come in squares and various types of material are available, but the requirements are that:

1 They will not restrict root development.
2 They, preferably, break down in the soil after replanting of the tree.
3 Capillary action of the material should prevent drying out of the ball.
4 They hold the weight and contain the rootball during all the handling and transporting.
5 They are easy to handle and quick to tie and knots will not slip when tied.

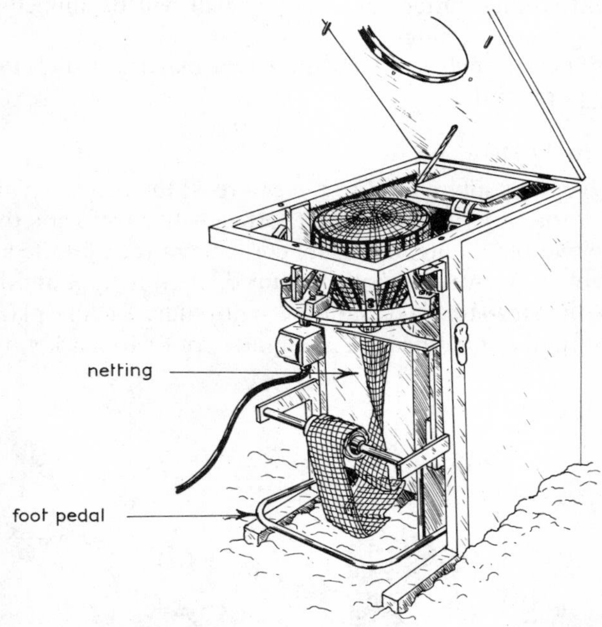

Fig. 63 Rootwrapping machine for conifers

ROOTBALLING MATERIALS

Hessian: a natural cloth product from hemp or jute, which is used as it resists natural breakdown. It is obtained in rolls or squares from 450 mm (18 in) up to 1 m (3 ft 3 in) in size. Some producers are now making foam-lined squares to conserve moisture.

Acrylic/jute: a mixture of jute and acrylonitrile, a liquid derived from the oil refining and coal carbonization process, can be obtained as rootwrap squares. This material will protect the rootball for a 12-month period without restricting the root, although it does not break down in the soil as readily as hessian.

Elastic netting: a fairly new material for horticultural use, this product can be used with rootballing machines and is very effective as a rootball container.

Rot-treated burlap: a product used in the USA which is composed of hessian impregnated with copper naphthalate or copper sulphate to prevent rotting. Often the wrapped ball will be slipped into a plastic bag for marketing.

Woven polypropylene: A plastic-based material which must be removed at planting.

WRAPPING PLANTS

The conifer is simply placed in the centre of the rootwrap and the opposite corners of the square are knotted, with a reef knot, over the ball. The two remaining, opposite, corners are then knotted, again with a reef knot, over the ball. Ensure the ball is tight and lift the plant by the stem to make sure the ball holds. Finally plants are stood out on the standing area and graded prior to marketing.

Fig. 64 Rootwrapping machine in the field

ROOTBALLING MACHINES

Equipment is being developed to wrap conifers and evergreens in a more efficient manner. Machines can either be used in the field or operated in a shed, whichever is more efficient for the particular nursery. The machine being used must be simple to handle, speed up the operation and produce a strong ball in a range of sizes.

Machines currently available have been developed in Holland, France and the USA. Some are merely simple tools to assist handling, while others will provide the complete rootballing operation (see Plates 10 to 14).

Grading

The grading of field-grown conifers is based on height, spread, and size of rootball. As a rough guide the measurement ratio of height to spread should be no less than 5:3, and the rootball specification should be as follows:

1 Balls with diameters of less than 500 mm (20 in)—depth not less than 75 per cent of diameter.
2 Balls with diameters of 500–750 mm (20–30 in)—depth not less than 66 per cent of diameter.
3 Balls with diameters of 750–1,500 mm (30–60 in)—depth not less than 60 per cent of diameter.

Rootball widths and depths will obviously vary according to soil conditions and this specification is only intended as a guide.

× *Cupressocyparis leylandii* production

One cannot complete a chapter on conifer production without mentioning Leyland cypress production. This hybrid between *Cupressus macrocarpa* and *Chamaecyparis nootkatensis* originated at Leighton Hall, Welshpool, and six seedlings were planted at Haggerston Castle, Northumberland, in 1888. In recent years this plant has become the most commonly grown ornamental conifer for hedging and screening in the garden and landscape situation, replacing the original favourites of *Lonicera nitida*, *Ligustrum* species and *Crataegus* species.

Various clones have originated giving much confusion in the nursery trade. Table 17 indicates the present situation.

Table 17 Clones of × *Cupressocyparis leylandii*

'Haggerston Castle'	Clone 1 'Green Spire' Clone 2 'Haggerston Grey' Clone 3 Clone 4 Clone 5 Clone 6
All hybrids between *Chamaecyparis nootkatensis* ♀ and *Cupressus macrocarpa* ♂.	
'Leighton Hall'	Clone 10 'Naylor's Blue' Clone 11 'Leighton Green'
Hybrids between *Cupressus macrocarpa* ♀ and *Chamaecyparis nootkatensis* ♂.	
'Stapehill'	Clone 20 Clone 21
Cupressus macrocarpa ♀ and × *Chamaecyparis nootkatensis* ♂.	

Other forms introduced include × *Cupressocyparis leylandii* 'Castlewellan', a golden hybrid between *Chamaecyparis nootkatensis* 'Lutea' and *Cupressus macrocarpa*. Variegated forms, × *Cupressocyparis leylandii* 'Rostrevor' and 'Robinson' are now being raised.

Apart from golden forms, four clones are commonly raised, although 90 per cent of the total is 'Haggerston' No. 2, the other 10 per cent being 'Leighton Hall' 10 and 11, and 'Stapehill' 20. 'Haggerston' No. 2 is easily propagated but is less vigorous, producing a badly shaped tree and often needing staking in the nursery. For hedging and screening purposes the clone we recommend is 'Leighton Hall' No. 11.

Leyland cypress can be grown either in the field or in containers, although, because of the coarse root system, most growers are turning to container production.

Field versus container production

Conifer production generally, except for large specimens, is changing from field to container growing. The reasons for this change are numerous, but the main one is market preference for a container-grown plant which is clean and easily handled by the customer, who can purchase and plant any time of the year.

The grower has a higher investment with container plants at the beginning of the crop, having to purchase pots and compost, while a field-grown crop has a high investment at lifting, that is, labour and rootwrap materials.

Many producers of field-grown conifers have found the disease *Phytophthora* has become a problem, resulting in plant losses, and this has also had some influence in the change-over.

32

Lifting and storing field-grown crops

One of the highest labour peaks in nursery production occurs in the autumn when large numbers of plants have to be lifted and prepared for sale in the shortest possible time. Historically, hand lifting has been the standard method, but mechanical means are now replacing this method, being quicker, cheaper and often leaving the root in better condition than if it was hand lifted.

LIFTING

Hand lifting

The spade is still the main tool for lifting and it is important that a lifting spade (one with a metal reinforcement up the shaft) is used, otherwise the shaft will often be broken when under pressure. The majority of hand lifting is carried out by retail growers who are unable to lift a whole batch in one operation but need to select to customers' requirements.

Firstly, the operative must select the tree or shrub to be lifted, and any support and ties must be removed before lifting commences. Then one must assess the distance from the plant at which lifting should begin; if the spade encounters too many roots then the trench is too near and if no roots are encountered then it is too far away.

With large subjects a trench of one spit or more in depth is required around the plant. If the plant is small then a slit with the spade all the way round should be adequate.

After lifting, the plant should be inspected, and damaged and very long roots removed. Ensure individual plants or batches are labelled. They should then have their roots protected until storage or dispatch.

Mechanical lifting

Wholesale lifting is carried out with special lifting ploughs, which undercut the plants and partially, or completely, lift them out of the ground. Most lifters leave the root in better condition than in hand-lifted plants and therefore survival should be better (see Plate 9).

The simplest lifters are based on strongly constructed under-cutters. Some of these have p.t.o.-driven shaking mechanisms which loosen the soil from around bare-root plants and assist with the lifting. Most lifters are either U- or J-shaped. A large U is ideal for lifting plants on a bed system; and a J, often off-set from the tractor, is ideal for single rows.

Some lifters are pulled along the rows by a tractor-mounted winch, which is ideal for larger stock, although heavy equipment is needed, and then single or double cable can be a hazard. Winched lifters are useful where off-set J-blade undercutters are not strong enough to lift the plants concerned.

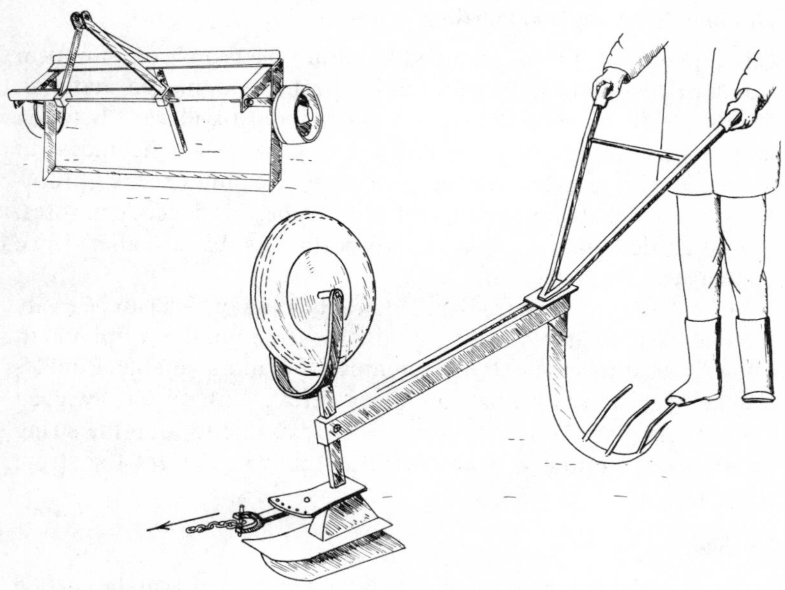

Fig. 65 Lifting equipment

A more recent development in lifting equipment is the use of a U-shaped blade coupled with a share, which lifts the plants between two rubber conveyor belts and shakes any remaining soil out of the root system, assuming it is a bare-root plant. The conveyor then delivers the plants to a separate trailer or bundling machine. This eliminates excessive handling of plant material, but is only useful where large numbers of an individual species are required at one time.

Dehydration

Earlier we mentioned the importance of protecting roots and this cannot be over-stressed. Dehydration occurs when the plant is deprived of water. Drying easterly winds on unprotected roots soon kill the root hairs and often the plant does not have sufficient food reserves to produce new ones, resulting in a check in growth.

Delay = Dehydration

Delay often occurs at lifting, awaiting collection, on the journey to the storage area, at unloading, awaiting packing and at packing. At all these points roots must be protected as necessary.

Grading, trimming and bundling

Lifted plants need to be trimmed to ensure the crop is of a uniform standard for the customer and also to remove damaged material. Plants are then graded, although the standard will vary between crops and growers. Some plants are graded on height and stem circumference, e.g. trees; others on stem circumference, e.g. rootstocks; and others on the number of branches produced, e.g. roses. A well-graded bundle of plants is important as this will affect price and customer satisfaction.

Once graded, plants are bundled into batches, which can be easily handled. Each batch should contain the same number of plants to allow for easy assessment of the number of plants available. Bundles are tied with string or other suitable material. With smooth-twigged subjects such as *Cornus* and *Salix* it is advisable to loop the string around a few branches when tying as this will prevent the string slipping.

Mechanical bundling

Bundling of plants such as roses, soft fruit and shrubs can be carried out mechanically by using a bundling machine. The standard machine is driven by an electric motor and can also be linked to a tractor p.t.o. for use in the field. Operation of the machine is simple and plants are tightly bundled.

STORAGE

Any storage area should have easy access for loading and unloading plant material. It is often advisable to have an area close at hand where plants can be assembled for packing and dispatch. Storage of plant material can be divided into two groups: short-term and long-term storage.

Short-term storage

Plants in short-term storage should only be held for a few weeks before being replanted or dispatched. Storage always increases the cost and should only be used if there is no alternative or if there will be an increase in profit. With this in mind short-term storage facilities should be cheaply constructed and an earth floor is adequate within structures.

The simplest is an open store in the field. Many nurseries construct cheap 'heeling-in' areas where bays have been constructed, and peat, leafmould or straw are used to protect the plants. It is important that these areas are protected from winter winds and are not built in an area likely to suffer from waterlogging.

The next type of store is the covered 'heeling-in' area (construction of a roof over the bays) to allow sorting and packing in wet or snowy weather.

Finally a fully enclosed building can be constructed with ground-level bays or racks. Natural or artificial light is essential to allow work in the area. Doors and passages must be wide enough to allow access by tractors and dispatch vehicles. A water source should be near at hand to damp down plant material if the atmosphere becomes too dry.

Long-term storage

Plant material can now be stored throughout the winter and into the following summer. When long-term storage is planned, more sophisticated equipment is required and this is inevitably linked to a higher capital investment.

Interest in cold stores for nursery stock first started in the 1950s in Denmark. Originally, direct-cooled apple stores were considered. A direct-cooled storage unit is an insulated building with the evaporator (cooling unit) within the storage area. The result of this is that air movement occurs in the store, which means plant material is exposed to dehydration and any disease spores which are in the air. When using a direct-cooled unit nurserymen have to place material in polythene bags to avoid drying out; this is time-consuming and, in many cases, impractical.

Because of the above problems growers now prefer indirect or jacket stores. In these stores a second inner wall is built separated by a cavity from the outer wall. Cold air is then circulated through the cavity and around the jacket (inner wall) by the evaporator; this cools the inner wall and therefore, indirectly, the air within the store. The result is no air movement within the store and nursery stock can be stored bare-root without fear of dehydration.

INDIRECT STORAGE

Inside the 'jacket' the heat generated is only slight and the cool air circulating around the unit maintains a very low temperature inside

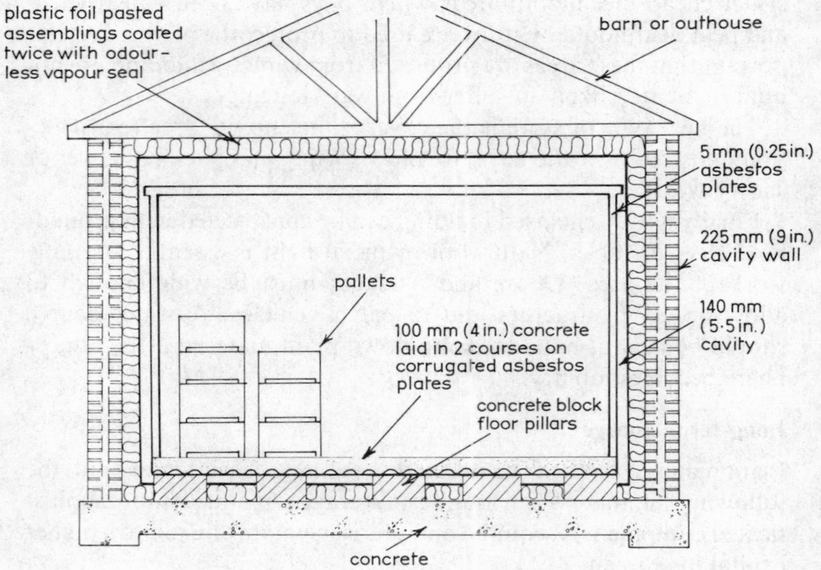

Fig. 66 A jacketed cold store

the store. A number of considerations need to be taken into account when storing plant material. Firstly, humidity should be maintained at a relative humidity (RH) of 95 per cent; this will prevent drying out of plant material. Humidity can be checked by using a whirling hygrometer and maintained by watering the floor, or in more advanced stores, by a misting unit in the ceiling.

Temperature regimes should remain between 0 and 2 °C (32–35·5 °F). Below 0 °C (32 °F) damage to plant material will occur due to freezing. Above 2 °C (35·5 °F) plants start to grow and fungal moulds reproduce rapidly.

The main concern in cold storage is the development of fungal diseases. Fungi will attack unripe parts of plants or wounded areas, which often appear during lifting. Weak plants, especially those which have been given high nitrogen, are particularly at risk, and wet foliage can also be affected. It is therefore important that foliage should be dry and plants lifted carefully. A fungicide can be used in the store and dichlofluralin is recommended as it remains active down to 2 °C (35·5 °F) while others are inactivated below 5 °C (41 °F).

A problem that often occurs with evergreens when stored for long periods is browning of the foliage. The reason for this is that they will continue to grow above 0 °C (32 °F) with the result that their nutrient store is depleted. One way of overcoming this problem is to spray the foliage at monthly intervals with 1 per cent urea, 1 per cent magnesium sulphate and 98 per cent water.

Some plants cannot withstand cooling and darkness for longer than a six-month period and are therefore not recommended for very long-term storage. These include: *Buddleia davidii* 'Black Knight'; *Camellia* 'Campbellii'; *Cedrus atlantica* 'Glauca'; *Clematis* (under one year old); young *Cotoneaster* plants; *Escallonia*; *Hypericum* 'Hidcote'; *Ilex aquifolium* 'Golden King' and *Rhododendron russatum*.

THE ADVANTAGES OF COLD STORING NURSERY STOCK

1 Time used for 'heeling-in' can be replaced by cold storage.
2 Plants can be lifted in ideal weather conditions and cold stored until required.
3 Land can be cleared and prepared for the next crop in favourable conditions.

4 Plants are stored under cover so packing and dispatch can continue during inclement weather.
5 Plants in store remain dormant which means the planting season can be extended, even up to July, without damage.
6 Plants can be exported or transported to northern areas, e.g. Scandinavia, and receive no check in growth due to differing climatic conditions.

Uses of a cold store

The obvious use of a cold store is for the storage of hardy ornamental plants between lifting and dispatch, but to make maximum value out of the store it must be considered for other uses.

1 Seed storage and seed germination: seed can be stored in cold conditions and a store is especially useful for subjects such as *Acer pseudoplatanus* and *Quercus* species; often deep freezing of −10 to −20 °C (14 to −4 °F) will be of no harm. Some seed needs cold to assist in germination and the store could also be used for this purpose. An example is apple which requires ten weeks at 5 °C (41 °F) prior to germination. Not all subjects can be germinated in this way, for instance *Rhododendron* and *Azalea* seed need light as well as cold treatment for germination.
2 Storage of cuttings: hardwood cuttings of material such as *Malus*, *Prunus*, *Platanus* and *Populus* can be stored in cold conditions until the rooting area has been prepared.
3 Storage of strawberry runners and herbaceous plants: the maximum yield of strawberries from maiden plants is from the early planting of runners, and there is a large demand for early lifted runners. Growers are therefore lifting and storing runners so they can deliver for planting when required. During the summer these runners establish better than freshly dug plants, provided irrigation is supplied, and the result is a far heavier yield of fruit.

   Herbaceous plants can also be treated in the same way and produce healthy plants during the next summer.
4 Storage of budwood: budwood can be stored for up to one year enabling grafting and budding to be more precisely planned.
5 Plant-growth control: many growers display their produce at various local and national flower shows. By using a cold store they can manipulate plants so that, for example, they will flower out of their natural season, but in time for the show.

Cold-stored container-grown roses can also be induced to produce a second flush of bloom which could assist retail sales.

6 Tree seedlings: as mentioned earlier one can retard growth so that it matches a climate to the north of the grower. This enables the grower to sell plant material to northern outlets such as Scotland, Scandinavia or northern USA and Canada.

Prior to sale, plants should be graded. Bare-root material is bundled with all shoots facing in the same direction. Any foliage on the plants should be surface-dry to reduce any possibility of heating up. Bundles are tied with string, twine, plastic strip or other suitable material which will not damage the plants. If trees are being bundled then the heads must be securely tied in to reduce damage.

Part 6

SPECIALIST PRODUCTION SYSTEMS

33

Alpines and herbaceous plants

In Chapters 33–7 we deal with the more specialized crops in detail, from their propagation to saleable stage. There are nurseries, of course, which are true specialists, for example, growing only alpines, aquatic plants, or perhaps clematis or herbaceous plants. These nurseries have organized their production systems to a fine art and the staff on such nurseries have acquired a deep knowledge of their particular crop. Of course there is very little that we can offer to such growers and so this section is aimed more at the general nurseryman who may be growing one or more of the following crops together with a range of other crops. The first group of crops we plan to discuss are alpines and herbaceous plants.

ALPINES

There are various methods of producing alpines such as by seed, division, stem cuttings and root cuttings. There are also one or two subjects that can even be raised from leaf cuttings. We will deal with each of these systems in turn, emphasizing that we are only considering the more common and popular plants here, not the really choice specialist subjects which are better left to the really knowledgeable alpine enthusiasts.

Stock plants

As with other hardy nursery stock, you will need a collection of stock plants of alpines, from which you can obtain propagation material at the optimum times of year. Probably one of the most convenient ways of growing stock plants of alpines is in low raised beds constructed perhaps of railway sleepers, bricks or concrete blocks. The plants can then be planted in groups on these beds in a gritty well-drained compost, which they enjoy. The fact that the beds are slightly raised will also help to ensure well-drained conditions. The surface of the beds can be covered with a layer of shingle which helps to prevent growth of moss and liverwort, conserve soil moisture and keep the roots of the plants cool. Most alpines like a situation in full sun but there are some which need partial shade and these could be grown under a lath area (see Plate 15).

Production from seed

Many species are easily seed-raised and this is an especially useful method for those which are impossible to propagate by other methods, such as plants which have no suitable vegetative parts which could be used for increase, for instance, *Meconopsis*, some *Papaver* species and various *Primula* species. Some subjects, although they make vegetative growth which appears to be suitable propagation material, are virtually impossible to propagate by anything other than seed—for instance some *Androsace* species come in this category. But for many other subjects seed probably offers the most productive means of increase.

The main period for sowing seed of alpines is January and February. A suitable compost is John Innes seed compost but for ericaceous plants and other lime haters you will need to omit chalk and use an acid loam. Often pans are used for sowing small quantities of seeds, although for large amounts standard seed trays could be used. Pans are really to be preferred as of course they hold a greater depth of compost, which is useful if pricking out cannot be carried out at the optimum time. Also some seed which is slow to germinate may remain in the containers for many months and will be less prone to rapid drying out if in pans.

A layer of fine grit can be placed on the surface of the compost and the seeds sown on this. The seeds can then be covered with another layer of the same material. Of course, for very fine seed, such as that of many *Primula* and alpine *Rhododendron* species, one should sow on a finely prepared compost surface and leave the seeds uncovered. The seeds can be germinated in cold frames and should be given good ventilation at all times. In fact, if the seeds are periodically frozen this will considerably help germination.

Some seeds have a short viability period and should be sown as soon as ripe. Sound seed will then germinate quickly. Examples of subjects include some of the *Primula* species, especially those in the Petiolaris section such as *P. gracillipes* and *P. whitei*; *Androsace*; *Corydalis*; *Lewisia*; *Meconopsis* and *Ranunculus*. The method of sowing and germinating is as outlined above.

You may well find that some subjects are slow to germinate and may need a long period of cold treatment before germination commences, so do not be in too much of a hurry to discard pans of seed if they do not germinate in the spring after sowing. Some may well need another winter in the propagation frames and then, in the second spring, will germinate like mustard and cress. Some of the dwarf or alpine bulbs have this characteristic as do various other plants such as some species of *Gentiana* and *Trillium*.

When seedlings are large enough to handle they should be pricked out – ideally into individual 75 mm (3 in) pots. If some seedlings are very tiny then it would be better to prick them out first of all into seed trays and then move them on into pots when larger. But try to avoid this double handling if possible. More details of pots and composts will be found further on in this section, together with growing-on procedures.

Production by division

Division or splitting of alpines is the simplest form of vegetative propagation and is widely practised on nurseries dealing with this crop. The mat-forming and carpeting alpines, which spread by rooting at the nodes, and those which form runners and offsets, can be increased by division. Examples include *Androsace sarmentosa* (offsets), *Chiastophyllum*, dwarf grasses, *Gentiana sino-ornata*, *Geranium*, *Lysimachia*, *Polygonum*, *Pratia*, *Primula*, *Raoulia*, *Saxifraga* (e.g. mossy and rosette-forming types), *Sedum*, *Sempervivum* (offsets) and *Thymus*.

Use young outer portions of stock plants and discard the old centre portion. Excess saleable plants could be used for division, retaining every portion of the entire plant. It is difficult to indicate the precise size of divisions but one should aim to ensure saleable plants which fill a 75 mm (3 in) pot in 12 months from propagation. Each division should equal approximately one-third to half the compost surface of a 75 mm pot.

The best time for division is during the period April and early May when the plants are starting into growth. Ensure each portion has an adequate amount of fibrous roots. Offsets, as produced by *Sempervivum*, are easily detached from the parent plants and are generally fairly well rooted. Each offset can be given an individual 75 mm (3 in) pot. Further details of pots and composts and growing-on procedures are discussed later in this section.

Stem cuttings

Many alpines can be propagated from softwood stem cuttings taken in the period April to early July. Try to propagate from young lateral growths after flowering, otherwise remove any flower buds during cutting preparation. The cuttings are of the straightforward nodal type, the length depending on the subject, but most are in the region of 50–75 mm (2–3 in). Strip off the lower leaves before insertion and treat with a hormone rooting powder formulated for softwoods, and add a fungicide to it to reduce rotting off.

Cuttings can be rooted in trays of cutting compost consisting of 75 per cent grit and 25 per cent sphagnum peat—this gives a well-drained and aerated rooting medium. The cuttings can be rooted in a mist-propagation unit with a bottom temperature of 21 °C (70 °F). It is essential to provide good ventilation at all times—in fact the cuttings do not require a high air temperature. It is better not to root woolly- or hairy-leaved subjects under mist as excess water can be trapped by the hairs and may cause foliage to rot off. Instead, root them on a glasshouse bench with soil-warming cables, again providing a temperature at the base of 21 °C and good ventilation. Depending on the subject, cuttings will root in approximately three to four weeks, at which stage they can be potted off and grown on as described further on in this section.

There is a very long list of plants that can be increased from softwood cuttings, but some typical examples include: *Achillea*; *Alyssum*; *Arabis*; *Armeria*; *Artemisia*; *Campanula*; some *Cytisus*; *Daphne cneorum*; *Dianthus*; *Genista*; *Gentiana sino-ornata*; *Helianthemum*; *Hypericum*; *Linum*; *Lithospermum*; *Origanum*; *Penstemon*; *Phlox subulata* and cultivars; *Saponaria*; some *Saxifraga*; *Sedum*; *Silene*; some *Thymus* and *Veronica*.

Aubrieta, although it produces plenty of soft young growth in the spring, seems to be more successful from hardwood cuttings taken in October or November and rooted in cold frames. Take three or four stems together and pot them off into 75 mm (3 in) pots of potting compost.

Root cuttings

Some alpines can be propagated from root cuttings taken in autumn and rooted in trays of cutting compost in cold frames. Full details of this method are given in Chapter 11. Examples of plants which can be increased from root cuttings are also given in Chapter 11.

Leaf cuttings

Two hardy members of the *Gesneriaceae* family, *Haberlea rhodopensis* and *Ramonda myconi*, can be propagated from leaf cuttings in June or July. Take entire young leaves and leave the petiole intact. The cuttings should be inserted so that two-thirds of the leaf blade remains above compost level. Use a cutting compost consisting of 75 per cent grit and 25 per cent sphagnum peat. Cold frames are preferred for these leaf cuttings which should be well rooted by August, at which stage they should be potted off.

Pots and composts

When potting off alpines, whether seedlings, divisions or rooted cuttings, use 75 mm (3 in) pots—the plants are sold in these. Ideally square pots should be used as these take up far less growing space than round pots. When growing on, the plants are generally stood pot thick. There are many different types of potting compost for alpines, and in fact some of the choice and difficult species do require rather special mixes if they are to survive. But for the easily grown common plants we have found that a modified John Innes potting compost No. 1 is suitable. All we do is to add an extra quantity of coarse grit (say about one-third of extra grit) to a given volume of John Innes potting compost No. 1. Alpines need a well-drained and well-aerated compost and this extra grit ensures these conditions. Do not forget that if you are potting lime-hating alpines then use an acid ericaceous mix. Very often an acid loamless compost is suitable for these plants.

Growing on to saleable stage

Once young seedlings, divisions, rooted cuttings, etc., have been potted off they can be stood pot thick in open cold frames on a bed of sand or ashes. There is no need to wean off young plants as they have been propagated in well-ventilated conditions. Small pots will, of course, dry out rapidly in warm weather and therefore a permanent overhead irrigation system should be installed in the frames. Water regularly in the summer but keep the plants only slightly moist in winter.

In fact, throughout the winter the young plants should be protected from excessive wetness by replacing the frame lights. However, alpines do not need to be coddled for they are perfectly hardy – they just need protection from excess rain. So prop up the frame lights to ensure good ventilation at all times.

Weed control in pots can be a problem and hand weeding is often carried out. However there is a residual herbicide which can be used on many plants. This is propachlor which is applied in granular form, but granules should be prevented from lodging on the foliage of mat-forming and carpeting plants. It is effective in preventing weed-seed germination for up to six weeks. Apply according to the manufacturer's instructions. It would be advisable to carry out small-scale trials on as wide a range of plant material as possible to ascertain which plants tolerate this herbicide before using it on a regular basis.

With many subjects saleable plants can be produced in 12 months from propagation. This applies, very often, to seed-raised plants, and certainly to those from divisions and cuttings. Dwarf bulbs, incidentally, generally take up to three years to reach flowering size and they would be sold as dry bulbs. Very often alpines are marketed in mixed collections for garden-centre sales. The main sale season is late March to mid-June.

HERBACEOUS PLANTS

There are various methods of producing herbaceous plants, such as division, root cuttings, softwood cuttings and seed, but for most nurserymen division is probably the most important. However, we will discuss each method in turn. We are including evergreen perennials in this chapter as well as true herbaceous subjects.

Division

Our policy is to use the least amount of stock material for the maximum increase and to do the work in the comfort of a potting shed during the winter in a slack period.

The dormant crowns are lifted when required and thoroughly washed free of soil. Our stock material is in fact taken from the crop of young saleable plants and we allow for this during propagation (of course, two- to three-year-old plants would yield far more propagation material). The crowns are split into as many pieces as

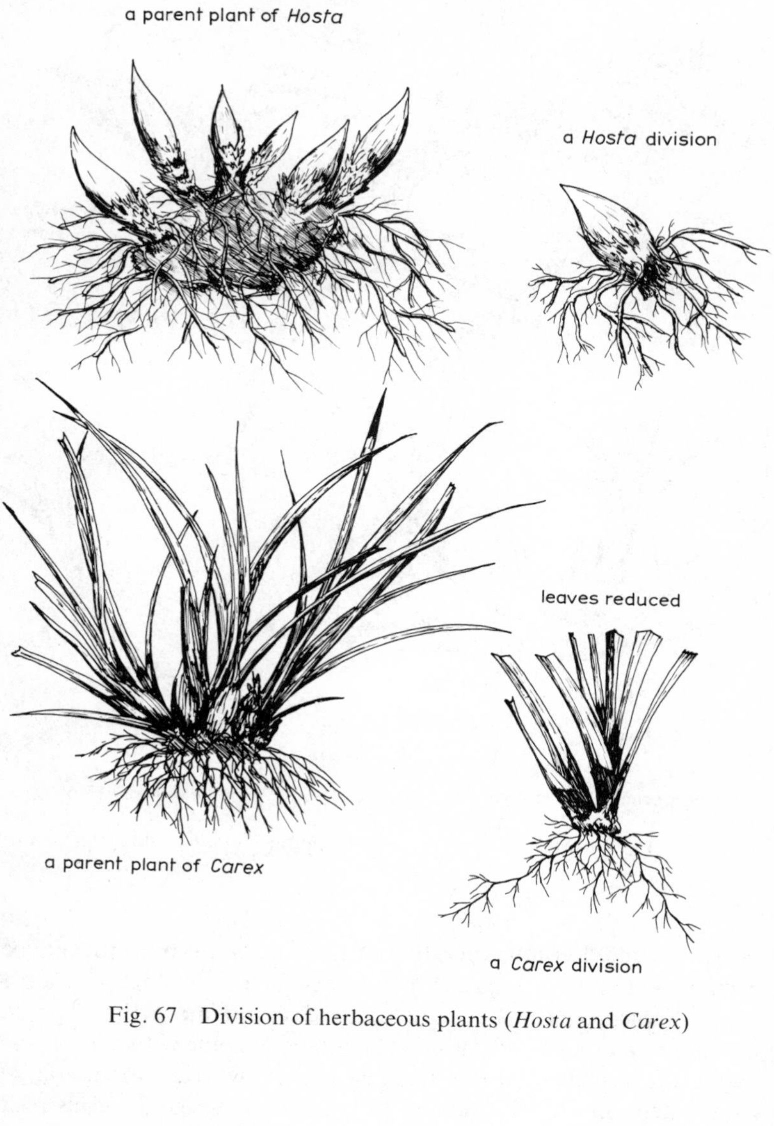

Fig. 67 Division of herbaceous plants (*Hosta* and *Carex*)

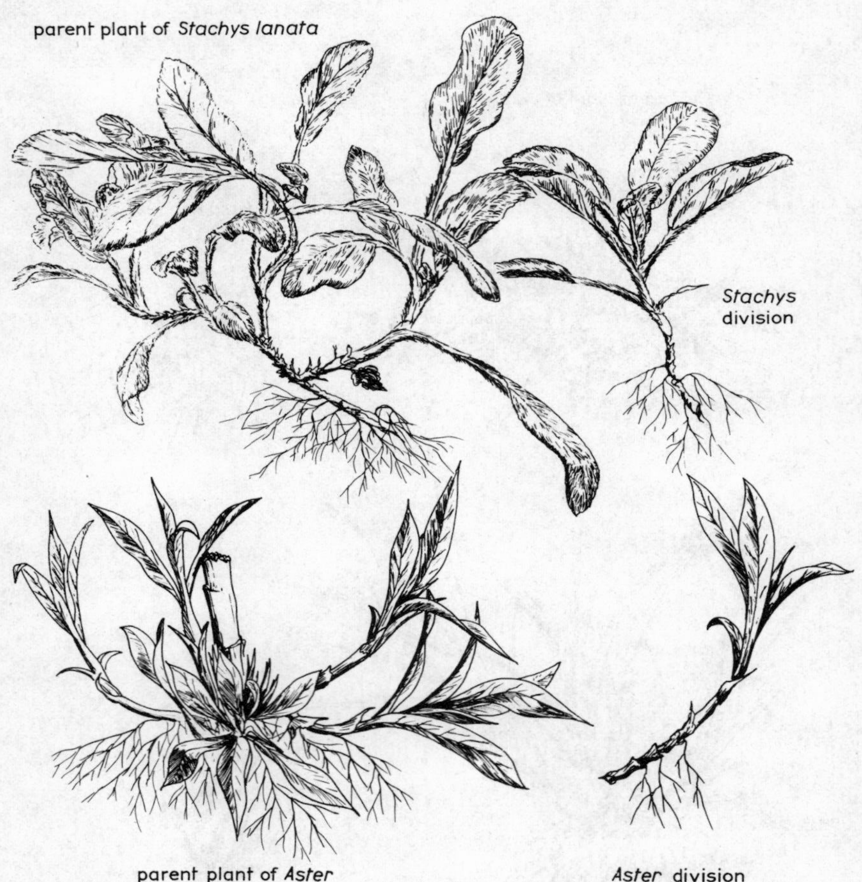

Fig. 68 Division of herbaceous plants (*Stachys* and *Aster*)

possible, each division consisting of some dormant buds (or maybe even a single bud in the case of subjects such as hostas) plus some roots. Subjects like asters are reduced to no more than rooted cuttings – in other words, a short length of rhizome with a few roots and a tuft of leaves. At this stage we are not worried about a large root system on each division as we aim to encourage vigorous root activity between propagation stage and lining out.

During splitting, any dead leaves and stems are removed and with evergreen perennials, with tufts of long foliage, such as *Carex*, *Liriope* and ornamental grasses, we reduce the leaves by about half their length. This cutting back encourages very vigorous and compact growth in the spring.

The next stage is to lay the divisions in wooden trays, such as tomato trays, in a well-aerated and well-drained compost to encourage the development of a substantial root system prior to lining out in the spring. We use a standard cutting compost consisting of equal parts sphagnum peat and crushed grit. It is possible to pack up to 100 divisions in a tomato tray, or 40 to 50 larger ones. They can be packed fairly close together in rows across the tray. By April or May even those divisions that had only a few roots at the time of splitting will have made a substantial amount of fibrous root.

The trays are then placed in a sheltered standing area out of doors on polythene topped with shingle. They are left until the ground is in a suitable condition for planting in the spring.

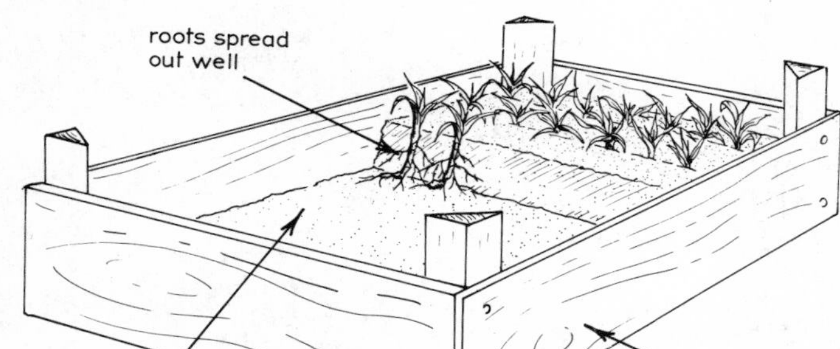

Fig. 69 Boxing divisions of perennials

The divisions are lined out into well-cultivated and manured, weed-free soil. We line out in 1 m (3 ft 3 in) wide beds separated by 600 mm (2 ft) wide paths. The beds are raised about 75 mm (3 in) to ensure reasonably good drainage particularly if the soil is rather wet.

The divisions are lined out across the width of each bed in blocks of one species or cultivar, allowing about 600 mm (2 ft) between each block. The number of divisions in each row depends on the vigour of the subject but we space the rows about 300 mm (1 ft) apart. On a small scale lining out is done by hand in slit trenches taken out with a spade. However, the well-rooted divisions are suitable for lining out by machine if large-scale production is contemplated.

It is important to apply a herbicide immediately after lining out to control germinating weed seeds. The soil-acting herbicide lenacil applied as an overall spray to moist soil is particularly useful and gives very good weed control over the entire growing season and we do not have to hand weed or hoe. However, some perennials are rather sensitive to lenacil—we have found this to be the case with many ornamental grasses and also members of the *Liliaceae* family. We prefer to control weeds among these by manual methods.

By the following autumn, provided the plants have been adequately irrigated during dry conditions, the plants are of a saleable size and are sold as bare-root specimens.

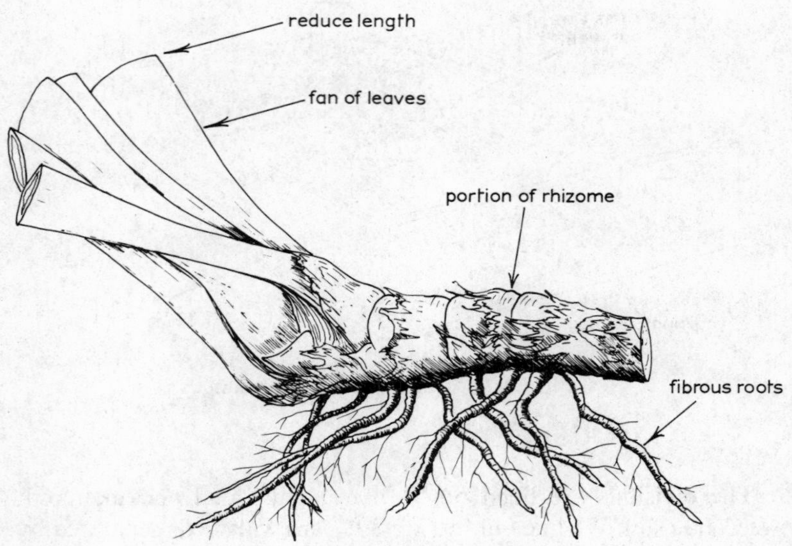

Fig. 70 Division of a bearded iris

There are some exceptions to the timing of this method of production. These are early-flowering subjects like *Iris*, *Doronicum*, *Pyrethrum* and *Epimedium*. Ideally these should be split immediately after flowering (when they are, in fact, starting to make vigorous growth) and lined out straight away. The usual time for *Iris* division is in June or early July. Each division should consist of a portion of rhizome (swollen stem), with roots attached and a fan of leaves which can be reduced by half. With *Epimedium* the rhizomes, which are being vigorously produced after flowering, can be cut up, each piece having some roots attached, and lined out in the field.

Dicing *Bergenia* rhizomes

The evergreen bergenias can be increased by cutting up the thick fleshy rhizomes. In January the plants are lifted and thoroughly washed free of soil. The old rhizomes (obtainable from two to three-year-old plants) are then cut up into 25–35 mm (1–1·5 in) long pieces each containing a dormant growth bud. They are dusted with captan fungicide to prevent rotting. The diced rhizomes are then inserted horizontally, bud uppermost, in seed trays of Perlite, which is a sterile rooting medium. There is no need to cover the sections of rhizome completely—just press them into the Perlite, leaving the buds showing.

The seed trays are placed on a heated bench with a bottom temperature of 21 °C (70 °F) and for the first few days are covered with clear polythene sheeting, the edges of which should be tucked under the trays to ensure high humidity within. Do not forget to water in the rhizomes before covering with polythene. The dormant buds are forced into growth within a matter of a few days, after which the polythene can be removed. The trays should remain on the heated bench to encourage root development.

As soon as roots have been produced the bergenias should be potted off—we use compressed peat pots. Allow the plants to become well established, preferably under heated glass, and then gradually harden them off in frames or tunnels ready for lining out in May. One should then have saleable plants by the following autumn onwards.

We find this a useful method for quickly building up stocks of the newer more expensive *Bergenia* cultivars like 'Sunningdale', 'Ballawley', 'Abendglut', 'Morgenrote' and 'Silberlicht'.

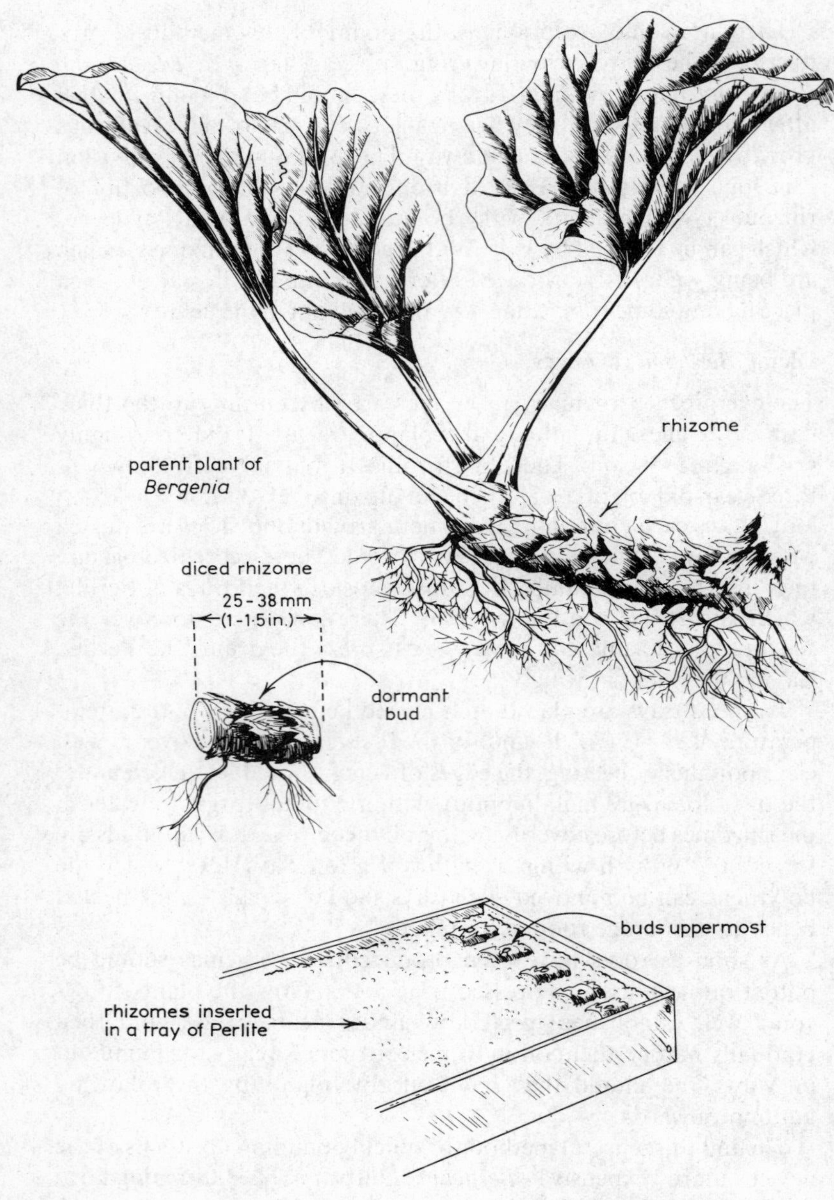

Fig. 71 Dicing of *Bergenia* rhizomes

Root cuttings

As will be seen in the list of plants included in Chapter 11, quite a wide range of herbaceous plants and other hardy perennials can be produced from root cuttings. As this method of production has been discussed in detail in Chapter 11, we only intend to give a brief mention of it here. Generally, if the root cuttings are inserted in cold frames then sizeable plants will be obtained within 12 months. These can be either lined out to make further growth or containerized. Stock plants of about two to three years old yield a far greater amount of suitable roots than, say, one-year-old stock, although some nurserymen do take propagation material from 12-month-old plants during lifting.

Softwood cuttings

Many herbaceous plants can be propagated from the soft young shoots produced by the crowns in the spring. Examples include *Lupinus*, *Delphinium*, *Kirengeshoma*, *Sedum spectabile* and cultivars, *Euphorbia* species and cultivars, *Scrophularia*, *Veronica*, *Valeriana*, *Achillea*, *Coreopsis*, *Gaillardia*, *Helenium* and *Scabiosa*.

Aim to take cuttings about 50–75 mm (2–3 in) in length and remove them from as close to the crown of the plant as possible. They can be rooted in trays of cutting compost either in a mist-propagation unit (but not for hairy-leaved subjects) or under polythene with bottom heat. Try to choose non-flowering shoots wherever possible. Once rooted they can be potted off and hardened off in tunnels or cold frames, eventually to be containerized or lined out in beds. Again 12 months should see saleable-sized plants.

Leaf cuttings

This is a method which can be used for the ground-cover perennial *Tolmiea menziesii*, for this subject produces young plants at the base of the leaves. This is known as viviparous reproduction. Leaves, complete with petioles, can be removed in the spring or early summer and inserted up to the base of the leaves in seed trays of cutting compost. The trays can then be placed in a heated propagation house to root. If the leaves do not have plantlets at the base during collection, they will soon produce them under heated conditions. As soon as the leaf cuttings have rooted and the plantlets are starting to develop, they can be potted off and hardened off in tunnels or cold frames. Saleable plants can again be obtained within about 12 months from propagation.

Root grafting *Gypsophila*

Cultivars of *Gypsophila*, such as 'Bristol Fairy' and 'Flamingo', are produced by root grafting. The rootstocks on which the cultivars are grafted are roots of *Gypsophila paniculata*, these being raised from seed. They are lifted in the autumn and kept fairly dry under tunnels until required for grafting in March. Roots about 12 mm (0·5 in) thick and about 75 mm (3 in) long are required.

The scion material is obtained from plants grown in cold frames to produce soft growth. The scions are prepared about 50 mm (2 in) in length and they have their lower leaves removed and the base cut to a wedge shape.

The top of the *paniculata* root is firstly cut flat and then a 12 mm (0·5 in) vertical cut is made in the top of this stock. This cut is then prised open, the scion is inserted by pushing it in, the pressure is released and the scion is then held firmly in place. However, it may be necessary to tie in the scion as it can become dislodged during subsequent handling.

The grafts can then be planted out into heated frames and will take five to six weeks to unite. Generally one can expect a high 'take' in the region of 80–90 per cent.

By May the grafts can be lined out in field beds or, of course, they may be containerized for garden-centre sales. One season's growth is needed to produce saleable-sized plants. If field grown, lifting can therefore commence from October onwards.

Seed

Finally, we should mention the production of herbaceous plants from seed. This is a useful method for producing straight species, especially if your stock plants set good crops of fertile seed.

Sowing is quite straightforward, it can be carried out in the open ground in April or May for the majority of subjects; but for very fine seed it would be better to sow in more controlled conditions, such as in seed trays and germinating under glass. Once seedlings in the open ground are large enough to handle they can be lined out in beds and grown on to saleable size. Or they could be containerized. From seed, the majority of species will make saleable-sized plants in one year. However, subjects like *Bergenia* will take two years from seed to make saleable plants while *Helleborus* species will take up to three years.

Marketing herbaceous plants

There are various methods of marketing herbaceous plants. For instance, many nurserymen who grow plants in the field market them as pre-packs or root wrapped. Often these are offered in collections of plants for retail sale. For local retail sales plants could be offered bare-root, thereby reducing the cost of packing materials and therefore the cost of plants.

We have already indicated that herbaceous plants can be containerized for garden-centre sales and indeed this is now a popular method for retail sales. Most nurserymen use 90–100 mm (3·5–4 in) polythene bags, although to our way of thinking some of the subjects that make large plants, like *Hosta* for example, would probably be better in a 150 mm (6 in) bag. Herbaceous plants can, however, be a difficult container crop, for the plants can end up rather straggly and with undersized flowers. Flower quality is important for retail sales as herbaceous plants are generally bought on impulse when in full flower. Often the plants need caning to prevent flopping over whereas in the field they seem to make more sturdy growth.

In garden centres the turnover is often low and therefore many establishments reduce their range to the most popular six to ten subjects. There are some nurseries which specialize in the more unusual plants and they find that there is often a steady demand from discerning gardeners.

34

Lime haters

RHODODENDRONS

Rhododendrons comprise one of the biggest groups of plants, and are found in Asia, Europe and America. The diversity of wild species has produced many hybrids, giving variation in size, flower, foliage and hardiness. Rhododendrons can be produced by various methods, and production is best studied by dividing the genus into smaller production systems.

Deciduous azaleas

Deciduous azaleas either root easily from cuttings or are exceedingly difficult; the degree of rooting varies with different cultivars. The following is a list of cultivars likely to root without difficulty:

1 Knaphill and Exbury azaleas: 'Berry Rose', 'White Swan', 'Persil', 'Galipoli', 'Marion Meriman', 'Toucan', 'Gibraltar', 'Klondike', 'Harvest Moon'.
2 *Mollis sinensis* azaleas: 'Koster's Brilliant Red', 'Baron E. de Rothschild', 'Queen Emma', 'Lemonora', 'Dr M. Oesthoek', 'Mrs Peter Koster', 'Adrian Koster', 'Dr Moerlands', 'T.D. Seidel'.

To obtain early cutting material it is advisable to plant the stock plants in a polythene structure, which is left unclad until January. When cladding, also give the plants a mulch of spent hops to conserve moisture.

Cuttings can be taken from forced plants between mid-March and May. Material is dipped in a rooting hormone before being inserted in pure peat and placed under a mist unit with a bottom heat temperature of 21 °C (70 °F). Rooted cuttings should be weaned from the rooting environment by July, when they are grown on in a deep frame equipped with spraylines and supplementary lighting. Maximum growth can be induced by using lighting between July and

September to give three hours' extra light per day. Dormancy should be induced in September although heating cables can be used in the frames to keep cuttings frost free. During the autumn dead leaves should be removed to reduce the risk of infection by disease.

In the spring, March–April, the young stock can be bedded out in a polythene tunnel with a growing media of peat to a depth of 150 mm (6 in). Fertilizer should be added to encourage growth. During the summer the plants should have their growing points 'stopped' two or three times to encourage bushy plants. In September the polythene cover to the tunnel should be removed to encourage hardening off.

Plants can be containerized into 150 mm (6 in) or 230 mm (9 in) polythene or rigid containers during late winter, January–March. The growing media should consist of peat, although grit may be added for stability. The following fertilizer regime is recommended per bale of peat:

675 g (1 lb 8 oz) slow-release fertilizer
450 g (1 lb) magnesium limestone
340 g (12 oz) single superphosphate
90 g (3·5 oz) trace elements mixed with sand

During the summer the plants are grown on under polythene. *Botrytis* may be a problem in this growing environment, especially as the disease can be carried over during the winter on azalea leaf scales. To combat this thiram should be applied to the crop at 10-day intervals during the summer.

Marketing of the azaleas can be carried out from October onwards, making deciduous-azalea production a two-year cycle.

Rhododendron **species and hybrids**

Rhododendrons can be produced from cuttings, seed, layering or grafting. Most producers prefer plants on their own roots as plants are produced more quickly and often more successfully.

PRODUCTION FROM CUTTINGS

The system of production is bound to alter slightly according to the species, as rooting potential and time of rooting will vary.

Cuttings should be taken from stock plants, generally between October and December when plant tissue has matured. The cut should be directly under a node leaving a 75 mm (3 in) long cutting which is then wounded by making a slice 25 mm (1 in) long. Lower leaves are removed completely leaving two or three terminal leaves. With large-leaved species and cultivars some growers will reduce by half the size of the remaining leaves.

Cuttings should be dipped in a rooting hormone and it is also suggested that they should be dipped and sprayed with benomyl to control *Pestalotiopsis* species, a common leaf-spot disease that enters the stem, causing rotting of the cutting. Cuttings should be dipped in benomyl at a rate of 10 g/9 1 (1 lb/100 gal) of water, and cuttings in the propagation area should be sprayed at a rate of 5 g/9 l (8 oz/100 gal) of water. Care must be taken when using this chemical and any varietal damage noted for the future.

Hormone treatment varies between species and cultivars. Generally four strengths are used, but variation in treatments will occur from nursery to nursery. The following is recommended for these species and cultivars:

1 0·25 g (0·007 oz) IBA in 100 ml (3·5 pt) 50% methylated spirits for *Rhododendron* 'Elizabeth, *R.* 'May Day', *R. cinnabarinum* and *R. griersonianum*.
2 0·5 g (0·015 oz) IBA in 100 ml (3·5 pt) 50 % methylated spirits for *R.* 'Alice and *R.* × *morelianum*.
3 1 g (0·03 oz) IBA in 100 ml (3·5 pt) 50 % methylated spirits for *R.* 'Pink Pearl', *R.* 'Hugh Koster' and *R.* 'Doncaster'.
4 2 g (0·06 oz) IBA in 100 ml (3·5 pt) 60 % methylated spirits for *R.* 'Britannia'.

Cuttings are placed in a rooting environment where bottom heat – 20 °C (68 °F) – and a humid atmosphere can be achieved, normally by covering with polythene. Rooting should have taken place by December–March when the polythene cover can be removed and the cuttings weaned. If a bushy plant is required the growing point should be pinched out at this stage. Rooted plants can be containerized into 90 mm (3·5 in) pots during early summer, using a peat-based growing medium, and stood in a polythene tunnel or protected growing area for 12 months.

At the beginning of the second growing season the plants can be pinched again to obtain a second flush of bushy growth, and also sprayed with malathion or gamma – HCH (BHC) to control Rhododendron Bug (*Stephanitis rhododendri*).

The final potting should take place in the autumn, when plants are potted into 180 mm (7 in) containers and left on the standing ground for one year. In the final growing season plants should again be pinched and sprayed, and will be saleable by the autumn.

SEED-RAISED RHODODENDRONS

The wild species and understocks are often raised from seed, together with new hybrids. *Rhododendron* seed can ripen at any time from three to ten months after flowering, depending on the species and climate. As a rough guide, alpine rhododendrons produce ripe seed in a short time, while large-leaved rhododendrons from temperate low-valley regions take a long period for seed ripening.

Seed should be stored in a dry atmosphere at room temperature and should not be stored for more than a few months as viability quickly drops. Sowing should take place in January or February to produce as large a seedling as possible by the end of the first season.

Rhododendrons will germinate very successfully in clean seed trays of moist shredded sphagnum peat, firmed before sowing. *Rhododendron* seed is very small and thick sowing can easily occur, with the resulting seedlings being overcrowded. Sparse sowing is important as pricking out should not occur until the seedlings are 19 mm (0·75 in) tall.

Once sown, the seeds should not be covered with peat or any other material, nor should they be watered as seed will be washed into the moss peat. Cover with a pane of glass and a sheet of newspaper to give the ideal germination conditions. Covered seed trays are placed in a glasshouse at a temperature of 21 °C (70 °F) and germination can take place from 10 days onwards.

The growing on of the crop from this stage is the same as any other seed-raised crop in containers.

RHODODENDRONS FROM LAYERING

The traditional way of raising rhododendrons is layering. The disadvantages of this system are that it is slow and a large number of stock plants is required to produce young plants. Often layer-produced plants are badly shaped compared with those produced from cuttings or grafting. An advantage of layering is that it is reliable and does not need expensive facilities and equipment.

The technique of layering rhododendrons is similar to other ornamental plants (see Chapter 15) and is recommended for propagating rare and unusual species and cultivars where only small numbers are required.

RHODODENDRONS BY GRAFTING

Grafted plants often suffer from weak graft unions and suckers can arise from the roots – these will need removing for a number of years after the plant has left the nursery. As in other grafting situations the rootstock can affect the growth habit and adaptability of the plant.

A number of rootstocks may be used for rhododendrons and they can be classified as follows:

1 *Rhododendron ponticum*: most of the more common species and cultivars are grafted on to this rootstock as it is vigorous, has a large root system and suckers can be easily identified. The root system produced is very hardy although it is prone to Rhododendron Wilt.
2 *Rhododendron maximum*: this rootstock has been used in the USA by some growers who claim it is more resistant to Rhododendron Wilt.
3 *Rhododendron catawbiense*: this rootstock has been tried in the USA and Holland. It produces a slightly dwarfer plant, but the crop is more uniform.
4 *Rhododendron* 'Cunningham's White': this is becoming a more common rootstock, being more easily produced from cuttings, and is tolerant of less acid soil conditions. One problem is that suckers are very similar to the cultivars.

Rootstocks are produced from cuttings or seed as mentioned in other production systems.

GRAFTING

Three bench grafts can be used in *Rhododendron* production: the side, veneer and saddle grafts, during November/December.

Potted or balled rootstocks should be prepared for grafting by placing them in a glasshouse at 15 °C (60 °F) six weeks prior to grafting. During this forcing period they should be syringed twice a day and they will have produced new white roots by the time grafting takes place.

Scions are selected from current year's growth and should be strong, straight and have the same diameter as the rootstock.

After grafting, the plants are placed in a grafting case with a bottom heat temperature of 21 °C (70 °F). Callusing should take about three or four weeks and from then on the plants can be slowly hardened off. It is important that this process is done slowly as too quick a hardening off will result in wilting of the scions.

BUDDING

Rhododendrons can be produced by budding during the summer, normally between mid-June and late August. T budding is practised although the technique is only recommended when it is not possible to produce the plants from winter grafting.

This section has only briefly discussed *Rhododendron* production. There are over 1,000 species, as well as many hundreds of hybrids, and it is recommended that before producing rhododendrons a clear understanding of the particular species and hybrids is obtained.

HEATHERS

In heather production the plants we are dealing with are cultivars of *Calluna vulgaris*, the native Ling or heather; *Daboecia cantabrica*, the Irish heath, and its cultivars; and species and cultivars of *Erica*, the heaths. There are six species of *Erica* commonly produced by nurserymen: *E. herbacea* (syn. *E. carnea*); *E. erigena* (syn. *E. mediterranea*); *E. arborea*; *E. vagans*; *E. ciliaris* and *E. cinerea*. Heaths and heathers belong to the family *Ericaceae* and this family is associated with soils that have a low pH, such as the peaty bogs of mountain areas, which means that one of the important factors in producing a good heather crop is providing the correct growing media.

Heathers are generally considered a specialist crop and certainly growers of a wide range of nursery stock all too often do not have as much success with them as they do with other lines. The main demand for heathers is from garden centres and local authorities.

Heathers can be a very useful crop, for very little space is needed to produce sizeable numbers and overheads are very much less than for other intensive crops. Heat can be used, particularly to speed up propagation, but because of hardening off and subsequent growth patterns there is often little to be gained in the long run. However, the cheaper the production system the more erratic the results.

Heathers can be produced in two ways: from summer cuttings and from winter cuttings.

Stock plants

Whichever production system is used it is important that cuttings are taken from vigorous clean stock plants. The main disease is the soil-borne fungus *Phytophthora* which causes root rot and die-back.

If rooted plants are bought in to start the stock area these should be isolated and grown in sterilized, disease-free compost before being planted out in beds. Any doubtful plants should be burned.

Because heaths and heathers are low-growing they are more prone than many other plants to this soil-borne disease. It is therefore advisable to drench stock plants with a fungicide such as zineb and to spray them every 14 days during the summer using 1 kg (2 lb) of zineb in 455 litres (100 gal) of water.

In the past many nurserymen have collected cuttings from established plantings. These plants often have a doubtful history as far as health is concerned and it is easy to carry disease to a nursery not already infected. Therefore it is important that growers establish stock areas which are renewed on a four-year cycle as clean material will save money in production. However, staff need to be trained to cope with *Phytophthora* and good hygiene is absolutely essential.

Production from hardwood cuttings

With this system propagation is undertaken in winter, the cuttings being collected in February. When collecting use clean polythene bags for each cultivar to maintain a high standard of hygiene.

Tip cuttings 25–30 mm (1–1·5 in) in length are taken from the stock plants. In the propagation area the bottom leaves are stripped off leaving the lower third of the cutting leafless. Cuttings are then dipped into 0·3 per cent IBA hormone rooting powder and inserted in trays of sphagnum peat which has had the larger lumps removed. We would recommend inserting 100 cuttings per standard tray.

Label the trays adequately, water in the cuttings and stand the trays in a glasshouse with a bottom heat temperature of 20 °C (70 °F). The trays are covered with 19 μm (75 gauge) clear polythene to maintain high humidity. The polythene is taken off twice a week to allow for watering, removal of any dead cuttings and air circulation. The latter is most important as it prevents fungal diseases such as *Botrytis* from infecting the cuttings – if this should occur spray the cuttings with the systemic fungicide benomyl.

First rooting normally occurs after 16 days and the polythene is completely removed by mid-March. The rooted cuttings are slowly weaned by gradually reducing the bottom heat. Rooted plants can be either potted or planted in cold frames by April. Whichever system is used it is important that the plants are not over-watered or placed in poorly drained conditions as either will lead to deaths through *Phytophthora*.

If plants in pots are preferred then a 75 mm (3 in) polythene bag or plastic pot can be used. The compost will vary from one grower to another but it must be of a lower pH than that used for conventional lines. The following mix can be recommended:

3 bales sphagnum peat—each bale 0·34 m^3 (9·3 cu ft)
2 level barrows sand—barrow of 0·12 m^3 (3·3 cu ft) capacity
750 g (1 lb 10 oz) controlled 9 month fertilizer (18:11:10)
1·3 kg (3 lb) dolomitic limestone
1·3 kg (3 lb) single superphosphate
300 g (10·75 oz) fritted trace elements
75 g (2·5 oz) etridiazole (used for *Phytophthora* control)

The three bales of peat and two barrows of sand give 1 m^3 (1·3 cu yd).

Once plants are potted they are placed in a shade house or in cold frames, or alternatively they can be bedded out in 100 mm (4 in) deep clean sphagnum peat in a frame. Space the plants 100 mm (4 in) apart each way to allow good air circulation. Water in the plants and then cover with shaded Dutch lights or white polythene sheeting.

A feeding programme is commenced a few days after planting and a 1 per cent solution of a liquid feed containing 9 per cent nitrogen, 9 per cent phosphate and 7 per cent potash, plus trace elements, is applied as a drench at fortnightly intervals.

With both of these methods of growing it is important to keep the plants free of weeds. Weed control can be achieved by a half-rate application of chloroxuron. Immediately after spraying, the foliage should be washed off with plain water to prevent damage. Repeat the application of chloroxuron at six-weekly intervals.

Plants will be saleable in September/October, eight months after propagation. Bedded-out plants can either be containerized or sold as balled plants. This system aims to reduce handling costs and to produce a cheap plant which will dictate the selling price. Frames are left free for other crops during the winter.

Production from summer cuttings

This is the more conventional way of producing heathers. The propagation season can be staggered from May/June through to September.

Table 18 The propagation programme for heathers

Species	*Optimum cutting season*	*Remarks*
E. arborea *E. erigena* (syn. *E. mediterranea*) *Erica herbacea* (syn. *E. carnea*)	May/June	Take cuttings as early as possible
E. vagans	June	As soon as stems are long enough
E. ciliaris *E. cinerea* *E. tetralix* Summer hybrids	July/August	As soon as flowering material is long enough
Calluna vulgaris *Daboecia cantabrica*	August/September	Take cuttings before growth hardens

Cuttings are taken in the same way as in the previous system and inserted into clean trays of 50 per cent medium-grade peat and 50 per cent sand with a pH of 5·5. The finished boxes are placed under mist or polythene with a bottom heat temperature of 22 °C (72 °F) and no shading should be given.

The cuttings are left under mist for 14 days—if left for longer than this they will deteriorate, especially *Erica cinerea* and *Calluna vulgaris*. Rooted cuttings are removed to a close, shaded polythene house where they are weaned off into the normal watering programme within two days.

Potting normally takes place between September and May, using 75 mm (3 in) containers. The compost is the same as that recommended in the other system. The potting order is important: plants such as *Calluna vulgaris*, *Erica cinerea* and *E. vagans*, should be potted first as they will make saleable plants by the end of the growing season, while *E. herbacea* (syn. *E. carnea*) will take two growing seasons to make marketable plants.

Potted plants are stood down in a polythene house until April when they only require shading. Most plants will be saleable from the autumn onwards, although they could be grown on for a second season to produce larger plants which are sometimes required by retail outlets. It can be seen from this system that plants are on the nursery for a longer period and have to be overwintered before they reach the saleable stage.

Table 19 Summary of systems for heather production

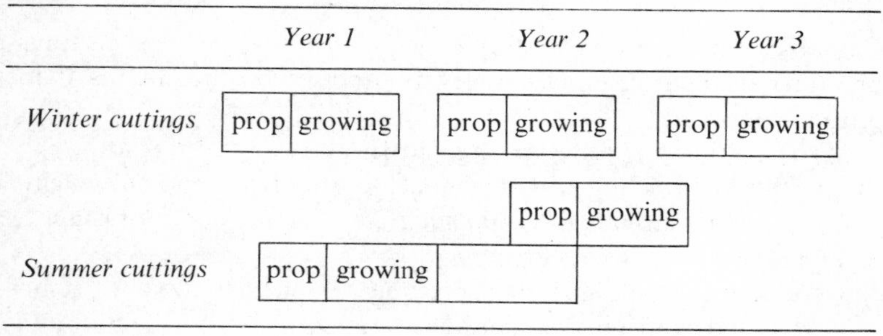

	Year 1	*Year 2*	*Year 3*
Winter cuttings	prop | growing	prop | growing	prop | growing
		prop | growing	
Summer cuttings	prop | growing		

Other methods of propagation

New cultivars of heathers and heaths are constantly being introduced and in recent years we have seen the introduction of dwarf *Calluna* such as *C. vulgaris* 'Foxii Nana' and *C.v.* 'Humpty Dumpty'. With these cultivars it is often difficult to get small cuttings to root, and so a method that can be used instead is mound layering. Once the shoots have rooted they can be removed from the mother plants and grown on in the normal way.

Trends and developments

Heathers are becoming more popular for use as ground cover in low-maintenance areas and as a result the landscape and local-authority market for these plants is increasing, with the opportunity for nurserymen to produce more plants with this outlet in mind. The alternative market is for small numbers of high-quality plants to be released through garden-centre outlets.

CAMELLIAS

The aim in *Camellia* production is to produce well-shaped, branched plants with a good set of flower buds. Very tall, single-stemmed plants do not represent top quality but by cultural and chemical means one can achieve good shape, branching and flower-bud initiation. Plants sold when about 600 mm (2 ft) in height have a better chance of survival when planted out than very small specimens. This of course helps to ensure customer satisfaction.

Propagation

Camellias can be propagated from stem cuttings, leaf-bud cuttings or grafting. Stem cuttings, however, produce bushier plants than grafted specimens.

Many cultivars can be propagated from stem cuttings although the percentage rooting will vary considerably from one cultivar to another. Most cultivars of *C. japonica* and *C. sasanqua*, for instance, can be raised from stem cuttings.

Take cuttings in August or September, using current year's semi-mature wood, and make them about 150 mm (6 in) in length and ensure they have three nodes. Cut below a node at the base and wound heavily. Treat with 0·8 per cent IBA and insert in a cutting compost consisting of 60 per cent peat and 40 per cent grit. Ideally the cuttings should be inserted in individual containers to minimize root disturbance when potting on. Root the cuttings under mist with a bottom heat temperature of 21 °C (70 °F). There is no need to wean off the rooted cuttings if in unit containers – it is only necessary if potting off from trays is carried out.

Propagation from leaf-bud cuttings is useful if cutting material is limited or if a cultivar is new and the nurseryman wants to increase stock quickly. A leaf-bud cutting consists of one leaf with a bud in the axil and a portion of the stem – about 35 mm (1·5 in). Again take these in August or September, using semi-mature wood of the current season. Dip in 0·8 per cent IBA and thereafter treat as for normal stem cuttings.

GRAFTING

This is a useful method if propagation material is limited or if some cultivars prove difficult from cuttings. It is possible to obtain saleable plants in one year from grafting, that is, 600 mm (2 ft) high plants, but the plants will not be as bushy as those raised from cuttings.

Camellia japonica is used as a rootstock – 18-month-old seedlings, well established in 150 mm (6 in) pots. Grafting can be carried out in October, ensuring the soil in the pots is on the dry side. Use a side graft and prepare 200 mm (8 in) long scions from current year's wood. Bind the grafts with plastic grafting tape. Then place in a grafting case with high humidity and a bottom heat temperature of 21 °C (70 °F).

Growing on young plants

Young plants can be containerized in spring, using 150 mm (6 in) polythene bags or, preferably, rigid containers. A suitable compost for containerizing would be an acid John Innes potting compost No. 2 or No. 3. Use an acid loam and omit the chalk.

Generally, plants are grown on in unheated plastic tunnels or glasshouses to ensure good flower-bud initiation. The plants must be well hardened off from August onwards prior to sale in the winter or spring. Plants should be saleable within approximately 20–21 months from cuttings.

Plants can also be field grown if desired and containerized in their final year. Line out young plants in late spring. Some nurserymen find that this treatment often results in very good flower-bud initiation. The plants have one season in the field – the spring and summer after propagation.

Flower-bud initiation and shaping

To ensure well-branched plants remove the top 50–75 mm (2–3 in) of growth in the spring following propagation. In natural conditions flower-bud initiation takes place in the spring and summer and factors which influence it include the cultivar, the feeding of the plants and the use of growth regulators. In recent years a good deal of research has been carried out in respect of feeding and the use of growth regulators. The use of a growth regulator to help initiate flower buds is of most benefit in a poor summer, as more buds are produced in a good summer.

Some cultivars bud more freely than others irrespective of any treatment given to the plants. Cultivars have been classified under the headings of 'easy budding', 'moderate to good budding' and 'difficult budding'. Below are listed a few popular cultivars from each section.

1 Easy budding: 'Donation'; 'J. C. Williams'; 'Lady Clare'; 'Leonard Messel'; 'Polar Bear' and 'St Ewe'.
2 Moderate to good budding: 'Adolphe Audusson'; 'Apollo'; 'Donckeleri'; 'Inspiration'; 'Lady Vansittart' and 'Nagasaki'.
3 Difficult budding: 'Drama Girl'; 'Imbricata Rubra'; 'Preston Rose' and 'Reg Ragland'.

Feeding can also help to initiate flower buds. Nitrogen increases the number of buds and also improves the colour of the foliage, but feeding with nitrogen must not be carried out beyond early August owing to the danger of bud and leaf drop. Phosphorous also increases the number of flower buds and is important if the compost is low in phosphorous. It has been found that a top dressing of superphosphate in spring can considerably increase flower buds. The growth regulator chlormequat has been found to improve flower-bud initiation, especially in a poor summer. It must be used with care for it can result in a reduction in plant height.

As the result of research it has been suggested that the following programme could be carried out in the year the plants attain flowering size:

1 Early spring: top dress pots with superphosphate. If phosphorous index less than 3, apply 180 g (6 oz) per 60 pots. If phosphorous index 3–4, apply 120 g (4 oz) per 60 pots.
2 May to August: weekly liquid feeds of 420 ppm nitrogen and 230 ppm potash. Dissolve 450 g (1 lb) potassium nitrate and 900 g (2 lb) ammonium nitrate in 4·5 litres (1 gal) water and dilute this stock solution to 1:200. Apply 4·5 litres (1 gal) of the dilute feed to 60 pots. If the feed comes in contact with the foliage wash it off immediately.
3 Early June, repeating early July: apply 36 ml (1·25 fl oz) of chlormequat in 4·5 litres of water per 60 pots.

The above recommendations are based on 120 mm (4·75 in) pots in each case.

35

Aquatics

There is no doubt that the demand for aquatics is increasing as water gardening is becoming very popular with private gardeners. Many garden centres nowadays sell water plants, as well as fish, pools and associated equipment. Many also have attractive display pools which further help to encourage customers to make purchases.

Although there are, now, quite a number of specialist aquatic-plant producers we feel that water plants could still be a profitable line for the general nurseryman. For anyone contemplating growing aquatics in a big way it is likely there will be a high initial outlay for the growing tanks and stock tanks. However, the general nurseryman could well concentrate on those plants which are easy to produce and which fit in, more or less, with existing production programmes. For instance some of the marginal plants do not need to be grown in tanks but could be grown in moist soil in much the same way as field-grown herbaceous plants.

Setting up tanks

The majority of aquatic plants, however, need to be grown in shallow tanks of water – both young plants for eventual sale and the stock plants. Tanks can be formed of materials such as railway sleepers, bricks or concrete blocks and lined with butyl rubber sheeting or plastic sheeting. The stock plants will need to be grown in a suitable growing medium and for most subjects a medium to heavy loam would be suitable. A layer of this could be placed in the stock tanks in which to plant the aquatics (see Plate 16).

Marginal plants

These are plants which are grown in the more shallow water around the edges of a pool and they are among the most popular plants with private gardeners. They are suited to production by the general nurseryman and are generally sold in pots.

As we mentioned earlier, some of the marginals can even be

grown in moist soil instead of in tanks, for instance the *Iris* like *I. laevigata* and *I. pseudacorus*, *Caltha palustris* and *C.p.* 'Plena', *Acorus calamus* 'Variegatus' and *Glyceria aquatica* 'Variegata'. All of these are very popular plants and are in demand at the present time—this in fact applies to all the plants which we will mention in this section. *Typha* and *Scirpus* are also popular subjects and these need to be grown in tanks. The same comments apply to *Calla palustris*, *Butomus umbellatus* and *Menyanthes trifoliata*.

The marginals are generally easily propagated by division of the roots in the spring and early summer—April to July. The divisions can be potted off to grow on to saleable size. Use a loam-based compost for potting. When propagating long-leaved subjects do not cut back the foliage as is the practice with herbaceous plants as this can lead to rotting of the remaining foliage. This applies particularly to plants with hollow leaves like the *Juncus*—water can collect in these leaves and this results in decay.

With *Menyanthes trifoliata* the rhizomes can be divided and boxed up, until they start into growth. Quite small divisions can be made. The same applies to *Calla palustris*. *Butomus umbellatus* produces bulbils in the axils of the leaves and these can be used for propagation. Simply detach them and box them up to grow on.

Some marginals can also be propagated from cuttings about 50 mm (2 in) in length taken in the spring and inserted three cuttings per pot, in loamy compost. Subjects which respond to this method include *Myosotis scorpioides* and *Mentha aquatica*. Grow them on in shallow water—the rims of the pots being just below the surface.

Seed is a cheap method of producing plants in large quantities. It is best to sow fresh seed, generally as soon as it is ripe. With *Pontederia cordata* it is in fact best to sow the seed while it is still green. Subjects like *Calla palustris*, *Alisma plantago* 'Aquatica' and *Aponogeton distachyus* germinate well from fresh seed, sown as soon as ripe.

Sow the seed in trays using a loam-based compost and cover them with a thin layer of coarse sand. The trays are then partially submerged in water. The seeds and seedlings should be protected during the winter, for instance by covering the tanks with Dutch lights or by placing the trays in a glasshouse. Once the seedlings are large enough to handle they can be potted off using a loam-based compost.

Submerged oxygenating plants

There is a constant demand for submerged oxygenating plants as they are so important in maintaining a balanced pool and are essential if fish are to be kept. What is more they are an ideal crop for the general nurseryman as they are so easy to produce. One simply takes cuttings approximately 75–100 mm (3–4 in) in length and secures them in small bunches. They can, in fact, be leaded so that the bunches sink to the bottom of the growing tanks. A cheaper method is to hold the cuttings together at the base with an elastic band but then of course the bunches are liable to float on the water surface.

The bunches of cuttings will quickly root if taken in the spring and summer and they are simply dropped into the water in the tanks. Submerged oxygenators need a large volume of cool water—in shallow tanks the water will quickly heat up in hot weather and this results in discoloured or even decomposed foliage.

Stock plants should be grown in a fertile medium, such as a medium to heavy loam to which a slow-release nitrogenous fertilizer has been added.

Several different types of oxygenators, such as *Elodea crispa* and *Myriophyllum spicatum*, should be grown. Plants can be retailed either bare-root or they can be pre-packed in polythene for garden-centre and shop sales.

Floaters

The floating aquatics like *Stratiotes aloides* and *Hydrocharis morsus-ranae* are also very easy to produce by the general nurseryman and are in popular demand. As they float in the water or on the surface it is not necessary even to plant them—they are just dropped into the water. Often they can be propagated from runners which are detached in the spring or summer and dropped into growing-on tanks.

Some floaters, like *Hydrocharis*, form winter-resting buds or turions which sink to the bottom of the pool or tank where they spend the winter. These rise to the surface in the spring and develop into new plants. These turions can be collected up in the autumn from the stock tanks and kept in the growing-on tanks to provide saleable plants for the following spring and summer.

Waterlilies

Waterlilies or *Nymphaea* are classed as a high-value crop and like the other plants mentioned are much in demand at garden centres and the like. There are many cultivars and species one could produce but we would suggest the range is restricted to a few of the most

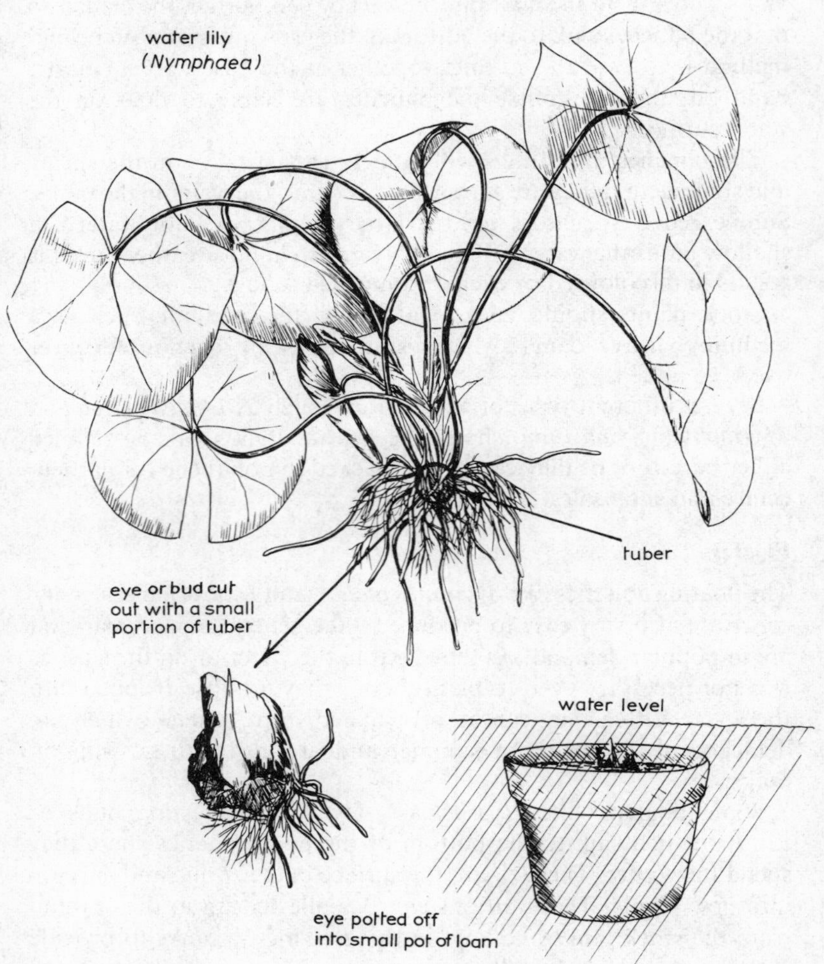

Fig. 72 Waterlily propagation from 'eyes'

popular types, for instance the *N. pygmaea* cultivars which are small growers and in much demand for small private pools. Medium to large growers which are popular include 'Froebeli', 'Sioux', 'Mrs Richmond', 'Escarboucle' and *N. marliacea* 'Chromatella'.

Waterlilies are propagated from 'eyes' or buds which are born on the thick tuberous roots of the parent plants. The parent plants should be lifted in April and the eyes cut out with a sharp knife so that they include a small portion of tuber. Dust the cuts of the eyes and roots with powdered charcoal to prevent infection from diseases. One can take eyes from young plants before they are sold and this does not affect saleability.

The eyes can now be potted off individually in a loam-based compost—preferably one in which medium to heavy loam was used. The eyes can in fact be grown in pure loam. The pots should now be stood in growing-on tanks with the water just above compost level. As the plants grow the water level can be raised so that the leaves are floating on the surface of the water at all times, rather than sticking up above it. Pot on the young plants as they grow so that eventually the plants are in pots of about 100 mm (4 in) in diameter, in which they are sold.

Maintenance

In new tanks containing fresh water, algae very quickly builds up. This is the suspended type and it turns the water green, rather like pea soup. Generally the water gradually clears as plants become established in the tanks but there are algicides available which speed up the process. These are rather expensive though, and therefore it may be better to wait for the water to clear naturally. On no account change the water in new tanks in the hope of clearing up the problem for it will merely prolong the trouble. Blanket weed is another type of algae and is a filamentous type. If allowed to become established in tanks it will smother and choke the aquatics. It should be pulled out by hand or with a rake.

It is a good idea to keep fish in the tanks, especially in the stock tanks, as they help to control the larvae of mosquitoes and gnats which can be troublesome in the adult stage.

Marketing

Probably the main outlets will be garden centres and shops. In this instance it is best to grow as much as possible in pots, say of 100 mm

(4 in) diameter. Plants can also be pre-packed by sealing them in polythene bags and this is an acceptable method for selling in shops and stores. Submerged oxygenating plants, floaters and waterlilies are certainly best pre-packed for shops and stores.

For sales in garden centres potted aquatics can be displayed in shallow tanks – preferably raised about 1 m (3 ft 3 in) or so off the ground. The oxygenators and floaters are simply dropped into the display tanks. Remember that deeper tanks will be required for the oxygenators. The main sale period for aquatics is April to June or early July.

36

Clematis

In *Clematis* production the traditional practice of grafting cultivars on to a rootstock is being replaced by propagation from cuttings. This is due to the high cost of production with grafting and the greater risk of Clematis Wilt disease.

Stock plants

Stock plants for the production of soft cutting material are grown in pots, either under glass or polythene tunnels. The first batch of cuttings can be taken as early as March and after this growth comes in flushes so that further batches of cuttings can be taken up until August.

Cuttings from the earliest batches will result in saleable plants by the autumn of the same year, but cuttings rooted later in the season, for example, July or August, are left in their rooting trays over the winter, potted off in February or March and make saleable plants during the following summer.

Preparation of cuttings

Cuttings are prepared from shoots which are starting to turn pinkish in colour, but the very soft tips are discarded. The cuttings are inter-nodal and contain a double-budded node at the top. They are prepared as follows: cut immediately above a node at the top and allow about 35 mm (1·5 in) of internodal growth below this. Remove one leaf completely just above the bud. The other leaf may be reduced in length if considered too long. Difficult cultivars like 'Henryi' and 'Gipsy Queen' can be wounded at the base of the cutting. It is advisable to immerse cuttings in a captan solution to reduce infection by diseases. The bases of the cuttings can then be dipped in 0·3 per cent IBA to encourage rooting.

The cuttings can be inserted in seed trays—up to 100 cuttings per tray. They should be inserted up to the buds in compost of equal parts peat and coarse sand or, alternatively, a mixture of peat and

Perlite could be used. In any case a well-drained and aerated rooting medium is desirable to reduce losses resulting from rotting off. We have tried peat blocks for *Clematis* cuttings but have found that they remain too moist and heavy losses can result.

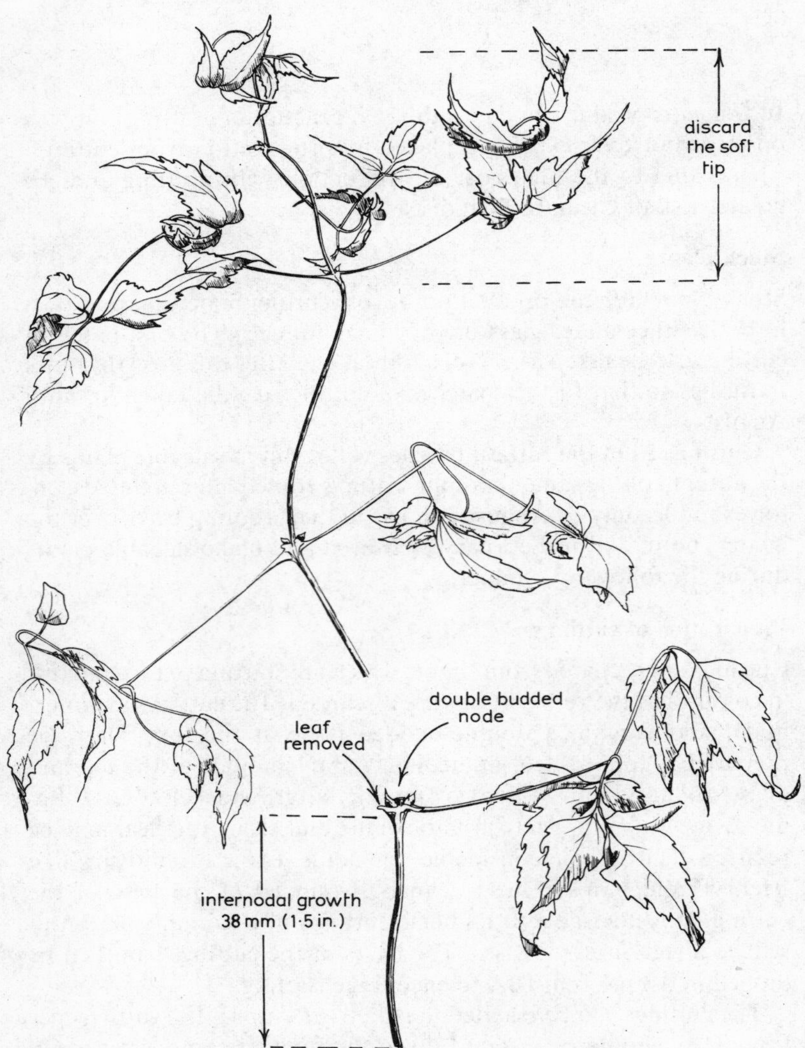

Fig. 73 Leaf-bud cutting of *Clematis*

Rooting conditions

The cuttings can be rooted under mist with a bottom heat temperature of 21–24 °C (70–75 °F). At all costs avoid excessive misting as the cuttings will rot if the compost becomes too wet. Provide a minimum air temperature of 15 °C (60 °F). Also, provide shading for the cuttings while they are under mist, using a 70 per cent shading material. Rooting will take approximately six weeks and the percentage of rooting will vary between 40 and 60 per cent depending on the cultivar. The rooted cuttings should be gradually weaned off the mist. Reduce the shading but do not dispense with it completely and gradually increase the ventilation over a period of time.

Potting

The cuttings will be ready for potting 10–12 weeks after propagation. They should be graded out for size and quality and the roots should be trimmed. Ideally a loam-based compost should be used which contains a slow-release base fertilizer. Use a loam with a pH of approximately 6·5.

A good pot size is important—the best plants will be sold in 125 mm (5 in) pots and, if available, use deep pots. When potting, the buds should not be too high above the compost—in fact they should be level with the surface. When carrying out late potting the buds should be slightly below the surface.

Late-flowering cultivars like 'Jackmanii' do not establish well if potted too late in the season but, conversely, early-flowering cultivars establish a bit better if potted late. Finish potting by the middle of August. After this rooted cuttings are best left in their trays over the winter, placing them in polythene tunnels, to be potted in the following spring. You will find that young plants with good, well-established root systems overwinter far better and produce stronger growth in the following spring. Pinch out the tips of rooted cuttings to ensure the development of side shoots—one should aim for three to four shoots per plant by the sale date. Avoid overwatering young plants as they are still susceptible to over-moist compost.

Growing on plants

Growing on the plants under polythene tunnels reduces production time. If you cannot keep the plants under polythene for their entire nursery life, then at least overwinter the plants under tunnels, and also of course rooted cuttings. A minimum temperature of 10 °C (50 °F) can be provided to encourage growth but do not provide artificial heat in the winter. It is important that the *Clematis* plants are not grown too soft in tunnels as this could lead to frost damage during cold periods.

Some producers use dusk to dawn lighting (fluorescent tubes) for a six-week period on young plants during the growing season and can obtain 12 weeks' growth in about eight weeks. Once the plants are well established in their pots liquid feeding can be commenced.

A 1 m (3 ft 3 in) bamboo cane should be provided for each plant and the shoots regularly tied in. Some growers contain the shoots by enclosing them in a netting sleeve. This certainly prevents tangled shoots while the plants are on the nursery.

Wilt disease can be a problem and some growers are now drenching the compost in the pots with a solution of benomyl in order to try and prevent trouble. Several drenchings should be given to young plants on the nursery.

Hardwood cuttings

Some clematis, particularly *C. montana* and *C. viticella*, can be propagated from short hardwood cuttings in the period January to February. They should be nodal cuttings, prepared by cutting just above a node at the top and just below a node at the base. Dip the bases of the cuttings in a hormone rooting powder containing 0·8 per cent IBA and insert in deep trays of cutting compost – equal parts peat and coarse sand. Provide bottom heat – a temperature of 18 °C (65 °F) would be suitable.

Alternatively, the cuttings could be inserted in cold frames during the autumn, using a peat/sand compost in the base of the frames. After insertion cover the cuttings with 19 μm (75 gauge) polythene sheeting and shaded Dutch lights. The cuttings can remain in the frames until January, at which time they should be lifted and potted. Young plants raised from hardwood cuttings can be grown on in the way described above.

Marketing

Generally plants are sold when 1 m (3 ft 3 in) in height although of course these constitute expensive plants in a garden centre and many people are reluctant to pay a high price. It may therefore be necessary to market smaller plants which can be retailed at far lower prices. *Clematis*, however, have most sales appeal when in flower, which is in the spring and summer, or even early autumn, depending on the cultivar or species.

37

Soft and top fruits

Raising soft fruits for commercial and private fruit growers is today a highly specialized business. Many of these producers now participate in the Ministry of Agriculture's Certification Schemes for strawberries, raspberries and black currants: these schemes were started to improve and maintain quality in soft fruits throughout the country. Growers obtain Elite stocks, which are virus free (there are numerous viruses which can affect soft fruits and seriously reduce their cropping potential) and true to name, from the Nuclear Stock Association. These stocks are used to produce plants for sale to commercial and private fruit growers.

In order to ensure the plants remain virus free, generally healthy and true to name, production is carried out under strictly controlled conditions of isolation and cultivation. The plants are inspected twice during the growing season by Ministry officers and, if they pass inspection, are issued with a certificate in respect of their health and trueness to type. There are two schemes in operation: the Special Stock (SS) Certification Scheme and the Ordinary ('A') Certification Scheme. For black currants, only the Ordinary ('A') Certification Scheme is now in operation.

Obtaining clean stocks

Obviously there are many general nurserymen who want to produce soft fruits for retail sales, such as through garden centres, without the necessity of participating in the Certification Schemes. However, even these producers should feel morally obliged to ensure their plants are healthy and true to type. It is strongly advisable to buy stock plants which have been certified from a specialized producer and to propagate from these. Stock plants should be replaced regularly every few years, for although the plants are supplied virus free there is no guarantee they will remain healthy. There are registers of growers of certified strawberry, raspberry and black currant plants and these are made available as soon as possible after plants have been inspected. Generally notification of their availability appears in the trade press each year.

STRAWBERRIES

Strawberries are propagated from runners or young plants which are formed on the stolons or stems. These are produced in the summer, when they can be layered, and saleable plants will be produced from August onwards. The parent plants, ideally, should not be allowed to fruit.

Soils

It is important to choose a suitable soil for runner production. The most suitable is a medium or sandy loam, free from eelworm and other pests and diseases. The soil should be in good heart and as free as possible from perennial weeds. Ideally the runner bed should not follow a previous crop of strawberries.

Planting

Specialized growers participating in the SS Certification Scheme plant on the isolated-block system to reduce risk of viruses, pests and diseases spreading. This system takes up a lot of land but the ordinary nurseryman could, instead, plant his stock plants in continuous rows. The rows can be spaced 1 m (3 ft 3 in) apart, with the plants spaced 450 mm (18 in) apart in the rows. The runners are then allowed to root in the space between the rows. Young plants are planted in the autumn – to ensure they are free from aphids they can first be dipped in dimethoate.

Management

It is best to de-blossom the plants in the spring to strengthen them and increase runner production. As the runners develop, from about June onwards, they should be laid in the space between the rows. Runners can be allowed to grow and root on both sides of the row, or on one side, or runners from two rows can be trained together to leave alternate inter-row spaces free of runners. If the site is prone to wind, the runners can be pinned down to the soil with galvanized-wire pins. This will ensure they are not blown about by the wind, which would inhibit rooting.

There is no limitation to the number of runners that can be taken from one parent plant, but generally the best plants come from the first plantlet produced on each runner. Any produced beyond this first plantlet can be removed.

Weeds should be controlled during the summer by hand weeding or hoeing. Strawberry aphids are the chief vector of viruses and should be controlled by spraying the plants with dimethoate. To prevent mildew spray the plants with a sulphur fungicide. Keep the plants well irrigated in the summer as a moist soil will encourage quicker rooting and growth of runners.

One should be able to recognize the major virus diseases which infect strawberries and, if any plants are seen to be infected they should be immediately removed and burnt. The main viruses are Yellow Edge and Crinkle and they are spread by the strawberry aphid (*Pentatrichopus fragaefolii*). They are identified as follows:

1 Yellow Edge: the young leaves in the centre of the plant are the first to show symptoms. The edges of the leaflets are devoid of chlorophyll and appear yellow. This yellow edge gradually merges into the green part. The leaves are dwarfed and their margins cup upwards and the petioles are abnormally short. Eventually there are many such leaves and the entire plant presents a dwarfed and flattened appearance.

2 Crinkle: small pale spots appear on the young leaves. The leaf at these spots does not grow and as the rest of the leaf develops it becomes distorted and crinkled, often with a reddish coloration. The petioles are not shortened in this instance and therefore the plants remain upright.

Lifting

The main period for lifting and selling rooted strawberry runners is August–September, although lifting can continue until November. Runners planted by the customer in late summer/autumn will fruit well the following year.

Strawberry runners can be cold stored to provide customers with plants for even earlier planting – in June and July. Such plants will give very heavy crops the following year. Cold-stored strawberry runners must, however, be planted as soon as possible after removal from the store, so customers should be advised of this.

Well-rooted runners for cold storage are lifted in December and loosely packed into 38 μm (150 gauge) polythene bags, which should then be secured at the top with an elastic band. They should be placed in the cold store and maintained at a temperature of −1 °C (30 °F) until removal in June or July.

For sale in garden centres, shops and the like, rooted strawberry runners can be potted off into 90 mm (3 in) pots and allowed to become established in them prior to sale.

RASPBERRIES

These are propagated by suckers from virus-free stock plants grown in beds known as 'spawn' beds. The parent plants are not allowed to fruit. Raspberries are sold as one-year-old canes.

Soils

Again the land should be in good heart. Stony or heavy soils are really unsuitable as on these it is difficult to dig out the young canes with a spade. Also the land should be as free as possible from perennial weeds like couch, bindweed and so on. Such weeds make lifting difficult, and there is the risk of selling weeds with the canes.

Apply a heavy dressing of farmyard manure prior to planting the mother plants and also ensure the soil has an adequate supply of phosphorous and potash.

Planting

Plant stocks obtained from specialist growers to ensure they have been certified healthy and virus free. Plant the canes in the autumn 600 mm (2 ft) apart in rows spaced 2 m (6 ft 6 in) apart.

Management

Cut down newly planted canes to within 250 mm (10 in) of the ground to leave several buds. When new basal shoots are developing well cut away completely the old stubs. Keep the plants weed free either by hoeing or by the use of paraquat and simazine.

In the following winter dig out all the strong canes with a narrow-bladed spade to leave as much fibrous root as possible in the soil. Cut out all weak canes to ground level.

In the second year an abundance of new canes should be produced and it is the usual practice to regularly cultivate between the rows to ensure the spaces do not become filled with growth. One could limit the width of the beds to about 1 m (3 ft 3 in), so that there is a space of 1 m between the rows. All flowers should ideally be removed.

At the end of the second year canes can be lifted for sale, again using a narrow-bladed spade, and lifting with an adequate portion of fibrous roots. Weak canes unsuitable for sale should be cut down to ground level. During the winter a dressing of manure should be lightly incorporated into the beds.

If any plants are suspected of being infected with virus they should be immediately dug out of the beds (complete with all roots) and burnt. The main virus diseases are Raspberry Mosaic and Rubus Stunt, identified as follows:

1 Raspberry Mosaic: the symptoms vary according to the cultivar and the virus involved. They range from pale yellowish-green mottling to sharply defined yellowish sunken spots on the leaves, often accompanied by crumpling and twisting of the leaves. The plants are also very often stunted. It is interesting to note that some cultivars show no symptoms. This virus is spread by aphids so spray with malathion or dimethoate to control these pests.
2 Rubus Stunt: we have called this a virus, but to be correct one should refer to it as a mycoplasma. It is spread by leafhoppers (*Macropsis* species) which should be controlled by spraying with malathion. Symptoms are many dwarf, spindly shoots producing a 'witch's broom' effect.

Saleable canes

The canes, when lifted, should be graded into large, medium and small. They can be sold bare-root, direct from the nursery if retail, or they could be pre-packed if for garden centre or shop sales. Canes can also be containerized for garden-centre outlets but do ensure they become established in containers before being offered for sale.

BLACKBERRIES AND LOGANBERRIES

Soils

Stock plants ideally need to be planted in a well-drained medium loam, which retains adequate moisture and has been well supplied with organic matter. Light soils are also suitable, provided plenty of organic matter is incorporated and moisture can be given in dry periods. Heavy soils and clays are not very satisfactory as rooted layers can be damaged during lifting. Ensure the site is as free as possible from perennial weeds.

Planting

Plant one-year-old stock plants in the autumn, ensuring the plants are healthy and free from virus. As these two fruits are generally propagated by tip layering, the parent plants need to be well spaced out. Plant them 2·7–3·6 m (9–12 ft) square, and then cut them down to within 250 mm (9 in) of the ground to encourage shoots from below soil level.

Management

In July and August the tips of the new shoots are layered. The tips are buried in holes about 150 mm (6 in) deep: one side of the hole should slope towards the parent plant and the tip of the shoot or cane should lie along the sloping side. Backfill with soil and firm in lightly.

The tips of the canes will form roots and dormant growth buds, and if well rooted by the autumn can be carefully lifted and severed from the parent plant. If not well rooted, leave until the spring. When cutting the rooted tips away from the parent, retain about 300 mm (1 ft) of cane with each tip.

The rooted tips should be planted as soon as possible after lifting as they will dry out quickly if exposed. Plant either in nursery beds or in containers. If they are to be lined out in the field, space the young plants 300–600 mm (1–2 ft) apart in rows 1 m (3 ft 3 in) apart. If they are to be containerized, use 150 mm (6 in) polythene bags and any normal potting compost, either loam-based or loamless.

Once the tips have been lifted, the canes of the stock plants should be cut back to ground level and the beds manured and cultivated. The stock plants will continue to produce suitable canes for tip layering for several years.

Blackberries and loganberries are often sold as one-year-old plants, but two-year-old material is excellent for retail sales, especially in containers. Blackberries and loganberries can also be attacked by Rubus Stunt; for details see under raspberries.

BLACK CURRANTS

Black currants are propagated from hardwood cuttings taken in the autumn and they are generally sold retail as two-year-old bushes.

Soils

A deep medium soil, which contains plenty of humus and is water retentive, is ideal for growing the stock plants. So plough in adequate farmyard manure prior to planting, and ensure the soil is not deficient in phosphorous and potash.

Planting

Obtain certified plants for use as stock plants—two-year-old bushes—and plant in the autumn. The parent plants can be spaced about 1·2 m (4 ft) apart in rows 1·5 m (5 ft) apart. The parent plants are grown as stools—each autumn all the current year's shoots are removed to as near the stool as possible. After planting the stock plants, all shoots should therefore be cut down to the ground. These will make ideal cutting material.

Propagation

The ideal time to take and insert cuttings is in the autumn—October being a good month as the soil is still warm. The cuttings will then make good growth in the spring. However, cuttings can be taken any time in autumn, or even in winter, but very often cannot be inserted if taken late in the year, due to the soil being too wet and cold. In this instance the cuttings can be bundled up and heeled in a callusing bin until soil conditions improve in the spring.

The current year's shoots from the stools are used for cutting material, and the whole length can be used if well lignified. Discard soft tips, however. Use secateurs for making cuttings and cut immediately above a node at the top and just below a node at the base. Cuttings can be from 175 to 300 mm (7–12 in) long—shorter cuttings are necessary if they are to be machine planted. Use longer cuttings for hand planting. All buds should be left intact as black currants are grown as bushes with growth coming from below ground level.

A light or sandy soil is best for cuttings—ensure it is well supplied with humus and not deficient in nutrients. Cuttings can be machine planted or inserted in a narrow trench taken out with a spade. It is important to insert them deeply—allowing only one bud to show above soil level—and to firm them well in. The cuttings may need refirming after frost.

Cuttings can be inserted in rows 1 m (3 ft 3 in) apart with 150 mm (6 in) between the cuttings in the rows. This is adequate spacing for two years' growth if it is not intended to lift the bushes before saleable stage.

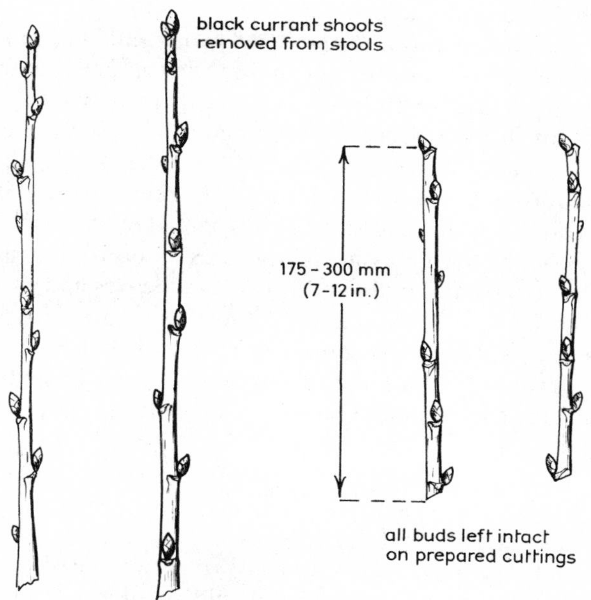

Fig. 74 Preparation of hardwood cuttings of black currant

Management of young plants

To control weeds among cuttings and young plants apply simazine or lenacil immediately after insertion and thereafter as required. Once the cuttings start to grow in the spring and leaves are produced, one will need to spray against gall mite and mildew. For gall-mite control, spray with endosulfan in late April followed by two more sprays at two to three week intervals. Mildew can be controlled by preventive sprays of benomyl, dinocap, lime sulphur, triforine and other fungicides. Irrigate cuttings once rooted if the soil is dry, but do not overwater as this may result in lush growth and a weak root system.

At the end of the first season the rooted cuttings can be lifted and planted out into nursery beds, or containerized into 150 mm (6 in) polythene bags; or they can be left where they are to grow on for another year. It is advisable to cut back all new shoots in the first winter to within one bud of their base, to ensure well-branched bushes in the second year.

In the second year continue spraying against gall mite and mildew and maintain chemical weed control. In the autumn or winter of the second year, field-grown bushes can be lifted for sale; ensure the roots do not dry out. Containerized plants will also be ready for sale at this time.

It is important to know about one of the most serious viruses of black currants, that is, reversion. This is spread by the black currant gall mite, hence the necessity of rigorously controlling this pest. Reversion results in changes in the growth of leaves and shoots and eventually the entire bush takes on the appearance of having reverted to the wild state. Symptoms show most clearly from the end of June onwards: the number of leaf veins is reduced and the leaf serrations are less definite. Grub out and burn any affected plant material.

RED CURRANTS

Red currants are propagated and grown on in the same way as gooseberries and therefore details should be obtained under that heading. Like gooseberries, red currants are grown on a leg and are propagated from hardwood cuttings. These root more readily than gooseberries and grow much more vigorously. Bushes are sold as two-year-olds, and can either be field grown or containerized in the autumn of the first year. Some growers also retail three-year-old bushes. We must add that red currants are one of the least popular of the soft fruits, but there may be a small demand from private gardeners.

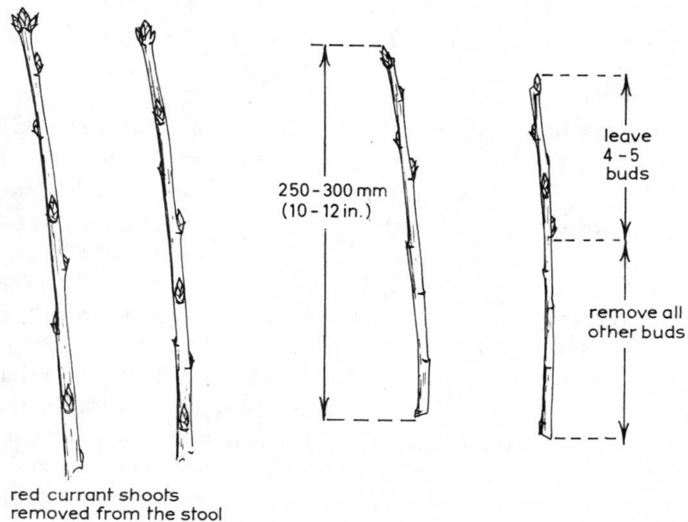

Fig. 75 Preparation of hardwood cuttings of red currant

GOOSEBERRIES

Gooseberries are propagated from hardwood cuttings taken in the autumn and two- to three-year-old bushes are ideal for retail sales in garden centres and the like. They can be bare-root bushes or containerized.

Soils

Soils for the parent bushes that supply cutting material should be well drained as poor drainage is disliked by gooseberries and can result in their death. A medium soil of good depth, well supplied with organic matter, is the ideal; while light sandy types and shallow soils result in poor growth due to dryness and lack of nutrients.

Planting

Stock plants or parent bushes can be planted in the autumn and may be spaced about 1·2 m (4 ft) apart in rows 1·5 m (5 ft) apart. The bushes are grown as stools for the annual production of hardwood cuttings and therefore each autumn all the current year's growth is removed. After planting new parent plants, therefore, all the growth can be cut off and used for cutting material.

Propagation

The site for propagation is the same as for black currants. Gooseberries for fruiting are grown on a short leg or stem about 150 mm (6 in) in length, and when propagating account must be taken of this. Try to ensure a good straight strong stem in the saleable plants.

Cuttings are made from current year's shoots which are well ripened and straight. The ideal time to take and insert cuttings is in the early autumn. Prepare the cuttings with secateurs and make them 250–300 mm (10–12 in) in length. Discard the soft tip of each shoot, by cutting just above a bud and cut just below a bud at the base. Remove all buds, together with the spines, except for the top four or five. This will ensure that no growth will arise less than 100–200 mm (4–8 in) from ground level, so that the bush is on a clean leg.

Insert prepared cuttings either by machine or in a slit trench taken out with a spade. Ensure they are inserted to the optimum depth, that is, to half their length. For example, a 300 mm (1 ft) long cutting is inserted 150 mm (6 in) deep so that a portion of bud-free stem is above soil level with, of course, the four or five remaining buds at the top.

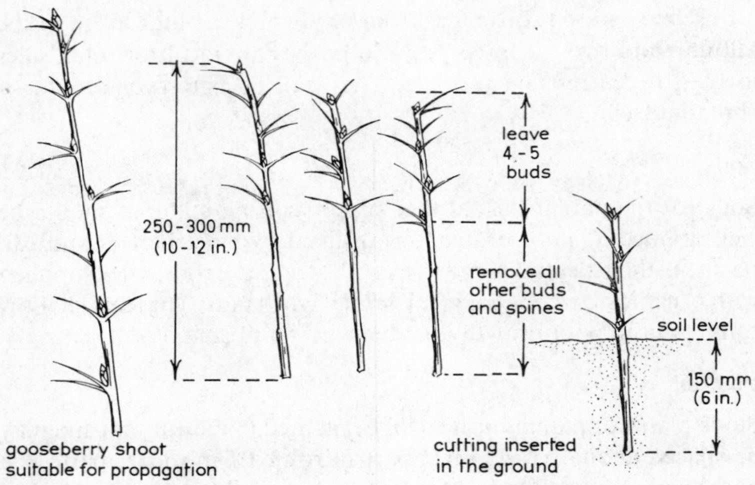

Fig. 76 Preparation of hardwood cuttings of gooseberry

If bushes are to be lifted at the end of the first season, either for planting out into nursery beds to grow on, or for containerizing, then the cuttings can be spaced 150 mm (6 in) apart in rows 600–750 mm (24–30 in) apart. If you intend replanting the lifted bushes, space them 300–450 mm (12–18 in) apart in rows 1 m (3 ft 3 in) apart. They can then be grown on for another one or two years. If you do not intend lifting after the first season then space the cuttings 300–450 mm apart in rows 1 m (3 ft 3 in) apart.

Management

Young bushes should be pruned on the nursery in the autumn to ensure strong well-branched growth. This can be done in the autumn of the first and second year.

From spring onwards, as new leaves start to appear on both cuttings and parent plants, you may need to start sprays of benomyl or dinocap to control the serious and crippling fungal disease, American gooseberry mildew. This appears as white powdery patches and quickly spreads to all parts of the plant.

Control germinating weed seeds among cuttings and parent plants with residual herbicides like simazine or lenacil. Apply adequate irrigation if the soil starts to dry out—both to cuttings and stock plants.

GRAPE VINES

Grape vines (*Vitis vinifera* cultivars) are becoming an increasingly important crop, especially containerized vines for sale in garden centres. The grape can be propagated from cuttings, layering, budding or grafting. In this country we generally propagate from eye cuttings, details of which will be found in Chapter 13. Conventional hardwood cuttings can also be used, rooting them in heat as described in Chapter 13. Eye cuttings, of course, are more economical of propagation material. In the USA, especially, an important method of propagation is grafting, and also chip budding, very often using eelworm- and phylloxera-resistant rootstocks. Budding or grafting is also used to increase the life of the vines, and to produce more vigorous plants and heavier yields.

Grape vines from cuttings

As we mentioned above, propagation from eye or conventional

hardwood cuttings in heat is probably most applicable to UK nurserymen. It has been found that hormone rooting compounds are not particularly helpful with vine cuttings, adequate rooting of most cultivars being achieved without this added stimulation. Cuttings should be collected from healthy, vigorous stock plants, which should be fed on a regular basis with a compound fertilizer to prevent nutrient deficiencies which could result in a lower-percentage rooting in the cuttings. The stock plants must be grown in a position in full sun and in a well-drained soil.

When cuttings are well rooted (eye cuttings are generally rooted in unit containers) there is no reason why they should not go into final containers. We use 150 mm (6 in) diameter polythene bags and generally a loamless compost, although a loam-based type is often considered better for vines. After containerization transfer to a walk-in polythene tunnel to harden off the young plants. Once they are well established and making vigorous growth they could be transferred to a standing ground—at any rate the plants must be acclimatized to outdoor conditions by late summer so that the wood ripens well in the autumn. During containerization it will be necessary to provide a 1 m (3 ft 3 in) bamboo cane for support. Regular tying in will be necessary throughout the summer.

One season's growth in the nursery should produce plants large enough for sale, especially if polythene tunnels were used in the early part of the growing season. Single-stemmed vines are quite acceptable for garden-centre sales and also for setting out in vineyards.

CONTAINER-GROWN TOP FRUIT

In recent years a buoyant market has been created for trained fruit trees in containers. In previous chapters we have discussed container growing and fruit rootstocks. In this section we will concentrate on the training of fruit for this market.

Espalier trees

Young bush apple trees are containerized for training. A good-quality espalier should have evenly spaced branches and be two or three tiers high, depending on the age it leaves the nursery. The distance between the pot and the bottom tier should be 300 mm (1 ft), and between each tier of branches 300–400 mm (12–16 in). In pruning one should aim for laterals opposite each other to produce a well-balanced tree.

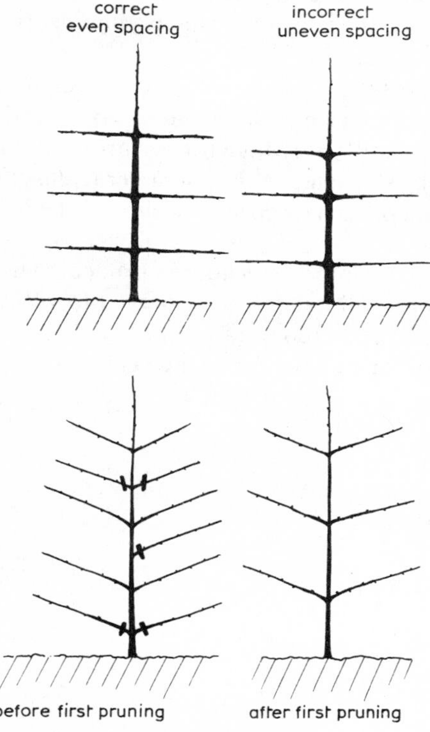

Fig. 77 Espalier tree training

The first pruning operation is to remove, to one bud, all unwanted laterals to leave the branch framework required for an espalier. For ease of management we then suggest you use a ready-made frame which can be fitted in the container although some growers use canes and a frame. Once the frame has been placed in position the grower can then tie in the layers of branches. The basal layer is tied in first, securing the old wood to the frame before the young wood, using raffia. Depending on the length of the lateral, three ties may be needed on each layer. The same procedure is adopted for the next two layers to produce a fully trained tree.

Next year, the leader is removed to encourage buds to break and a fourth tier can be made. All prunings must be collected and burnt to ensure that hygiene is maintained in the growing area.

At the point of sale the framework can be removed as customers will no doubt have their own training requirements.

Cordons

Fruit trees grown on a single stem and normally trained at an angle of 45° are called cordons. Maiden trees are containerized at a 45° angle and a cane is inserted in the container to ensure that a straight stem is maintained. As new growth occurs on the leading shoot it is tied to the cane.

During the first winter the leader is pruned back by half to just above a bud, while all laterals are removed to within 25 mm (1 in) of their bases. This is repeated in the second winter and plants should be ready for sale the following year.

Part 7

EFFICIENT WORKING ON THE NURSERY

38

Work organization

The aim of this chapter is to illustrate how nursery operators can improve their existing methods of work. In nursery production we are constantly trying to improve our productivity to make growing more efficient; the term used for this is method study, which should not be confused with work measurement.

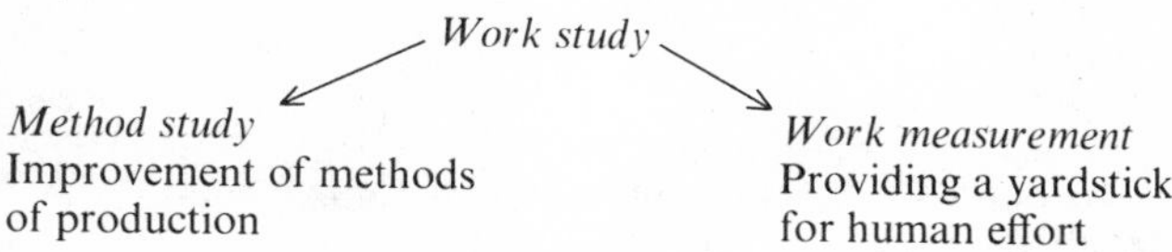

Method study is the systematic recording and critical examination of existing techniques and proposed ways of doing work with the aim of developing and applying easier and more effective methods of reducing costs.

The problem that exists is that once we have been trained in a method of carrying out a job, we tend to stick to that method, whether it is the most efficient technique or not.

Any operation can be broken down into components to produce the basic work content; that is the irreducible minimum time it takes to do the job. In practice, jobs take longer than we expect, often due to bad planning, unskilled staff, machinery breakdowns, safety hazards or bad weather. The main objective of work organization is to reduce this lost time to its minimum.

The first important aim in work organization is to be able to recognize a problem work area; once identified it can then be analysed and suitable alternatives developed. The indications of a problem area are bottlenecks, waste materials, idle labour, low output, breakdowns and people waiting around for other work to be completed. Once an operation has been selected for study one can then start solving the problem, but three things must be borne in mind:

1 Economic factors: is money available to implement the change?
2 Technical aspects: is it technically feasible to alter the system?
3 Human reactions: will the workforce react favourably to the change?

Table 20 Example: work content of containerizing nursery stock

		Analysis %
Time added: method Example: alternative is to reduce travel	Collecting and bringing plants to the shed	8
Time added: method Example: alternative is to buy in	Compost mixing	10
Time added: method Example: alternative use herbicides and peat pots	Cleaning and knocking plants out of the pots	5
Basic job time	Potting by machine	55
Time added: crop management	Watering	2
Time added: method	Travelling to standing area	5
Time added: method	Standing down plants	15
		100

Recording work

When a problem area has been identified it must be examined in detail before an improved technique can be found. It must be stressed that any job is made up of three parts:

1 Make ready.
2 Key doing operations.
3 Put away.

The whole operation needs to be studied to gain any benefits.

A number of types of recording techniques can be used according to the type of operation being studied.

FLOW PROCESS CHARTS

The most common means of recording is by use of the flow process chart. Firstly, decide on the subject to be charted, that is, a person, article, material or equipment; the same subject should be followed throughout, without change, and every detail on the chart must be about the one subject. The starting and finishing points must be firmly established and brief but concise details about the operation are written down as the work progresses.

Charting should be done in the work situation while the job is actually being carried out. One must bear in mind that no chart will solve the problem. It is simply used as an aid so that information can be set down, studied and the present method then improved.

Because it is difficult to write down in detail each activity in a piece of work we use symbols to simplify the recording. The symbols are as follows:

Symbol		
○	Operation	Main step in a process. Usually product or material is modified.
□	Check/inspection	Check for quantity or quality.
⇨	Transport	Movement from place to place.
D	Delay	Delay in sequence of events.
▽	Storage	Indicates a controlled storage.
⧇	Combined symbol	Operation and inspection occurring simultaneously.

The following flow process chart illustrates the technique as a material type chart.

STRING DIAGRAMS

The string diagram is an aid for measuring the distances travelled during an activity. In nursery production a nurseryman, during a day's work, could travel great distances and walking is unproductive time in the sense that it does not add value to the crop. Therefore

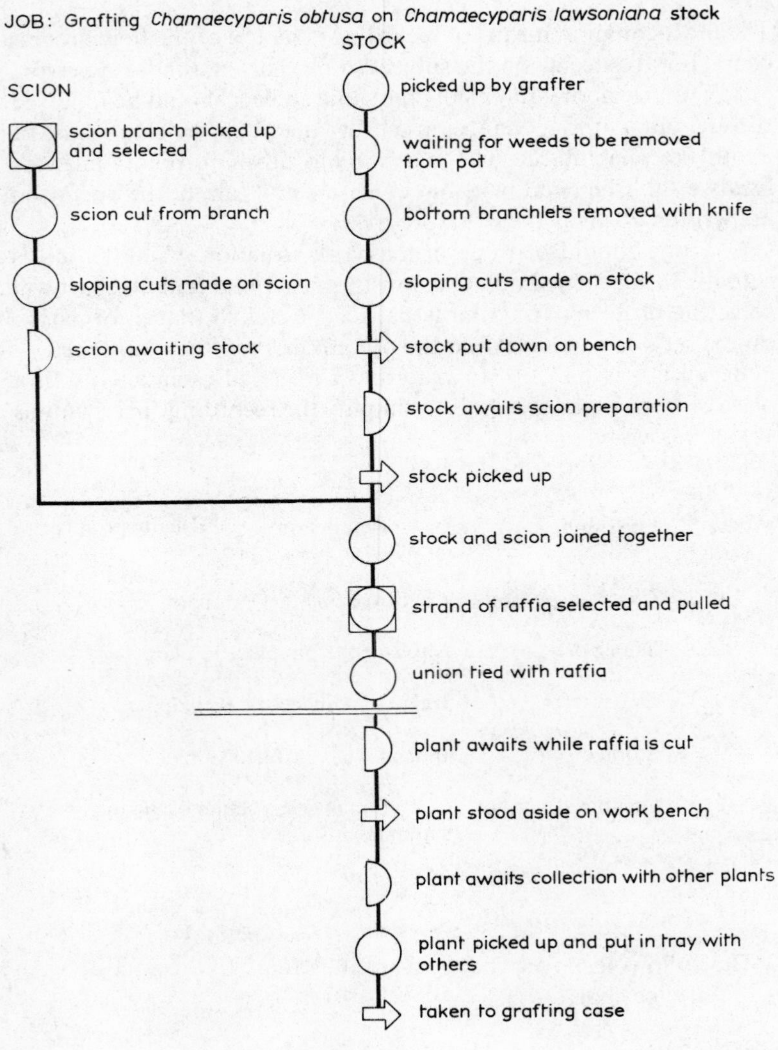

JOB: Grafting *Chamaecyparis obtusa* on *Chamaecyparis lawsoniana* stock

Fig. 78 Flow process chart

if we can reduce travelling time our operations should be more efficient.

When using a string diagram the following procedure is adopted:

1 List the workers' movements.
2 Plan the work area on a convenient scale to fit a sheet of paper.
3 Draw the area on the paper and then insert pins along the route of work. It is advisable to use large-headed pins where work is carried out. Once pinned out, the route can be followed by using cotton and the total distance walked can be measured.

A study of a string diagram can reveal which is the best route of travel as well as assist with designing new buildings and new routes of work.

MULTIPLE ACTIVITY CHARTING

Often it may be necessary to consider the activity of one subject in relation to another, or a group of activities.

Where this type of recording is needed then a multiple activity chart (MAC) is used. The important point with a MAC is that all subjects being studied have a common time scale. Each operator or activity being studied has a separate column on the chart and this then allows you to record clearly the amount of operations, movements, idle time and ineffective time. Charts can also be useful for showing when equipment is available for other uses or maintenance.

A time value needs to be obtained for every activity studied. These times need to be accurate to make the study effective. An MAC must be self-contained and include the following information:

1 Description of the operation.
2 Whether the present or proposed method is being studied.
3 Time scale used.
4 Key to abbreviations if being used.
5 A summary of the times incurred during the activity.

Every chart should cover the whole of the operation or a complete cycle of work. The charts are most easily explained by the exercise that follows.

Exercise example: containerizing

Three gangs are employed to containerize nursery stock. Compost mixers take 10 minutes to machine mix a *batch* of container compost.

Table 21 Compost mixing, handling and potting multiple activity chart: present method

Time, min	*Compost mixers*	*Potters*	*Trans-porters*	*Time, min*
0	First batch of compost for potters			0
10	Second batch	Potting		10
20	Third batch		Compost moving	20
30	Fourth batch		Compost moving	30
40	Fifth batch (second potters)		Compost moving	40
50			Plants to growing area	50
60	Sixth batch			60
70				70
80				80

Shaded areas show work time.

Summary:

	Work	*Idle*
Compost mixers	60 min	20 min
Potters	70 min	10 min
Transporters	50 min	20 min
	180 min	50 min

Potters work on the potting machine using up a compost mix in 40 minutes. Each shift requires some preparation and potting usually begins following the first mix of compost.

Transporters use a tractor and flat trailer and clear and stand down the potted plants in the growing area; they take an average of 25 minutes per compost batch of potted plants. Whenever they are waiting for a batch of plants they move by tractor and another trailer (tipping) a batch of compost from the compost mixers to another section of the nursery. This operation takes 10 minutes in total.

Compost *is not stored* but must be dropped direct from batch mixer elevator to potting machine hopper or into a tipping trailer for elsewhere.

A multiple activity chart should show:

1 The working time of each gang.
2 The total idle time of each gang.

Given this information one can set out a multiple activity chart.

Critical examination

Once a recording has been completed one can examine the work to see if improvements can be made by elimination or combination of any of the activities. When studying the records it is important to start by defining which are the important key operations. This is difficult to do objectively, especially if you are examining your own holding. To help, look at a job critically: it is best to study it under the following headings:

1 Purpose: what is being done? This should be the real reason for the operation and not how it is done. Ask if it is really necessary; if not, do not include it in the new method. If it is necessary, ask yourself why.
2 Place: where is the work being done and why is it being carried out there? Would a new site for the job increase or reduce the amount of movement?
3 Sequence: when is it done? What was carried out before and after this piece of work? Would it be easier to change the order? If so, what are the advantages?
4 Person: who does the work and why does he or she do it? Could anyone else do the job and are there any particular skills in doing that job?
5 Means: how is it done? The materials, equipment and method

should be described and then questioned as to why it is done that way and what else could be done.

It must be stressed that you will often come up with more than one solution to the problem. If this occurs it is advisable to look at the short-term modifications and long-term modifications as separate issues. It is important to bear in mind the technical considerations; quality and quantity should never deteriorate by altering the method.

Installing and maintaining a new method

It is possible to produce detailed recording and feasible efficient alternative methods, but to be effective the new method must be installed and maintained.

Conditions are liable to change from time to time and this may mean alterations in the method. Labour may be hesitant about adopting the new system or wish to make their own minor innovations. It is important to involve the labour force when the new scheme is being implemented and to take ideas and suggestions from them; the benefits of the new method should also be stressed to them.

Once adopted, the new system should be reviewed frequently. The reason for this inspection is to find if any discrepancies have crept into the system of work. If variations have occurred these should be investigated and if valid should officially be incorporated into the system. In accepting improvements you should ensure credit for the improvement is given where it is due. Where undesirable variations have occurred these should be corrected and the reasons for the correction explained to the workforce.

It is important to stress that any changes that take place should not result in a deterioration of quality or safety standards.

ERGONOMICS

In an intensive industry such as nursery production, labour plays a vital part in every aspect of the production cycle. It is important, with increasing costs, that manpower is used efficiently.

To be effective, labour should be provided with the correct conditions to produce the optimum performance. This means facilities should be made available to produce good work patterns, in the correct environment with the right tools and equipment. It is important to remember that one of the commonest reasons for reduction in productivity is fatigue, which can result from monotonous work, bad working environment or the wrong equipment being used.

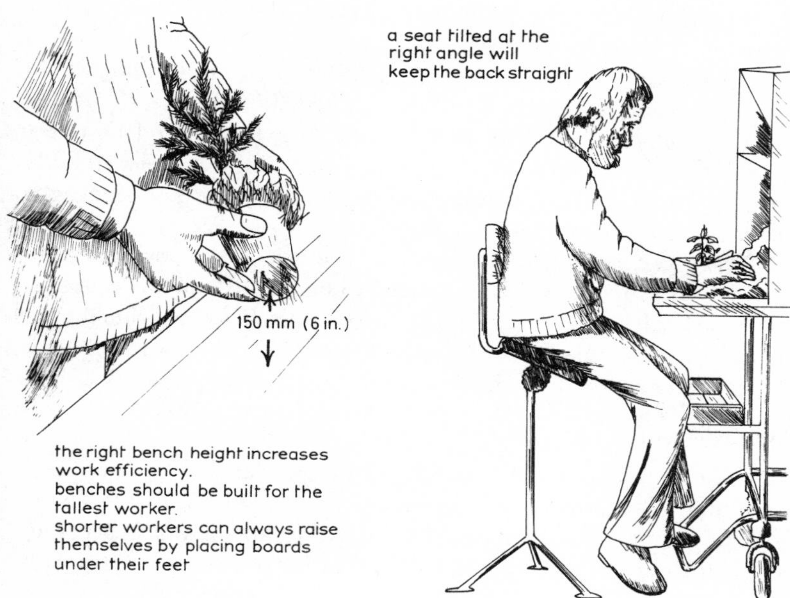

Fig. 79 Ergonomics in the nursery

Ergonomics is the study of work patterns, and the layout of the working area, to give the maximum comfort for labour as well as improving the work output.

When studying ergonomics there are several principles which must be considered:

1 Natural movements: labour should use muscles correctly and when carrying loads the strain should be equally and evenly spread.
2 Habitual movements: if the movements used in the operation are correct they will become habitual, or carried out as reflex actions.
3 Rhythmic movements: once an operator gets into a rhythm it normally speeds up the operation as well as reducing the fatigue of the operator.

4 Simultaneous and symmetrical movement: where possible, work should be arranged so that both hands are used, e.g. inserting cuttings.
5 Minimum movement: work should be well laid out so that unnecessary movement is eliminated.

When laying out a work area, e.g. potting shed, it is important to ensure it is adequately lit, heated, ventilated and safe. If it is possible to sit somebody down to do the work then this should be done. Seats should be tilted towards the work area to allow a relaxed body position and a straight back; this offers a solution to backache which is a common ailment and a major cause of lost working days.

When working next to a bench ensure it is at the correct height for the operator. If not, boards need to be placed under the worker to raise him or her if the bench is too high. The ideal height for benching should be approximately 150 mm (6 in) below the elbows. An operator should not have to stoop or reach to do a job.

Arrangement of the work place

Obviously it is far easier to arrange an indoor area, e.g. a propagation unit, for maximum efficiency, than an outdoor area.

Equipment and tools should have fixed stations so that it becomes habit-forming to go to a particular area for a piece of equipment. Tools should be pre-positioned to reduce searching and where possible gravity should be used to deliver materials, e.g. compost, to the work area. Materials and tools should be arranged to permit the best motions to do an operation, that is, a worker should not need to cross his/her hands to complete an operation.

DESIGN OF TOOLS

With hand tools, especially, we are confronted with varying designs of the same tool, making it difficult to select the right equipment. The best tool for the job can only be determined once you have studied your own working situation and tested the equipment available. Where possible use tools where two or more have been combined into one, e.g. dibber and firmer combined to fit a seed box. Handles should be designed so as to permit as much of the surface of the hand as possible to come into contact with the handle.

Planning work

In earlier parts of this chapter we discussed methods of how to make the most effective use of time. Whatever new techniques are devised we still have to plan the work programme. Basically there are five reasons for planning the day's or week's work schedule. These are:

1 To make the best use of available time.
2 To save human effort and machine working time.
3 To reduce cost of operation.
4 To avoid wastages.
5 To make sure the job is completed on time.

By careful planning it should be possible to improve output as well as making the job easier. When planning an operation the following points need to be considered:

1 Decide on the key points of the job.
2 Decide on the sequence of operations.
3 What are the limitations concerning materials which are available?
4 Is it possible to run more than one section of the job at the same time?
5 How long will the job take to complete?

In nursery production we are also governed by the weather and safety factors and these should be taken into account when planning the programme.

It is often advisable to have a diary work plan where activities for the week are written down, together with a separate list of 'wet weather' jobs.

39

Safety

The nursery trade is a labour-intensive industry dealing with a labour force of varying skills and intelligence. It is also an industry that is dealing with dangerous products, machines, chemicals and tools. Therefore, it is important that we train our workforce in the correct safety procedures of work and maintain a safe working place.

This chapter deals with various areas of safety in nursery production, but it must be stressed that in a developing industry we must keep up to date with safe working techniques and ensure that the workforce is trained adequately to carry out work safely.

Safe lifting

In nursery production we are constantly moving materials—plants, composts, pots and rubbish. As mentioned in a previous chapter, every time we move materials we add to the cost of the end product, but rarely increase the value. Therefore movement should be eliminated or minimized by combining operations or mechanizing them where practical.

Before considering any movement we should consider the following points:

1 Purpose: what are we achieving by moving the material? Is it really necessary?
2 Place: does the location of the material assist work flow at present? If not, can we move the material somewhere else and can direct floor contact be avoided?
3 Sequence: is the work being carried out in the correct sequence? A guideline here is that temporary storage should not occur in the ideal work-flow situation.
4 Person: are conditions safe to move materials?
5 Means: the way in which materials are moved is governed by a number of factors. Firstly, the nature of the material: its size, weight, shape and variety. Secondly, the nature of the move-

ment: intermittent, continuous, direction of travel and distance of travel. Thirdly, is gravity being used to the best advantage? If not, why not? And, finally, is there adequate provision for handling waste materials?

Rationalization of movement in nurseries has been of great interest in recent years and progress is now being made. Pallets are now a common feature in many large nurseries, particularly for moving plant material in and out of cold stores but also for movement to and from the nursery, especially with the introduction of cage pallets which collapse and stack easily when not being used. Obviously if pallets are to be used one needs to invest in tractor-mounted forks, either front or back loaded, or a fork-lift truck. Fork-lift trucks have a more limited use in the nursery than tractor-mounted forks as most need hard roads to work efficiently.

Many of the rough-terrain trucks can be fitted with fork lifts or shovels and are very manoeuvrable, in comparison to agricultural tractors, for moving pallets about or growing materials.

Obviously further developments will occur in the handling of materials in the future, but some materials still have to be moved by hand, some of these being heavy and care must be taken to ensure safe lifting.

The maximum weight which one worker should be asked to lift and carry unaided should be 81 kg (180 lb); anything heavier may damage the worker's vertebrae and this can also occur if materials are lifted badly, putting extra pressure on the back.

If you have to lift items it must be stressed that every time you bend your back to lift, risk of damage to the spine is possible. The golden rule is to use your strongest muscles, the thigh muscles, when lifting, and this is achieved by bending your knees.

The major points to remember when lifting can be summarized as follows:

1 Firstly, before attempting to lift or move any heavy object, stop, think, plan and test, as this may save a bad back, an important point when one considers that 80 per cent of the population suffers, at one time or another, with back pains.
2 Correct foot position is important; good balance should be ensured by placing feet at the correct distance apart, one foot in front of the other and pointing in the direction in which you wish to travel.

3 The correct arm position is important; arms should be held at the side of the body, again to ensure the correct body position.
4 When taking hold of an object grasp it if possible with the palm of the hand; many accidents have happened by using 'finger tip' holds which can result in dropping the article. Apart from this it can damage tendons and muscles in the hands.
5 The back, where possible, should be kept straight, with the chin tucked in and correct use of thigh muscles.
6 Never use jerky movements when lifting, but ensure smooth rhythmic movements.
7 If moving large or very heavy items by hand then at least two people should be employed on the task, if possible using a sling, e.g. moving large balled trees. Also long-handled tools will put less pressure on the back than short-handled kinds.

Apart from workers ensuring safety for themselves, other aspects of the nursery are important to ensure a safe working place. The following areas of safety are important and vigilance is critical.

Electricity

The use of electricity is increasing in nurseries to ensure adequate lighting and communication, and also to operate machines such as soil shredders, potting machines and soil sterilizers.

Electrical accidents are common and the following guidelines can reduce fatal accidents:

DO Ensure installations comply with regulations.
Make sure all leads are securely connected.
Check wandering leads and make them safe.
Test earth-leakage circuit breakers regularly.
Make sure all fuses are of the correct rating.
Protect lamp bulbs if they are liable to be damaged.
Check that machines which pass under distribution lines have adequate clearance for safe passage.
Take special care with metal ladders, irrigation pipes and so on near overhead lines.

DO NOT Make do-it-yourself extensions.
Fit three-core cable into two-pin plugs.
Extend wandering leads by joining on another length.

Use equipment if you suspect there is an electrical fault.
Allow damaged bulbs to remain in position.

Tractors

Many nurseries own a tractor, but unfortunately many accidents are connected with misuse of this machine. Tractors should be fitted with safety cabs, which have a rigid framework to protect the driver from being crushed if the tractor overturns.

The causes of overturning are due to tractors being driven too fast or driven too near a ditch or bank or up too steep an incline. To prevent overturning, vehicles should be driven slowly, especially on rough terrain and when cornering. If driving on a slope then the tractor should be adequately weighted to prevent somersaulting. (Care should also be taken during winching operations, particularly if working on slopes.)

Before allowing operatives to drive a tractor ensure they have experience and understand all the controls and their positions. Passengers should not be allowed and tyres should be regularly checked for equal pressure to prevent instability and skidding; at the same time tractors should be checked for servicing, especially brakes and steering.

Many accidents occur with the power take-off; while the engine is in motion this must be covered with a shield constructed of metal or other suitable material that will support at least 112 kg (250 lb) and protect workers from contact with it from above or from the sides.

Stationary machinery

All stationary equipment, such as potting machines, bundling machines and soil shredders, should be guarded whenever possible to protect workers and their clothing from moving parts. Stopping devices must be easily accessible so that a machine can be quickly stopped in an emergency. Ideally if a worker is working near moving parts then a means of disconnecting the machine must be within reach of his working position. Switches must be clearly indicated with how to stop and start the machine and if the equipment is indoors then the room must be adequately lit, either by natural or artificial lighting.

Chemicals

In the nursery industry we are using more and more chemicals, as pesticides, herbicides and growth controllers. Many of these chemicals are poisonous and care should be taken when storing and using them.

Chemical stores should be fire-proof and child-proof with chemicals adequately labelled and stored in a logical order. A register should be kept in the store with columns for chemical used, when used, by whom, time of spraying and on what material. This enables the manager to keep in touch with what chemicals are being used and if absence through illness occurs because of a chemical, he has a record of the history of the worker concerned.

Protective clothing should be supplied by the nursery manager and used as specified with poisonous chemicals. Gloves must be made of neoprene, not natural rubber which absorbs chemicals, and ideally should have cotton inserts. These should be kept in good condition and after use cleaned inside and outside. Overalls, rubber aprons and macintoshes must also be provided, being waterproof and made of polyvinyl chloride on a rayon base. For very dangerous products goggles should be provided which are resistant to oils and chemicals, with lenses made of acetate and, ideally, replaceable.

Operators using spraying equipment should be thoroughly trained and adequately supervised. Spraying should be carried out with well-maintained equipment and in suitable weather conditions for the particular product. During work, sprayers should maintain the same speed and pressure as used during calibration. Operators must not smoke, should keep out of spray drift and constantly keep a watch on wind direction and strength; if wind speed increases switch off the sprayer and seek advice. A constant watch should be kept on sprayer nozzles to ensure they do not get blocked, but never try to clear them by blowing or sucking down them.

After spraying, if any surplus chemical remains it must be sprayed on to waste ground where seepage into ditches, streams, rivers or domestic water supplies is avoided. Protective clothing must be removed and washed thoroughly and the operator should also wash thoroughly before eating or smoking.

Noise

Noise or unwanted sound is becoming increasingly more and more serious as we mechanize the nursery industry. Noise can be an annoyance, interfere with work efficiency by hindering communications and damage workers' hearing either temporarily or permanently depending on the exposure time to constant noise.

Sound is generated by vibration of surfaces and the level of sound is measured by the change in pressure it causes. The measure used is decibel, and the following is a guide to how much noise is harmful.

Table 22 Sound levels

Exposure as hours per day	*Maximum sound level in decibels*
8	90
4	93
2	96
1	99
0·5	102

Most noise generated in a nursery is caused by using a tractor with a cab, where noise levels can reach 110 decibels. It is therefore recommended that tractor drivers should protect their ears by wearing ear muffs or ear plugs. However, ordinary cotton wool should not be used as it is useless as an anti-noise device.

First aid

Whatever safety measures we take in the nursery, accidents are bound to happen from time to time and therefore an employer must provide a first-aid kit which is easily accessible. All boxes must be well equipped with enough contents to be adequate for the workforce on the nursery. All workers must know where to obtain first-aid equipment and someone should be responsible for maintaining the contents.

Safety policy

Safety regulations are constantly changing and it is the nursery manager's responsibility to keep up to date with new laws and codes of practice.

A nursery should have a safety policy as a written statement, and this should be available to all employees; this will ensure that lack of knowledge cannot be accepted as a reason for not complying with regulations and safety guidelines on the nursery.

Below is an example of a safety policy statement; this is meant as a guideline and should be adapted to suit the holding.

NURSERY SAFETY POLICY STATEMENT

1 This statement requires that all employees working in the nursery should at all times comply with current safety legislation, information upon which can be obtained from the nursery manager.
2 Employees must not remove any safety equipment or alter the controls of machines in any way that might cause an accident. Employees must ensure that all equipment is maintained in good order.
3 Proper servicing and checking routines on machines, as laid down from time to time, must be carried out.
4 Any faults affecting the safety of equipment, in particular wiring insulations, stop switches, leaking knapsack sprayers, identification of chemicals and failure to keep poisonous chemicals under lock and key, must be reported to the manager at the earliest opportunity. Work may not take place on the outside of glasshouse roofs without proper supports in the form of roof boards.
5 In case of fire or accidents, the following points should be observed:
   (a) Telephones are situated in the nursery office.
   (b) First-aid boxes are located in the nursery office.
   (c) Accidents must be reported to the manager and statements recorded in writing in the accident book.
   (d) Medical attention can be obtained at the doctor's surgery [address and telephone number to be given].
6 All chemicals received for use on the nursery must be recorded and a note made in the chemical book kept in the store by all users of specified substances of the date these chemicals are opened and the date the container is emptied. All poisonous chemicals must be locked up daily in the chemical store.
7 Empty containers must not be taken from the store but collected there until disposed of.

8 Any person having used a spray or other chemicals during the previous 24 hours and suspecting sickness due to chemical use must inform the nursery manager.

9 Chemical usage shall at all times follow the specific instructions given on the containers, with special regard to the use of PROTECTIVE CLOTHING. The supply and maintenance of this clothing is the responsibility of the nursery manager.

10 Queries regarding safety and the correct use of equipment and chemicals can be made by contacting the manager in the first instance. It is the policy of the nursery to encourage close co-operation between employers and employees in all safety matters and to seek suggestions from workers as to improved methods of safe working.

11 Information and instruction on use of any equipment or material will be encouraged and, where special requirements are recognized, training will be provided at a suitable establishment.

12 This policy statement is subject to revision as appropriate and workers will be notified of any such revision as they may be made.

40

Marketing

Hardy ornamental crops can basically be divided into three different products; bare-root, balled and container-grown plants. The packing and dispatch of these three products will differ and obviously the market place will also often be different; for example, a container-grown rose will often be sold through a garden centre, while a bare-root pre-packed rose will sell through supermarkets.

Whichever marketing outlet is selected it is important that quality does not deteriorate between the time that the product leaves the nursery and arrives at the eventual customer, often having passed through a number of intermediaries. Therefore material should never be allowed to dry out as desiccation will soon follow. Packing should be thorough to ensure no damage occurs to plant material during transit. Bare-root plants, especially, should have their roots protected as many plants are lost due to dehydration of the root system, even if only exposed for a short period in windy weather.

If straw is used as a packing material, check to make sure that it has not been sprayed with a harmful herbicide. Under dark, warm conditions the heat build-up can release fumes from the herbicide which result in adverse effects on the packaged plants.

The marketing of nursery stock is an increasingly complicated affair, especially as more growers are exporting and need phyto-sanitary certificates, agents' documents and other international documentation.

THE BASICS OF MARKETING

The first step in marketing is to produce what people want to buy and not to sell what we like to produce. This means that we put the customer first and that we organize and co-ordinate the business so that this happens. To achieve this aim we must carry out market research to find out what the customer needs in order that we can satisfy those needs. What we must offer is the correct marketing mix, that is, the right products at the right price, available through the right channels and presented in the right way.

Promoting nursery stock

Various means of promoting nursery stock are available to the nursery grower. Most growers rely on advertising, linking the advert to the plant's attributes. Normal means of advertising include the use of posters, leaflets and inserts in local and national newspapers. Whichever means is used the important element is impact to catch attention.

Often an inexpensive means of promotion is the use of sponsoring, either on a national basis, or on a local level such as flower shows and fêtes.

As in other industries merchandising is an important means of promotion. Displays should be attractive, presentable and the quality good.

Nurserymen rely on the catalogue as a major means of promoting themselves, which can be an expensive or cheap means of marketing. The first consideration is whether you are selling at a wholesale or retail level, as the information contained in the catalogue will be different with both types of outlet. In a wholesale catalogue the grower should give the name of plant, sizes available, origin, if known, method of production and the price per 10, 100 and 1,000.

Retail catalogues demand a higher standard of presentation and often have to be set by specialist printing houses. The catalogue needs to be individual, attractive and have maximum impact. The information it contains must include the plant name, often including the common name; price per plant; plant description; cultural details and often an illustration of the plant.

Labelling

A label is one of the most important considerations at sale. Again the information on the label will vary, depending on the market the material is being aimed at.

Wholesale plant material should be labelled with a weatherproof label and tie, giving the full Latin name, the quantity and the grade of plants in the consignment. At the retail level the label should again be durable, but should give the common and Latin name, a brief plant description (that is, when it flowers, how tall it grows, habit and soil requirement), as well as giving planting instructions and aftercare.

A wide selection of labels is on the market for the use of the retailer, the choice depending on the product and market outlet of the plant material. The aim of the label is to attract the customer and inform. A grower can purchase specific individual labels or blank material which he can fill in to his own requirements. The type of label depends on the plant material being sold, and the following acts as a guide to the type of label.

HERBACEOUS PLANTS

Often sold in rootwrap form, having no sales appeal. The label is the only guide the customer has to the eventual appearance of the product. In this instance the best type of label is a pictorial one with information either under the picture or on the reverse side of the label.

HERBS

These plants are often used for culinary purposes and often sold to an 'ignorant' public. This means that the buyer not only needs to know the name of the plant, but as much information as possible. This should include details on how to use the herb in the kitchen.

BEDDING PLANTS

Normally a quick-selling item and therefore the label need not be as durable as with other crops. Again, a pictorial label is of great assistance supplemented with planting instructions.

TREES AND SHRUBS

Most customers have very little plant knowledge and therefore each plant should be labelled with a very durable label. Information should include eventual height and width of the plant, as well as name, characteristics, soil requirements and maintenance. Pictorial labels can be a great asset, especially when selling plants that are not in their most attractive state. Ideally with trees and shrubs a tie-on label is preferable as there is little chance of this being mislaid.

Pricing

One of the most difficult decisions for the grower is setting a price for his product, which covers costs while giving him a fair profit.

The main factor which determines price is supply and demand, and most of us cannot fix a price until we have assessed the market demand. The grower's aim is to get as high a total return as possible, while keeping in mind the rate of inflation, otherwise working capital can soon vanish.

If the supply is correct one should have about 5 per cent of the crop left at the end of the season. If all is sold it is normally an indicator that prices are too low; if half the crop is left it is a sign that prices are too high.

NURSERY CO-OPERATIVES

The marketing of nursery stock is a complex business in its own right. Various organizations are available to assist the grower and now many nurserymen are combining to sell on a co-operative basis. Nursery selling groups have now been formed in a number of European countries to promote the sale of nursery stock. By forming a co-operative growers have a number of advantages over their competitors who are not in a group. Firstly, it should enable a grower to spend more time growing, while a marketing branch of the co-operative should be selling; this being more efficient and increasing outlets. Secondly, a group can bulk-purchase materials as well as having the benefits of machinery-sharing and the interchange of ideas and information.

All organizations have their disadvantages and the same goes for co-operative selling. Many growers are concerned about the loss of identity, accepting outside management decisions and geographical dispatch problems. A difficult problem to overcome is the standardization of quality, pots and growing methods between nurseries so that they can sell under a common logo.

In setting up a co-operative a number of guidelines need to be adhered to. The following should act as a guide:

1 Each member of the group should have equal standing.
2 Keep rules as simple as possible so that they can be changed at a later date if required.
3 Keep to as few members as possible.
4 Keep the membership as balanced as possible, that is, a group selling to garden centres may have an alpine specialist, ericaceous plant specialist, tree producer, container specialist, and so on.

5 Decide on the percentage sales which must go through the group.
6 Include penalty clauses for breaking the rules.

Co-operatives are now a permanent means of selling with an increasing number of international co-operatives being formed. It enables the grower to grow while still providing a very efficient marketing service to the customer. It also allows specialization by the grower doing what he does best.

OUTLETS

Nursery stock has many outlets which can be summarized in the following list:

Wholesale outlets

1 Municipalities or local authorities: parks and amenities departments in towns and cities purchase large amounts of plant material on a yearly basis for planting in parks, streets and housing estates. Purchasing can often be by tendering, a system where the buyer writes to a number of suppliers and accepts the most competitive reply to his requirements.
2 Landscape companies: many large landscape schemes are constructed and maintained by commercial landscape companies who purchase large amounts of nursery stock.
3 The government: government departments often buy nursery stock for forestry, motorway planting and other large schemes.
4 Exporting: the export market often looks attractive to nurserymen and can bring in large financial rewards, once the process of export documentation has been understood.
5 Sale to other nurseries: the industry relies on smaller specialist companies supplying larger companies. This allows growers to specialize in certain aspects of the industry, for example, rootstock or liner production. They would then sell to larger companies who grow and collect plants for dispatch.

Retail outlets

The sale of plant material to the buying public is obviously a large part of marketing; again, though, outlets differ:

1 Garden centres: during the last decade this has become a major outlet for the sale of nursery stock. Plant material can be dis-

played in mass and the public allowed to pick and choose, with payment at a central check-out point. An educated sales staff should be employed to offer advice when required.

2 Chain stores: in recent years the large stores have moved into the garden market with the result that more plant material is being sold through these outlets.

3 Nursery 'gate' sales: this was the traditional way of selling nursery stock. With more sophisticated means now being developed it is becoming less important as a means of selling nursery stock.

4 Mail order: still a major outlet for selling nursery stock although it does depend on a cheap, reliable postage system. Obviously, the increase in container-grown plants has resulted in a moving away from this type of marketing to garden centres.

Large marketing organizations are becoming increasingly interested in plant material as a lucrative side to their marketing and the grower must keep alert to these developments as well as taking advantage of national plant-publicity schemes such as Grün ist Leben in Germany, Green Survival in the USA and National Tree Week in the UK. All these schemes are aimed at promoting nursery stock and it is up to the grower to ensure he gets maximum benefit from them.

Here we have briefly indicated some of the important points, but it must be stressed that a nurseryman must obtain all the facts if he is to be successful in the most important part of his business—selling!

Bibliography

Agriculture Handbook No. 450, *Seeds of Woody Plants in the United States of America*, 1974.

Bailey, L., *The Nursery Manual*, Macmillan, 1920.

Baker, K., *The U.C. System for Producing Healthy Container-grown Plants*, University of California, 1957.

Berninger, L., *Profitable Garden Centre Management*, Reston Publishing Co., VA, 1978.

Bunt, A. C., *Modern Potting Composts*, Allen and Unwin, 1976.

Caborn, J. M., *Shelter Belts and Windbreaks*, Faber and Faber, 1965.

Centrale Marketing Gesellschaft der Deutschen Agrarwirtshaft mbH, *A Guide to the German Nursery Trade*, 1975.

Davies, B., Eagle, D., and Finney, B., *Soil Management*, Farming Press, Ipswich, 1972.

East Malling and Long Ashton Research Stations, *More and Better Fruit with EMLA*, 1973.

Forestry Commission Bulletin 43, *Nursery Practices*, 1972.

Forestry Commission Bulletin 54, *Seed Orchards*, 1976.

Furuta, T., *Environmental Plant Production and Marketing*, Cox Publishing Co., 1976.

Garner, R. J., *The Grafter's Handbook*, Faber and Faber, 1967.

Harris, A. G., Muckle, T. B., and Shaw, J. A., *Farm Machinery*, Oxford University Press, 1974.

Hartman, H., and Kester, D., *Plant Propagation Principles and Practices*, Prentice-Hall Inc., NJ, 1968.

Hawker, M. F. J., and Keenlyside, J. F., *Horticultural Machinery*, Macdonald, 1971.

HMSO Bulletin 4, *Bush Fruits*, 1977.

HMSO Bulletin 95, *Strawberries*, 1962.

HMSO Bulletin 135, *Fruit Tree Raising*, 1969.

HMSO Bulletin 156, *Cane Fruits*, 1971.

HMSO Bulletin 172, *Planning Farmwork*, 1960.

Lamb, J. G. D., Kelly, J. C., and Bowbrick, P., *Nursery Stock Manual*, Grower Publications, London, 1975.

Leach, D. G., *Rhododendrons of the World*, Allen and Unwin, 1961.

Lovegrove, H. T., *Crop Production Equipment*, Hutchinson, 1968.

Macbean, J., *The Soil*, Faber and Faber, 1961.

McMillan-Browse, P., *The Production of Hardy Woody Plants from Seed*, Grower Publications, London, 1979.

Ohio Coop Extension Service, *Proceedings: Woody Ornamentals Winter Storage Symposium*, 1977.

Patterson, J. M., *Container Growing*, American Nurseryman, 1969.

Pennsylvania State University, *Nursery Production*, 1971.

Stanley, J. B., *A Survey of Fruit and Ornamental Tree Production in the USA*, Merrist Wood, Guildford, 1976.

Toogood, A., *Propagation*, Dent, 1980.

Welch, H. J., *Mist Propagation and Automatic Watering*, Faber and Faber, 1970.

Wells, J. S., *Plant Propagation Practices*, Macmillan, 1955.

Index